Long-Eared Bats

Long-Eared Bats

Susan M. Swift

*With illustrations by
Ruth Lindsay*

T & A D
POYSER
NATURAL
HISTORY

Contents

List of Colour Plates

Plate 1   A brown long-eared bat (*Plecotus auritus*) in flight. The large, erect ears can be seen in torchlight. Photo: Frank Greenaway.

Plate 2   Grey long-eared bat (*Plecotus austriacus*). The tragus shape, dark brown facial colouring and short thumbs identify this individual. Photo: Frank Greenaway.

Plate 3   A brown long-eared bat at roost with ears in the 'ram's horn' position. The transverse folds in the conch close in a fan-like action as the ear relaxes. Photo: John Haddow.

Plate 4   Because long-eared bats fly inside roosts, their droppings become scattered around attics and may cover furniture or other possessions stored there.

Plate 5   *P. auritus* flying close to vegetation. During foliage gleaning, brown long-eared bats frequently stop echolocating and search for prey by passive listening. Photo: Frank Greenaway.

Plate 6   Insect remains accumulate beneath feeding perches. Clearly, the bat that used this perch had been hunting large yellow underwing moths. Photo: Frank Greenaway.

Plate 7   Flyways are consistently used by long-eared bats to avoid crossing open spaces while commuting between roosts and foraging areas. They fly close to vegetation along landscape features such as overgrown streams.

Plate 8   A group of brown long-eared bats in their normal roosting position in an attic. They were photographed from below and are huddled between the ridge beam and the sarking, in the angle formed by a rafter.

Plate 9   A female brown long-eared bat with a newborn infant. Babies are continuously attached to their mother's nipple during their first week of life. Photo: Frank Greenaway.

Plate 10   Brown long-eared bats have been found to select older houses with complex roof spaces. A colony of 80 roosted in this Victorian house and frequently moved between roof compartments.

Plate 11   Long-eared bat roosts are likely to be situated in wooded valleys. Well-maintained fishing rivers are an important feature of the ecology of the species.

Plate 12   *P. auritus* select houses which have woodland within 0.5 km. This roost is surrounded by mature deciduous and coniferous trees.

Plate 13   A hibernating brown long-eared bat with folded ears. The tragi hang down, superficially resembling the ears of other species. Photo: Frank Greenaway.

Preface

In recent years, a number of books on the biology, behaviour and ecology of bats have been published, in line with increasing knowledge of the group and developing interest in it. However, there have been very few in-depth monographs, and the time now seems right for more detailed reviews dealing with individual species. Long-eared bats are among the best known European species. They are distinctive, easily recognizable and attractive, and there are also aspects of their biology and behaviour which make them different from other bats and therefore worthy of being considered separately.

I hope this book will be of interest to amateur bat enthusiasts who want to discover more about long-eared bats, as well as to professional biologists. It is also intended as an introduction to the species for students embarking on research into their biology; I hope it will be helpful.

Sue Swift
May 1997

Acknowledgements

I am grateful to colleagues in the Zoology Department of the University of Aberdeen, both past and present, whose ideas and enthusiasm I have drawn upon and whose research on long-eared bats has formed the basis for much of this book. In particular I thank Professor Paul Racey, who was largely responsible for my initial interest in bats and who supervised and encouraged all my early work; he has also allowed me unlimited access to his collection of literature, for which many thanks are due. In addition, I am indebted to Abigail Entwistle for access to her unpublished PhD thesis.

Tony Hutson, Jens Rydell, Abigail Entwistle, Paul Racey and John Speakman read and improved early drafts of various chapters and devoted time and effort to finding references which I had missed – I am most grateful to them all. I also thank the library staff at the University of Aberdeen for help in tracing some of the literature.

During twenty years of field work, I have received hospitality and cooperation from many roost owners; I should like to take this opportunity to thank them all and to acknowledge the invaluable contribution which roost owners make to bat conservation throughout Europe. Finally, I am grateful to my family, John, Imogen and Marcus. Besides adapting to cope with my nocturnal way of life every summer, they have tolerated an even worse than usual standard of housekeeping during the months I was writing and have enabled me (more or less!) to maintain a sense of humour throughout.

CHAPTER 1

Who's Who — An Introduction to Long-Eared Bats

THE aim of this book is to describe the biology, ecology and behaviour of European bat species of the genus *Plecotus*. Long-eared bats are among the most distinctive and best known of our bat fauna and are immediately recognizable by their enormous ears which are about three-quarters of the length of the rest of the bat. With these huge ears and their large eyes and delicate faces, *Plecotus* bats are physically very attractive and photographs of them have appeared on the covers of several recent bat books aimed at the general public. They are also among the European species most closely associated with buildings, and as such are likely to be encountered by members of the public. Because they are so attractive, they have become seen as an important asset in the all-important 'Bats Need Friends' campaign to improve the public image of all bats. They have been featured on a number of logos in recent years, including those of the European Bat Research Organization and the Bat Conservation Trust. Because they frequently roost in houses and because of their habit of using feeding perches and therefore leaving interesting heaps of insect remains for humans to find, they are also bats which have long been of interest to amateur naturalists. Knowledge of their biology and behaviour has advanced rapidly over the last two decades; their foraging methods are different from those of other European species, and in a number of other ways they are also worthy of being considered separately. All bats are not alike, just as all rodents are not alike, and I hope the following chapters will begin to show how different and how fascinating these bats are.

Many bats worldwide have large ears, and the names 'big-eared' and 'long-eared' have been widely applied to species in no fewer than nine microchiropteran families. However, the genera *Plecotus*, *Corynorhinus*, *Idionycteris* and *Euderma* in the family Vespertilionidae are peculiar in that they have the ability to fold their ears while they are at rest. In effect, the ears are 'deflated' (Hill and Smith, 1984) by the closing of special valves in blood vessels which enter the ear conch, thus allowing the ear to collapse. When the bat becomes active, the vascular valves are opened and the inrushing blood causes the ear to become erect.

The genus *Plecotus* contains two Palearctic species which are widespread, a third confined to the Canary Islands and a fourth in Taiwan. There are also three North American species, which are now re-classified as *Corynorhinus* (see Close Relations, below).

The brown long-eared bat, *Plecotus auritus*, L.1758, occurs widely in Europe and is probably the second commonest British bat after the pipistrelle, *Pipistrellus pipistrellus* (Mitchell-Jones, 1990). It is a small to medium-sized bat of delicate build, weighing

5–10 g and with ears at least 25 mm long joined at their bases (Stebbings, 1986). These may be curled, resembling rams' horns when the bat is at rest. The tragus (inner ear) is slender and the face colour is usually brown or pink. The dorsal pelage is brown, with dark and light bands along the length of the hairs.

The grey long-eared bat, *Plecotus austriacus*, Fischer, 1829, is rare in Britain but is widespread in Europe, particularly in Mediterranean areas. It is very similar to *P. auritus*, but is overall slightly larger (7–14 g) and its coat colour greyer, with hairs evenly coloured along their whole length, although there is considerable overlap in both size and coat colour. Its face is grey to black and its thumbs are short and thick. The two species are very difficult to distinguish, especially when dealing with living specimens, and this has led to considerable confusion in a number of records of their distribution, especially in parts of their ranges where they are sympatric.

A third species, *Plecotus teneriffae* (Barrett-Hamilton, 1907), is found only in the Canary Islands, where isolation has led to the evolution of this endemic species (Boye *et al.*, 1990). Although it is larger than *P. auritus* and although, from geographic distribution, it has more in common with the southern species *P. austriacus*, Ibanez and Fernandez (1986) considered it to be more closely related to *P. auritus* than to *P. austriacus*. Little is known of the ecology or behaviour of the Tenerife long-eared bat. Long-eared bats in Taiwan, formerly considered to be *P. auritus* (Stebbings and Griffiths, 1986), are now recognized as a separate species, *Plecotus taivanus* (Yoshiyuki, 1991). This author also advocated separate species status for *P. auritus* in Nepal and India, but this has not been recognized by other authorities.

HISTORY AND ORIGIN OF THE SPECIES

The difficulty in distinguishing *Plecotus* species has, in the past, led to confusion. For many years, Europe was considered to have only one species, *P. auritus*; in 1907, *P. teneriffae* was described, and it was not until relatively recently that the existence of *P. austriacus* as a species rather than a variety of *P. auritus* was recognized. Jenyns (1829) described two species of long-eared bats in Britain, calling the larger, greyer one *P. auritus* and the smaller, browner one *P. brevimanus*. As Corbet (1964) pointed out, if these did, indeed, constitute two species, then Jenyns had them the other way round to the way in which we now accept the situation! Bell (1874) rejected *P. brevimanus* as being the young of *P. auritus*. Similarly, in Europe, two forms were recognized (Kuzyakin, 1944; Topal, 1958) but considered to be subspecies, *P. auritus auritus* and *P. a. wardi*, Thomas. It was not until 1959 that the existence of two good species, occurring sympatrically in Italy, was shown (Lanza, 1959). Lanza described the smaller, browner species as *P. auritus* and the larger, greyer one as *P. wardi*. After this, the presence of two sympatric species was shown in Austria (Bauer, 1960), Czechoslovakia (Hanak, 1962) and the Netherlands (Wijngaarden, 1962). Bauer (1960) named the grey species *P. austriacus*, which was the name originally given by Fischer in 1829 to a variety of *P. auritus* from Austria.

Corbet (1964) re-examined specimens of *P. auritus* in the British Museum (Natural History) and discovered among them several individuals of *P. austriacus*. One of these had been collected in Hampshire between 1873 and 1878, one came from Jersey in the Channel Islands and the rest were from mainland Europe. The presence of *P. austriacus* in

Britain was thus established. Corbet (1964) concluded that it was either very local in this country or that it was much less abundant than *P. auritus*; both conclusions have since been shown to be correct. Shortly after this, Stebbings (1966) identified both species in a colony in Dorset which he had been studying for some time. Mixed colonies, where the two species apparently live in close proximity to each other, have subsequently been reported widely in their common range. Even when the presence of both is suspected, identification can be very difficult.

From the above, it is obvious that to attempt to attribute records of *Plecotus* bats from before 1959 to one species or the other would be unreliable and so, prior to this date, records are referred to as *Plecotus* spp. unless they were from places where only one species occurs. Where identification cannot be made with certainty (e.g. in many hibernation records or in other cases where bats could not be handled), even those recorded since 1959 are, in many cases, identified only to genus.

Horacek (1975) attributed many of the differences in the ecology of *P. auritus* and *P. austriacus*, such as in diet and foraging (see Chapters 3 and 4), roosting behaviour and mating systems (Chapter 6) and choice of hibernation sites (Chapter 8), to differences in the history of the two species in Europe. While the ecology of *P. auritus* is that of an old but still adaptable species, that of *P. austriacus* indicates that it is a new species in the area and one which has spread only recently. *P. auritus* is known from the fossil record to have been present in Europe from the Pliocene (from 12 million to 2–3 million years ago) and to have been common in the Pleistocene, up to 2 million years ago (Horacek, 1975; Sese and Ruiz-Bustos, 1992). The species thus appears to have its origins in Europe. *P. austriacus*, on the other hand, is Asian in origin and is a remarkably new species in Europe (Horacek, 1975), spreading through the continent in historical time. It appears to rely heavily on human dwellings as summer roost sites and on artificial structures such as cellars as hibernacula, and it is possible that it only spread in Europe as such sites became available.

DISTRIBUTION

Both *P. auritus* and *P. austriacus* are widespread in the Palearctic Region. *P. auritus* occurs eastward as far as the Ural and Caucasus mountains. In Asia, it is found in Mongolia and north-east China (Zeng and Wang, 1989), Sakhalin and Japan (Corbet and Hill, 1991). It also occurs in South Korea and in isolated pockets in central China, as well as in parts of India and Nepal (Corbet and Hill, 1991). *P. austriacus* is distributed in southern Europe and north Africa, eastwards to Mongolia and western China and southwards to Senegal (Nowak, 1991) and Ethiopia (Largen *et al.*, 1974). In Europe, *P. austriacus* is the commoner species in southern countries where the climate is Mediterranean and relatively stable. The two species occur together in central Europe to approximately 53°N, and *P. auritus* occurs on its own at higher latitudes (up to 64°N), where the climate is cooler and more changeable (Stebbings, 1970). Figures 1.1 and 1.2 show the distribution of *P. auritus* and *P. austriacus* respectively.

P. auritus is common and widespread in Britain (Figure 1.3). It occurs everywhere except in exposed mountainous regions in north and north-west Scotland (Swift, 1991; Arnold, 1993). It is found in the Inner Hebrides and has been recorded on Orkney (Booth and Booth, 1994), but is absent from the outer islands and Shetland. Its absence from these

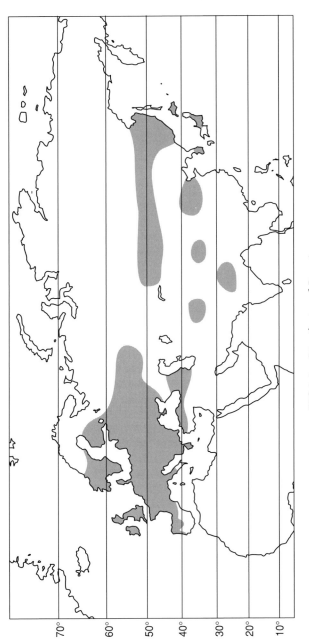

FIG 1.1 *Distribution of* P. auritus.

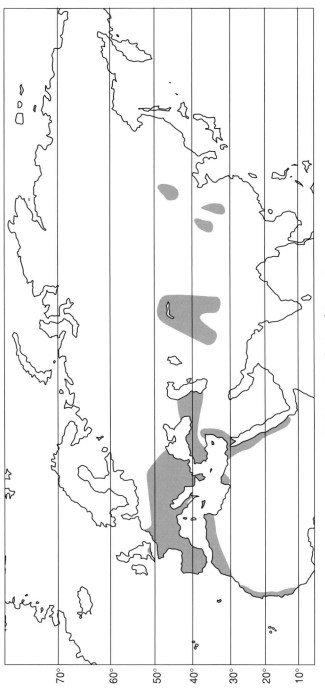

FIG 1.2 *Distribution of* P. austriacus.

FIG 1.3   *Distribution of* P. auritus *in the British Isles.*

areas may well be due to their lack of trees, since *P. auritus* is strongly associated with wood-land (Swift and Racey, 1983). It is common throughout Ireland (Moffat, 1938; O'Sullivan, 1994), where it occurs in large numbers in many areas (O'Gorman and Fairley, 1965). In Britain, *P. austriacus* is rare and is confined to the extreme south of the country (Figure 1.4); it has been recorded from Somerset, Dorset, Devon, Hampshire, the Isle of Wight and the Channel Islands (Arnold, 1993). There are several records from the extreme west of Sussex and, more recently, also from Brighton (Hutson, 1991) and Chichester (Hutson, 1996). It is reported to be the second commonest bat in Jersey after the pipistrelle (D. Laffoley, *pers. comm.*) and it has been recorded on all the Channel Islands except Herm. It is known to breed on Jersey and Guernsey and, possibly, also on Alderney; the Channel Islands are thought to contain about three-quarters of the British population of this species (D. Laffoley, *pers. comm.*).

   P. austriacus is absent from Scandinavia, but *P. auritus* is common in Denmark and occurs throughout the country (Baagøe, 1980–81). It is also common in central and south-ern Sweden (Gerell, 1980–81) and occurs as far north as latitude 63° or 64°N (Ahlén and Gerell, 1989; Schober and Grimmberger, 1989). It is present to similar latitude in Norway,

FIG 1.4   *Distribution of* P. austriacus *in the British Isles.*

in southern Finland and in Estonia. In Russia, it has been recorded as far north as 60°25′N (Revin-Yu and Boeskorov, 1989).

Both species occur throughout France, Switzerland and Austria. On the Austrian–Czech border, high numbers of both were netted in wooded areas (Gaisler *et al.*, 1996) and, also in Austria, both were found at heights of 350–1500 m above sea level (Spitzenberger, 1993). *P. austriacus* were found mainly in submontane areas and *P. auritus* mainly in montane areas. Both also occur in the Netherlands and Belgium. Jooris (1980) reported that *P. austriacus* was fairly common in the low-lying districts of Belgium, where it appeared to prefer more open habitats than the woodland areas inhabited by *P. auritus*. In the Netherlands, *P. austriacus* is uncommon and is mostly confined to the southern half of the country (Daan, 1980; Glas, 1982). *P. auritus* was formerly common, but appears to have suffered a sharp drop in numbers recently (Daan, 1980). The two species occur in the Czech and Slovak Republics (Gaisler *et al.*, 1980–81). Numbers of both vary but are locally high in forested areas (Gaisler *et al.*, 1996) and in areas where suitable hibernacula are found (Weidinger, 1994). In Poland, *P. austriacus* reaches the northern limit of its distribution at about 53°N (i.e. slightly further north than in Britain, where it is not found above 51°N) and is thus present in the southern two-thirds of the country (Ruprecht, 1971). In central and west Poland it is generally a lowland species, but in the east it extends to foothill regions. *P. auritus* occurs throughout the country, and the two species are thus sympatric below 53°N. Similarly in Germany, both species are found together as far north as around Berlin at 52°30′N (Haensel and Nafe, 1993), but *P. austriacus* has not been recorded further north. Both species occur in Bulgaria and Romania (Stebbings and Griffiths, 1986).

Further south in Europe, *P. austriacus* is the commoner and more widespread of the two species. Both occur in Portugal, but *P. auritus* is rare and was only recently recorded for the first time (Palmeirim, 1990). *P. austriacus* occurs throughout Spain and in the Balearic Islands (from which *P. auritus* is absent) and lives at a range of altitudes from sea level to 1600 m, although it is only in the south that it inhabits mountain areas (de Paz, 1984). An examination of museum specimens of *Plecotus* collected nationwide revealed that 77% were *P. austriacus* and 23% were *P. auritus* (de Paz, 1984). *P. auritus* appears to be widely distributed in the northern half of Spain, as far south as Sierra de Guadarrama and Gredos in the province of Madrid (de Paz, 1984; Benzal, 1991). It occurs at all altitudes in the north, but only higher than 1000 m above sea level further south. It is commonest in highland regions such as the Pyrenees, Cantabrian and Galician mountains, where it generally lives in either deciduous or *Pinus* forest (de Paz, 1984). In the Pyrenees, *P. auritus* was reported to be the commonest bat species netted at altitudes of 2000–2500 m (Bertrand, 1992). It does not appear to be present in the southern half of Spain. It occurs in Italy as far south as approximately 43°N (Crucitti, 1989) and is absent from Corsica, Sardinia and Sicily. *P. austriacus* occurs throughout most of mainland Italy except the southwest but is similarly absent from Corsica, Sardinia and Sicily (Vernier, 1987).

P. austriacus is the commoner of the two species in the former Yugoslavia and is widely distributed there (Krystufek, 1980). Two populations have been identified and these differ mainly in body size (Dulic, 1980). The larger specimens, of similar size to those of this species elsewhere in Europe, are found in northern and south-eastern areas, while smaller ones occur along the Adriatic coast and on adjacent islands. Populations in central Croatia and Bosnia contain specimens with characteristics intermediate between the two. Dulic (1980) proposed naming the smaller specimens as a subspecies, *P. austriacus kolombatovici*. Distribution of *P. auritus* in the area is much more limited; it occurs in Croatia, Bosnia and, uncommonly, in Slovenia (Krystufek, 1980).

P. austriacus is also much more prevalent than *P. auritus* in eastern Mediterranean and Middle Eastern countries (de Blase, 1980). Specimens of *P. austriacus* have been collected in Egypt (Madkour, 1989), Jordan (Revin-Yu and Boeskorov, 1989; Qumsiyeh *et al.*, 1992), Algeria (Gaisler, 1983–4) and Malta (Borg *et al.*, 1990). The southern limit for the species appears to be reached in the Cape Verde Islands (Azzaroli-Puccetti and Zava, 1988), an isolated island group in the Atlantic Ocean at 15°N. It is relatively common in Turkey, Greece and northern Iran (Steiner and Gaisler, 1994) and in Cyprus (Boye *et al.*, 1990). Although *P. auritus* is rare in this area, it does occur in mountainous, wooded habitats. Two specimens were mist-netted in Turkey at 600 m above sea level and one was caught at Assalem in northern Iran (Steiner and Gaisler, 1994). The species is also said to be regularly distributed in the higher mountain forests of Greece (Helversen and Weid, 1990). Thus, while *P. austriacus* prevails in southern Europe and has a well-defined northern limit to its range, probably delimited by its inability to survive the cool, changeable climate at high latitude, *P. auritus* is able to extend its range southwards by exploiting mountainous areas and taking advantage of the cooler climate in such areas. It is adapted to living in cool, temperate climates and so its range extends well into northern Europe.

CLOSE RELATIONS

The taxonomy of long-eared bats and their relatives has long been a subject of confusion and changing opinions. Five genera constitute the vespertilionid bats known as the plecotine group; they are *Barbastella*, *Plecotus*, *Corynorhinus*, *Idionycteris* and *Euderma* (Koopman and Jones, 1970). Of these, only *Barbastella* seems to have escaped the confusion. A genus of two Palearctic species, these bats have broad, triangular ears which are joined at the base and which do not fold when the bat is at rest (Stebbings, 1991). *Plecotus* was originally applied only to Palearctic long-eared bats, while three very similar species in North America, known as big-eared or lump-nosed bats, were classified under the genus *Corynorhinus*. Following Handley's (1959) revision of the group, however, it was decided by most taxonomists that *Plecotus* and *Corynorhinus* were so similar that they should be considered as a single genus. Thus, the American species were placed in a subgenus, *Corynorhinus*, within the genus *Plecotus* and became generally known as *Plecotus townsendii*, *Plecotus rafinesquii* and *Plecotus mexicanus*. The single species of *Idionycteris*, *I. phyllotis* was, at one time, classified as *Plecotus phyllotis* (Barbour and Davis, 1969) but later placed in its own genus (Corbet and Hill, 1991; Nowak, 1991). The genus *Euderma* contains one species, *E. maculatum*.

Recently, phylogenetic techniques have been used to re-evaluate relationships among plecotine bats. Using this method, Frost and Timm (1992) argued that *Idionycteris* and *Euderma* were far more similar than were *Idionycteris* and *Plecotus* and they should be synonomized. They also proposed that *Corynorhinus* should be removed from the synonym of *Plecotus*, although the relationships within *Corynorhinus* and *Plecotus* were not fully resolved. Tumlison and Douglas (1992) investigated phylogenetic relationships among the group, using 32 characteristics of the skin and skull. Cladistic analysis yielded one most-parsimonious tree. The cladogram indicated that each of the taxa should be regarded as a genus, which supported the contention that *Idionycteris* is a distinct genus (more closely related to *Euderma* than to the others but still distinct) and argued against the subgeneric designation of *Corynorhinus*. The authors therefore advocated elevating *Corynorhinus* to full generic status and limiting *Plecotus* to Palearctic species. This conclusion is congruent with that of Bogdanowicz and Owen (1996), who analysed relationships among plecotine species by means of a study of morphometric divergence of skull characteristics. The American plecotine bats thus form the following five species, assigned to three genera.

Corynorhinus townsendii. Townsend's, or western, big-eared bat is widely distributed and its range includes most of western North America from British Columbia in Canada, south to Mexico and eastwards through central USA from northern Texas to western Virginia (Ross, 1967). Colonies, including nursery colonies of up to 1000 females and young, live primarily in caves (Humphrey and Kunz, 1976), although attics and barns are also used (Ross, 1967). Besides the main population (known as *C. townsendii townsendii*), two other subspecies are recognized and both are currently considered to be endangered:

C. townsendii virginianus. The Virginia big-eared bat occurs in Virginia, West Virginia, Kentucky and North Carolina (Bagley and Jacobs, 1985). Little is known of its ecology, but recent studies aimed at promoting its conservation (Lacki *et al.*, 1993) found that cliff habitats were important and that the bats used fissures in the rock face as feeding roosts; moth wings were found under these roost sites.

C. townsendii ingens, the Ozark big-eared bat. Again, little is known of the ecology of this bat. It used to be found on the Ozark plateau of northern Kansas, southern Missouri and eastern Oklahoma, but surveys of caves during the late 1980s indicated that it is probably now absent from Missouri and Arkansas (Clark *et al.*, 1993). It is heavily dependent on limestone caves throughout the year (Ross, 1967).

Corynorhinus rafinesquii. Rafinesque's, or eastern, big-eared bat occurs in the south-east of the USA, from the Atlantic coast westwards to Louisiana, Arkansas and southern Missouri and from the Gulf of Mexico northwards to south Illinois, Indiana and Virginia (Barbour and Davis, 1969). It occurs in Kentucky (Meade, 1992) and has recently been found in southern Florida (Brown and Brown, 1993). It relies more on buildings to house nursery colonies than does *C. townsendii*, and rarely uses caves in summer (Barbour and Davis, 1969). Caves are, however, used for hibernation (Best *et al.*, 1992). As well as moths, this species has been reported to eat Tabanidae (horseflies) in considerable numbers (Ellis, 1993), and it has been suggested that it may be important for the control of these flies, which have few natural predators.

Corynorhinus mexicanus, the Mexican big-eared bat, occurs in northern and central Mexico. Formerly regarded as a subspecies of *C. townsendii*, it is now considered to be a distinct species (Hall, 1981). Handley (1959) revised the taxonomy of North American *Corynorhinus*, and his model was later re-evaluated by Humphrey and Kunz (1976). They suggested that *C. townsendii* spread across North America during the Wisconsin glacial period at the end of the Pleistocene, and that the Mexican population became isolated at this time and became specifically distinct. Subsequent isolation of segments of the *C. townsendii* population at the end of the Wisconsin resulted in the development of the sub-species detailed above (Humphrey and Kunz, 1976).

Idionycteris phyllotis. Allen's big-eared bat is distinguished by a pair of lappets projecting from the median bases of the ears anteriorly over the top of the snout (Hill and Smith, 1984). Its distribution is from southeastern Arizona and southwestern New Mexico to central Mexico (Ross, 1967), where it lives in montane forest to a height of about 2500 m above sea level. It flies late at night, about 10 m above the ground, and has been observed to hover and to glean insects from vegetation (Simmons and O'Farrell, 1977). In addition to a short, frequency-modulated pulse used by all plecotine bats, this species also uses a long, constant-frequency pulse at 27 kHz, ending with a short frequency-modulated element (Simmons and O'Farrell, 1977). It also emits loud, audible chirps at about 12 kHz (Hill and Smith, 1984).

Euderma maculatum, the North American spotted bat, is very distinctive in appearance, having black fur with three large white spots in a triangular pattern on its back, very large, pale pink ears and pale flight membranes (Hill and Smith, 1984). This colouration is thought to camouflage the bat in the conditions of changing light and shade on the rocky cliff faces on which it roosts. The spotted bat occurs in Arizona, California, Idaho, Montana, Nevada, New Mexico, Utah and Mexico and is thus sympatric with *I. phyllotis* over much of its range. It was once considered to be very rare and to fly only after midnight, but bat detector studies have shown it to be more abundant than was thought and to be active for most of the night (Leonard and Fenton, 1983). Its diet consists entirely of moths (Ross, 1961, 1967) which it catches in high-speed dives and not by gleaning; it hunts at a height of about 10 m above the ground and has been found to defend feeding territories (Leonard and Fenton, 1983). Its echolocation calls are audible to humans.

Chapter 2

Recognition and Design Features

THERE is no difficulty in distinguishing *P. auritus* and *P. austriacus* from all other European species, but telling them apart from each other is another problem altogether. This chapter addresses the question of identifying long-eared bats, their roosts and signs. It also describes the structure and function of features of these bats which distinguish them from other species and which particularly influence their behaviour and ecology.

RECOGNITION FROM OTHER BAT GENERA

In the Hand

Long-eared bats are easily recognized by their huge ears joined at the base – no other European bat has ears approaching this length (25 mm or more). The barbastelle (*Barbastella barbastellus*) has large ears, but they are less than 20 mm long (Stebbings, 1986), more or less triangular in shape, and are not folded when the bat is at rest. The only other species with relatively long ears is Bechstein's bat, *Myotis bechsteinii*. Its ears are about 18 mm long and are quite separate and positioned on either side of the head (Stebbings, 1986).

At Roost

Even at a distance and in torchlight, the profile of a long-eared bat is unmistakable if the bat is alert and has its ears erect (Figure 2.1a). At rest, the ears may be curled backwards, resembling rams' horns (Figure 2.1b) and, again, these are very distinctive and cannot be confused with any other bats. The only problem arises if the bat is torpid, in which case the ears are usually folded and tucked underneath the wings (Figure 2.1c). The tragus remains erect and looks, at a first glance, like the ear of some other species. Closer inspection will, however, reveal it for what it is.

In Flight

Identification of bat species in flight has been possible for some years, since the use of ultrasonic bat detectors became widespread. Some species are easier to detect than others, and long-eared bats are among the most difficult because they use very low-intensity calls and hence are generally known as 'whispering bats'. Most bat workers assume that, if a flying bat

12

(a)

FIG 2.1   *Ear positions of long-eared bats: (a) ears erect.*

is visible but no call is recorded on the detector, then it is probably a long-eared bat. The calls can rarely be detected unless the bat is within about 5 m of a detector and even then not always, since echolocation is sometimes 'switched off' by the bat. When calls are detectable, they are heard as a series of dry, very rapid 'ticks', similar to a crackle (Catto, 1994). They are more fully discussed later in this chapter. They sound similar to the ticks produced by *Myotis* species, but are softer and more rapid even than those of *Myotis nattereri*. The best frequency on which to detect them is around 45–50 kHz. Long-eared bats are most often detectable when they are flying in enclosed spaces such as attics or barns. In such places they can also be observed in flight by torchlight, when their large, erect ears can clearly be seen. They may also be recognized in such situations because of their slow flight, tight, stalling turns and high manoeuvrability. Even in the open, the ears can usually be seen if the observer is sufficiently close to the bat.

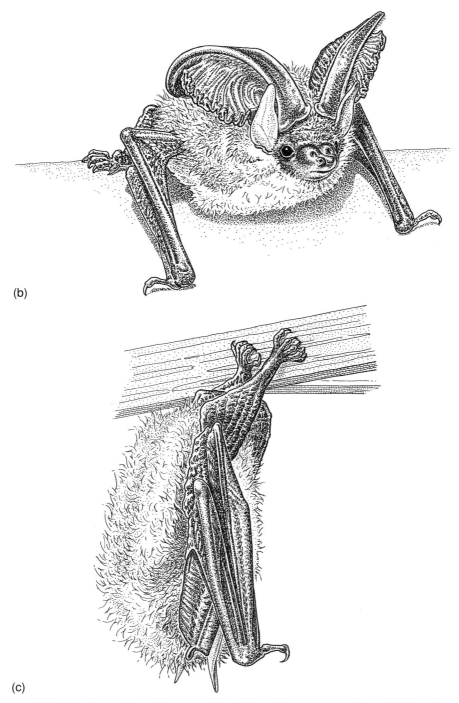

(b)

(c)

FIG 2.1   *Ear positions of long-eared bats: (b) ram's horn position; (c) ears folded and tucked under wings.*

Signs of Roost

In the absence of any bats, it is often possible to deduce the species which has used a roost. *Plecotus* species are among those most associated with roof spaces and particularly with attics since pipistrelles, the commonest species in buildings, usually roost in inaccessible crevices and signs of them are thus not visible. Droppings which are scattered in attics, particularly in a line underneath the ridge beam, are often a sign of long-eared bats. Because these bats fly inside roosts, their droppings are more scattered than are those of other species. Stains from secretions on the bats' fur may be present on roof beams, and the commonest position for these is on the wood in the angle of the ridge. The absence of cobwebs in an attic is also often a sign of use by *Plecotus*. Although long-eared bats are known to catch prey inside roosts (Roer, 1969; Swift and Racey, 1983), the reason for the lack of cobwebs is unlikely to be that the bats have eaten all the spiders. It is more probable that air movement, caused by the bats flying in the attic, prevents the build-up of cobwebs.

Droppings

The droppings of long-eared bats are 2.5–3.0 mm in diameter and 8–10 mm long, and their texture is relatively coarse. They differ from those of other similar sized bats in that they are frequently of irregular shape (described by Stebbings, 1986 as having a 'knobbly outline') and may have a shiny appearance due to the large numbers of moth scales they contain. If they are dampened and pulled apart under a dissecting microscope or powerful magnifier, many will be found to consist of a mass of moth scales, although they may also contain remains of other arthropods. On a number of occasions, I have found faecal pellets from long-eared bats, which, instead of being black like most bat droppings, were light brown in colour. On analysis, they were found to be made up of very pale coloured scales, probably from large noctuid moths. I have not found similarly coloured pellets from other species of similar size.

Feeding Perches

Long-eared bats frequently use feeding perches, which are a sign of their presence in an area. Insects too large to be eaten on the wing (mainly moths and beetles) are carried to a perch, or night roost, where the bat hangs up to handle and consume them. Gould (1955) reported that the average wingspan of moths whose remains were found under perches was 45 mm, thus confirming that the bats process only their largest prey items in this way. Perches may be situated anywhere sheltered where there is easy access for the bat and somewhere for it to hang. Common places to find them are in porches of houses and churches, or in barns and outbuildings. Poulton (1929) conducted a survey of observations made by amateur naturalists, and found that night roosts also included wall recesses, a stable loft, a pent-roof sheltering a garden seat, the roof of a station waiting room and a college study where the window was left open all summer and where the bat hung from a picture frame. Piles of droppings and insect remains rejected by the bat, mainly moth wings, accumulate under the perch; these may be scattered if the perch is high up, or in a neat heap if it is nearer the ground. There are often distinct tooth marks on the insect remains.

RECOGNITION FROM EACH OTHER

Separation of *P. auritus* and *P. austriacus* is only possible with certainty if the bat is in the hand, although face and pelage colour are used as diagnostic characteristics and can be seen without handling the bat. Most of the easily taken measurements overlap to some extent in the two species and thus identification is best made using a range of measurements. In dead specimens, certain skull parameters are diagnostic (Jooris, 1980), but in most cases identification will be made on living bats. Here, measurements have to be made accurately, which can be difficult under field conditions.

Baculum and Skull Measurements

Baculum

The baculum (penis bone) of males differs between the two species (Topal, 1958; Lanza, 1959) and has been used for identification. It is Y-shaped in both species and is described by Corbet (1964) as having slender proximal limbs, about three times as long as they are wide and with axis length 0.8 mm in *P. auritus* and as having stout proximal limbs, shorter than they are wide and with axis length 0.6 mm in *P. austriacus* (Figure 2.2). Strelkov (1989) examined bacula of long-eared bats over most of their ranges, and found wide variation in size and shape in both species. There was a distinct difference in the length of the bone between specimens of *P. auritus* from Europe and the Far East. Similarly, *P. austriacus* from Asia had shorter, narrower bacula than did those from central Europe. Strelkov noted that the differences in body and skull measurements on which differentiation of *P. auritus* into subspecies has been based were actually smaller than the differences in the dimensions of their bacula. Caution must therefore be exercised when using the baculum as a diagnostic character, but for European specimens its measurements and shape do separate the species.

Skull measurements

The most reliable skull measurements for separating *P. auritus* and *P. austriacus* are condylobasal length, the maximum diameter of the tympanic bullae and the lengths of the upper

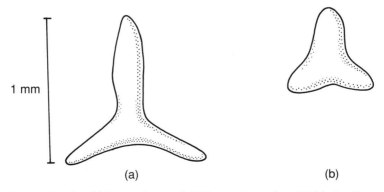

FIG 2.2   *Bacula of (a)* P. auritus *and (b)* P. austriacus *from Moldavia, Romania (redrawn from Strelkov, 1989).*

and lower tooth rows (Piechoki, 1966; Aellen, 1971; Jooris, 1980; Menu, 1983), although mandible length, maximum skull length (Haeussler and Braun, 1991) and the height of the ramus mandibulae (Ruprecht, 1983) are also reported to show clear differences between the species.

Condylobasal length, the length from the tip of the upper jaw to the posterior face of the occipital condyle (Greenaway and Hutson, 1990: Figure 2.3), is short (less than 15.6 mm) in *P. auritus* and long (more than 15.6 mm) in *P. austriacus* according to Corbet (1964). Piechoki's (1966) data agree with this – average length was 15.0 mm for male and 15.0 mm for female *P. auritus* and 16.3 mm for male and 16.7 mm for female *P. austriacus*, with no overlap between the two species.

Tympanic bullae, the bony cavities containing the middle ear, are also used for identification. These are oval-shaped and their maximum diameter is measured. It was found to be an average of 4.1 mm in *P. auritus* (range = 4.0–4.2 mm; *n* = 14) and 4.9 mm in *P. austriacus* (range = 4.8–5.1 mm; *n* = 11; Piechoki, 1966). The species are also clearly separated by expressing the maximum bulla diameter as a percentage of the condylobasal length. The value is less than 29% for *P. auritus* and more than 29% for *P. austriacus* in all cases (Piechoki, 1966; Aellen, 1971; Menu, 1983).

The length of the maxillary tooth row (C–M³) has been found to be diagnostic, being less than 5.6 mm in *P. auritus* and more than 5.6 mm in *P. austriacus* (Corbet, 1964). This is measured occlusally (along the biting surface), from the mesial edge of the cingulum of the

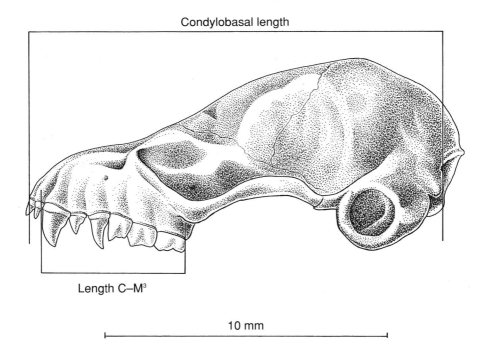

Condylobasal length

Length C–M³

10 mm

FIG 2.3 *Diagram of the skull of* P. auritus *showing measurements of condylobasal length and upper tooth row length (C–M³).*

canine to the distal extreme of the third molar of the upper jaw (Menu, 1983; Figure 2.3). Menu found C–M³ to be a mean of 5.5 ± 0.1 mm in *P. auritus* and 5.9 ± 0.2 mm in *P. austriacus*. He also measured the lower tooth row (C–M₃) in the same way and found that the two species similarly showed no overlap using this parameter. The lengths of C–M₃ were 5.9 ± 0.1 mm in *P. auritus* and 6.6 ± 0.2 mm (mean ± S.D.) in *P. austriacus*. Table 2.1, compiled from the above data, thus enables the species to be separated according to the four skull measurements which have been found to be most reliably diagnostic.

TABLE 2.1 *Principal diagnostic skull measurements of* P. auritus *and* P. austriacus.

Measurement	P. auritus	P. austriacus
Condylobasal length	<15.6 mm	>15.6 mm
Tympanic bulla diameter	<4.5 mm	>4.5 mm
% bulla/condylobasal length	<29%	>29%
C–M³	<5.7 mm	>5.7 mm
C–M₃	<6.2 mm	>6.2 mm

Morphological Measurements

Colour

It would seem logical to assume that brown long-eared bats are brown and grey long-eared bats are grey, but unfortunately the situation is not so simple. Juvenile brown long-eareds, for example, are sooty grey in colour and they remain grey for about 1 year. There is also wide variation in pelage colour within each species (Stebbings, 1967). Dorsal pelage in *P. austriacus* is generally grey, sometimes almost black, while that of *P. auritus* is much more variable, ranging from light buff, through brown to grey. The most reliable feature of dorsal pelage colouring is reported to be the variation in colour along the length of the hairs (Greenaway and Hutson, 1990), a feature widely used in identification of bat species. While the hairs of *P. austriacus* are dark coloured along most of their length, those of *P. auritus* have a broad basal (proximal) and a narrower apical (distal) band lighter in colour, thus forming zones of light and dark colouration. The ventral fur is usually whitish-grey in *P. austriacus* and creamy-buff in *P. auritus* but, again, there is wide variation.

Face colour is regarded as being a good indicator of species by some authors (e.g. Jooris, 1980). It is described as flesh-coloured to light brown in *P. auritus* and dark to very dark brown (not quite black) in *P. austriacus* (Stebbings, 1967; Jooris, 1980). However, face colour is generally considered to be less reliable for identification than colour along the length of the hairs (A.M. Hutson, *pers. comm.*).

Size

P. austriacus is overall larger than *P. auritus*, but intraspecific variation is great. In most vespertilionid species, females are larger than males (Myers, 1978). Stebbings (1967) found that sexual dimorphism in *Plecotus* species, while not as large as expected, did affect separation of the two on the basis of size and that more reliable results were obtained by treating the sexes separately. Weight is too variable through the year and between individuals to be of use, and head–rump length, overall length and wingspan are difficult to measure accurately on active bats. Forearm length is easier to measure, but there is some overlap between species (O'Gorman and Fairley, 1965; Jooris, 1980). Stebbings (1977) reported that forearm length in males was less than 39.0 mm in *P. auritus* and greater than 39.0 mm in *P. austriacus* and that in females less than 39.7 mm in *P. auritus* and greater than 39.7 mm in *P. austriacus*.

Thumb length

P. auritus have long, slender thumbs and feet, while those of *P. austriacus* are shorter. Thumb length is the easier of the two parameters to measure and is generally used as a separation character (Figure 2.4). Measurement is made from the proximal end of the first phalynx (i.e. the joint) to the tip of the thumb excluding the claw. This length is more than 6.0 mm (range 6.5–8.4 mm) in *P. auritus* and less than 6.0 mm in *P. austriacus* (Schober and Grimmberger, 1989). Because *P. auritus* is the smaller species but has longer thumbs, the ratio of thumb length to forearm length is useful, since it reduces overlap due to intraspecific size variation or sexual dimorphism. This ratio is about 17% in *P. auritus* and about 14% in *P. austriacus* (Corbet, 1964).

Tragus

The shape and width of the tragus are considered to be diagnostic. That of *P. auritus* is narrow and lancet-shaped (Figure 2.5), and is yellowish-white in colour with grey pigment towards the top (Schober and Grimmberger, 1989). Its maximum width is less than

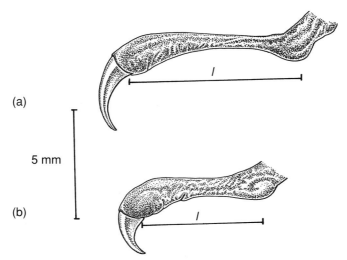

(a)

5 mm

(b)

FIG 2.4 *Thumbs of (a)* P. auritus *and (b)* P. austriacus, *showing the difference in length.* l *is the length from the joint to the end of the digit, excluding the claw (redrawn from Piechoki, 1966).*

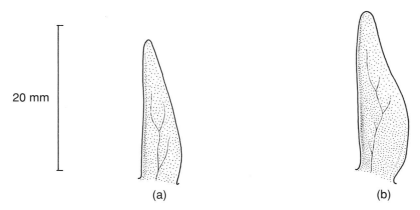

FIG 2.5   *Shape of the tragus of (a)* P. auritus *and (b)* P. austriacus.

5.5 mm. The tragus of *P. austriacus* is broader; its anterior edge is more or less straight and its posterior edge is strongly convex in the proximal half (Figure 2.5). It has grey pigment from the base up. Maximum tragus width in this species is more than 5.5 mm (Stebbings, 1986); when this parameter is measured, the tragus should be gently folded backwards to straighten its natural curvature. Tragus length and ear length are also greater in *P. austriacus* (Stebbings, 1967), but these are less useful parameters and are difficult to measure accurately.

Teeth
The dental formula for both species is $\frac{2.1.2.3}{3.1.3.3} = 36$. The length and shape of the upper canine teeth may be useful for separating the species (Figure 2.6). The tooth is measured from the cingulum to the tip and is longer (>1.9 mm) and relatively narrow when viewed from the side in *P. austriacus*, but relatively short (<1.9 mm) and broad in *P. auritus*. However, tooth wear can affect both shape and length, and for this reason the canines are less reliable for distinguishing the species than are the premolars (A.M. Hutson, *pers. comm.*). In *P. auritus*, the first upper premolar (P^2, since P^1 is missing in bats) is quite distinct, extending well above the cingulum of the canine and to more than half the height of the second premolar (P^4, since P^3 is missing in *Plecotus*). P^2 in *P. austriacus* is much smaller and is barely visible, hardly extending above the cingulum of the canine and not reaching half the height of P^4 (Corbet, 1964; Figure 2.6). The usefulness of this characteristic has been disputed (Menu, 1983), but it is considered by most workers to be reliable (A.M. Hutson, *pers. comm.*).

Penis
The penis of *P. auritus* is thin and narrows towards the tip, while that of *P. austriacus* is club-shaped at the end (Schober and Grimmberger, 1989), but the difference is very slight.
    The most reliable morphological characters separating the species are thus tragus width, thumb length, ratio of thumb length to forearm length, relative sizes of premolars P^2 and P^4 and colour variation along the length of the hairs.

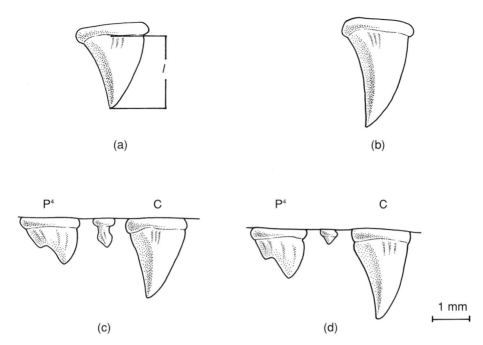

FIG 2.6   *Top: Relative size and shape of the upper canine teeth of (a)* P. auritus *and (b)* P. austriacus. *l is the length of the tooth from the cingulum to the tip. Bottom: The size and shape of the first upper premolar (P²) relative to the canine (C) and the second upper premolar (P⁴) in (c)* P. auritus *and (d)* P. austriacus.

Behavioural Characteristics

Aggressiveness

Stebbings (1967) found that juvenile bats of both species were difficult to handle but that there was a definite interspecific difference in the behaviour of adults. Adult *P. auritus* were mostly docile, and this is consistent with their reputation for being one of the easiest European species to handle and to tame. However, *P. austriacus* usually reacted vigorously to handling by persistently biting and struggling. Stebbings (1970) reported that one female struggled so violently it broke a humerus. He also recorded that the incidence of bats found with severe or fatal injuries was much higher (23%) in *P. austriacus* than in *P. auritus* (3%), and suggested this may have been due to intraspecific aggression. This characteristic varies among individuals, but excessive aggression in an adult bat, together with other characteristics, could well identify it as *P. austriacus*. Gaisler *et al.* (1990) studied the two species in the Czech Republic and reported that a characteristic of *P. austriacus* colonies was a low concentration of individuals which used a large number of roosts. This may well be associated with a high degree of intraspecific aggression.

EARS

The ears of *Plecotus* bats have been a source of interest to naturalists for many years, and there are frequent descriptions of them in bat literature. Among these is one by Bingley (1809), who kept a small group of long-eared bats and observed that their hearing was 'acute and delicate'. He suggested that hearing might well be the source of the dexterity with which even blinded bats were able to avoid objects – the so-called 'sixth sense' of bats described by Spallanzani (1784). Bingley (1809) also described the folding of the bats' ears during sleep. He called the tragus the 'inner ear' and deduced that its purpose was to keep out noxious insects and to prevent any other extraneous matter from entering the bat's head during sleep. By folding the ears and tucking them under the wings, the bat thus prevented intruders from entering. Although his suggested function for the tragus has been superseded, the idea that by folding the pinnae during sleep the bat is protecting them from invasion by dust or parasites is still considered to be valid.

The ear conch is thin and membranous, with 22–24 transverse folds in both species (Schober and Grimmberger, 1989). These close in an action similar to a fan as the ear is folded. The inner (anterior) border is slightly curved and is broadened, with a fringe of fine hairs. The tragus is long and lancet-shaped and points forwards even when the ear is folded. The medial lobules are small lobes which project laterally at a point just above where the ears meet (Hayward and Teagle, 1961). When the ears are erect, the lobules touch each other. They are thought possibly to be involved in the folding and unfolding of the pinnae (Howard, 1995), an action controlled by blood flowing in and out of the ear through special valves (see Chapter 1). Hayward and Teagle (1961) observed the medial lobules of a captive brown long-eared bat and noted that when the bat was torpid the lobules were pale flesh-coloured, considerably swollen and exuded a colourless liquid. When it was active in summer they were flesh-pink in colour, thickened along the outer margins and curved slightly inwards. In this bat, which was intermittently active in winter, the lobules were shrivelled and appeared dark red in colour during active periods. The change from swollen to shrivelled took place quite rapidly (over a few hours) and occurred before the bat changed from being torpid to active and back. Howard (1995) made a study of the medial lobules; he observed no changes in their appearance and never saw any dark red colouration. Their precise function remains obscure.

Folding the Pinnae

Long-eared bats fly with their ears fully erect – the forward-pointing pinnae can clearly be seen on those flying in torchlight and on bats caught in flight. The ears are erected shortly before taking flight (Schober and Grimmberger, 1989). My own observations in summer roosts indicate that, in long-eared bats which are not torpid, erection of the ears also occurs as a reaction to disturbance. As the ears become erect, the bat turns its head as if listening intently and then takes flight.

The normal position of the ears in roosts where bats are not torpid is the ram's horn position (Figure 2.1b), in which they are flaccid and curved backwards but are not folded. As the ears relax, the outer edges crinkle up like a concertina and the inner edges curve over and outwards (Cranbrook, 1963a). With the ears in this position, bats groom themselves and also consume prey at feeding perches. Captive long-eared bats can be observed moving about their cage, feeding and grooming with ram's horn ears.

Fully folded ears most commonly occur in hibernating *Plecotus*, although they can also be found on torpid bats in summer roosts (Speakman, 1988). The ears are folded longitudinally, stretched out to almost their full length and tucked under the wings parallel with the fore-arms (Figure 2.1c), with the tragi still pointing downwards and giving the impression of long, pointed ears. Cranbrook (1963a) observed that long-eared bats did not fold their ears in this way if they were asleep in a warm room, and concluded that the reason for the folding was probably connected with thermoregulation. Because most records of folded ears have con-cerned hibernating bats, it has been assumed over a number of years that ear folding does have a thermoregulatory function. Many field observations have indicated that long-eared bats with folded pinnae are torpid while those with erect pinnae have high body tempera-tures and are active (e.g. Stebbings, 1986). In order to clarify the position and to investigate whether the degree of ear folding could be used as an indicator of the thermoregulatory state of bats without having physically to handle them, Speakman (1988) conducted a study to assess the relationship between pinna position and thermoregulatory state during summer and autumn. He found that there was a significant association between the occurrence of tightly folded pinnae and torpidity, but that this association was statistical and not absolute, as was emphasized by the poor relationship between erection of the pinnae and body tem-perature. There was also no relationship between the elevation of body temperature above ambient and ear position for either torpid or active bats. He concluded that pinna position did not reflect thermoregulatory behaviour and suggested that, although long-eared bats may fold their pinnae to conserve heat in the first place, they may fail to keep them folded if they begin to move their wings and so allow the ears to unfold. Thus, activities such as grooming or adjusting hanging position may be incompatible with keeping the pinnae folded. Since torpid bats seldom move, they are more likely to keep their ears folded, and thus ear position depends principally on what the bat is doing and not on how warm or cold it is.

Besides reducing heat loss, a second possible function of pinna folding was proposed by Coles *et al.* (1989). Because the drastic alteration of shape involved in folding the pinna sig-nificantly reduces its acoustical efficiency, they suggested that folding may be used to reduce auditory sensitivity when the bat is inactive and so avoid acoustical disturbance. An analogy is the partial closing of the facial ruff in sleeping owls. Speakman *et al.* (1991) pursued this argument and suggested that, by folding their ears during torpor, long-eared bats reduce their sensitivity to sounds and so prevent frequent and unnecessary arousals which would waste energy. The failure of non-tactile stimuli to precipitate arousals in hibernating bats (see Chapter 8) is consistent with this theory. Bekker and Mostert (1990) suggested that long-eared bats fold their ears in order to reduce the likelihood of being pulled down from hibernation sites by predators, and another suggestion (J. Speakman, *pers. comm.*) is that they fold them in order to avoid frostbite.

Functions of Large Ears

Griffin (1958) compared the ability of a plecotine bat, *Corynorhinus townsendii*, with that of *Myotis lucifugus*, a bat with normal length ears, to avoid wires arranged in a grid in a flight room. He found that any loss of efficiency in *C. townsendii* caused by the faintness of its ultra-sonic calls was compensated for by its ability to hear much fainter echoes than did *M. lucifugus*.

However, its ability to avoid the wires was reduced if the shape or position of the pinna was altered in any way. The large pinnae were thus assumed to be an important component in the ability of large eared bats to echolocate using low-intensity ultrasound. Coles *et al.* (1989) recorded the neural audiogram of *P. auritus* and found that the most sensitive best frequency thresholds for single neurons were between 7 and 20 kHz, and that the lower and upper hearing limits were 3 kHz and 63 kHz respectively. The auditory system of this species is thus exceptionally sensitive to low-frequency sounds, well below those used in echolocation. The pinna was found to behave as an efficient pressure transformer above 7 kHz, due to its size and horn-like properties, and the external ear as a whole to provide about 20 dB in acoustic gain in the frequency range of 8–20 kHz (Coles *et al.*, 1989). Such amplification of sound pressure is likely to play a major role in enhancing low frequency sensitivity, the frequency range at which the auditory system of *P. auritus* is most sensitive. The main function of the huge ears thus appears to be connected, not with echolocation, but with detecting low-frequency, prey-generated sounds such as moth fluttering. It is an important component in the technique of gleaning, which is discussed in Chapter 3. Obrist *et al.* (1993), in a field study involving 47 bat species from 13 families, similarly found that the large pinnae of bats which used prey-generated sounds to find their targets supplied high sound pressure gain at lower frequencies.

Drag Effect of Large Ears

Large ears produce a high degree of drag (Norberg, 1976a), thus increasing the amount of energy long-eared bats have to expend in flight. Rayner (1987) found that drag, and therefore thrust to overcome it, varied with flight speed – the faster a bat flew, the greater was the drag caused by its ears. Norberg (1976a) observed that *P. auritus* often flies slowly and speculated that only bats which specialize in low-speed flight can afford to have large, drag-producing ears. Although this generalization holds true for most species, there are exceptions, such as the fast-flying, big-eared molossid *Otomops* (Hill and Smith, 1984).

EYES

The eyes of long-eared bats are relatively large compared with those of all other European species. Cranbrook (1963b) speculated that sight, as well as hearing, may be used to locate prey while gleaning. It is tempting to assume that the possession of big eyes means *Plecotus* species see better than other bats, but in fact very little investigation has been carried out. Eisentraut (1950) conducted visual acuity experiments on *P. auritus* and serotine (*Eptesicus serotinus*) bats in Germany. He trained the bats with food rewards to select cards coloured black or white. Both species were able to select 9 cm square cards of the appropriate colour from a distance of 5 cm, but both failed when offered a choice between a circle and a cross of similar size. It does not appear from these experiments that *P. auritus* has particularly good eyesight. However, as Ransome (1990) pointed out, the experiments were carried out in bright light, conditions in which all bats are likely to become confused and which they will not normally encounter in the wild. Ransome considered that the topic required further investigation and advocated experiments under low light conditions and using a range of species. Such investigations may discover whether *Plecotus* bats can, in fact, see better under these conditions than can bats with smaller eyes, such as *Rhinolophus* species.

NOSTRILS

Long-eared bats are unusual, but not unique, in that they produce ultrasonic calls through the nostrils and not through the mouth. They do not have specialized appendages such as the horseshoe-shaped noseleaf of the Rhinolophidae for producing the calls, but their nostrils are shaped differently from those of most other European vespertilionid species. They open laterally and appear to be slit-shaped rather than round as are those of, for example, *Myotis* species. Howard (1995) examined the nostrils of *P. auritus* in detail and recorded that, although they are apparently elongate, only the anterior part of them opens into the nasal passage. The posterior part opens into a circular pit-like structure separated from the anterior part by a septum. He speculated that this structure may be concerned with the production of resonance or with smell. The exact way in which ultrasound is produced by the nostrils of *Plecotus* species has not been determined, but it seems more than likely that the unusual structure of the nose is concerned with this function. Because ultrasound is not produced through the mouth, long-eared bats are also unusual in that they fly with their mouths closed. When alert in the roost and producing ultrasound (e.g. just prior to taking flight) or when being handled, they also keep their mouths shut. This may well be one of the reasons why they have such an appealing image and are seen by the public as 'friendly' bats – a mouthful of teeth appears threatening even if it is caused by bats simply 'looking around' to find out what is going on.

CHROMOSOMES

The karyotypes of *P. auritus*, *P. austriacus* and *B. barbastellus* are identical – $2N = 32$ (Fedyk and Fedyk, 1970). There are ten pairs of metacentric autosomes, five pairs of telocentric autosomes, a submetacentric X chromosome and a small, acrocentric Y chromosome (Fedyk and Ruprecht, 1983). $FNa = 50$–54 in *P. auritus* and 50–52 in *P. austriacus* (Zima and Horacek, 1985). Figure 2.7 shows a karyogram of a male *P. austriacus* from the Czech Republic.

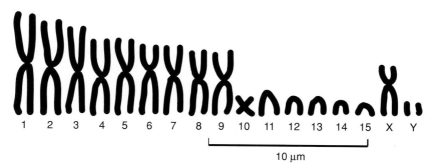

FIG 2.7 *Karyogram of a male* P. austriacus *from the Czech Republic (reproduced with permission from Baker, 1970).*

WINGS AND FLIGHT

Plecotus bats are generally considered to be slow-flying and manoeuvrable, able to hover and to fly and forage in cluttered environments. Because *P. auritus* adapts relatively easily to captivity and, with its ability to fly slowly, is suitable for experiments in flight tunnels and chambers, its flight characteristics have been studied more closely than those of any other European species. Data on *P. austriacus* are sparse, but the morphology and behaviour of the two species are so similar that it is unlikely that they differ greatly in respect of how they fly.

Wing Morphology and Shape

Figure 2.8 shows the wing structure of a *Plecotus* bat. The propatagium is the section of wing which lies anterior to the humerus and radius (Altringham, 1996). With the dactylopatagium minus (between digits 2 and 3), it acts as a wing flap on the leading edge. It can be raised or lowered using the thumb and digit 2, and is adjusted by the bat to prevent stalling at low speeds. The propatagium is greatest in area in slow-flying, manoeuvrable bats

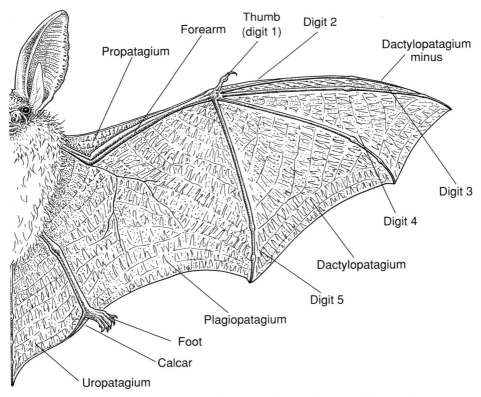

FIG 2.8 *Structure of the wing of* Plecotus, *showing the parts of the patagium.*

and is larger in *Plecotus* than in most European vespertilionid species. Long-eared bats also have relatively broad wings (measured as the length from the wrist to the end of digit 5). The area of wing between the body and digit 5 (the plagiopatagium) provides most of the lift in flight, and thus *Plecotus* bats are able to generate more lift than are many other species. Wing area is important when dealing with flight morphology, and it is usually measured by drawing around the entire flight membrane on graph paper and then counting the squares.

Wing loading is defined as weight of bat divided by total area of flight membrane and is thus a measure of the load carried per unit of membrane.

Aspect ratio is calculated as wingspan divided by area of flight membrane. It can be used to compare the length of wings in different bats in relation to wing area. As a rule, short, broad wings (low aspect ratio) are associated with slow flight (Norberg, 1976a) and long, narrow ones (high aspect ratio) with fast flight. Wing loading affects the speed at which bats fly – the higher the wing loading, the faster the bat has to fly in order to generate enough lift to stay airborne. Low wing loading bats can fly more slowly.

P. auritus has an average wing loading value of 7.2 N m^{-2} (0.072 g cm^{-2}) and an aspect ratio of 5.9 (Norberg, 1970a; 1976b; Norberg and Rayner, 1987). In *P. austriacus*, wing loading is 7.9 N m^{-2} and aspect ratio 6.1 (Norberg and Rayner, 1987). Similar values have been recorded for other plecotine bats: wing loading has been calculated at 7.0 N m^{-2} in *C. townsendii* (Farney and Fleharty, 1969) and 5.9 N m^{-2} in *C. rafinesquii* (Norberg and Rayner, 1987) and aspect ratio at 5.9 in both these species (Farney and Fleharty, 1969; Norberg and Rayner, 1987). Long-eared bats thus have low wing loading values and average to low aspect ratios compared with other bats (Norberg and Rayner, 1987). They have a large wing area and broad, relatively short wings. This combination is commonly found in bats which feed among vegetation, since it allows them to make tight turns and to hover. Low wing loading also enables such bats to carry heavy prey items to perches to consume them.

Another feature of slow-flying, tight-turning bats is that they often have short, rounded wingtips, and this is true of both *Plecotus* species. Also, the tips of digits 3, 4 and 5 are cartilaginous and flexible (Norberg, 1970b), so allowing flexibility of shape. Finally, long-eared bats have high-camber wings and the ability to control camber by flexing digit 5 and lowering the hind limbs.

Norberg and Rayner (1987) considered that the term manoeuvrability was too often loosely used, and they defined it precisely to distinguish it from agility. Manoeuvrability refers to the space required for a bat to alter its flight path when it is flying at a constant speed. It is greatest when wing loading is low and is also favoured by short wingspan; *Plecotus* bats are thus morphologically equipped to be highly manoeuvrable, and their ability to fly and turn in confined spaces confirms that this is the case. Agility is a measure of the ease or speed with which the flight path can be altered. It is favoured by low wing inertia and high lift production. Some fast-flying bats (e.g. the noctule, *Nyctalus noctula*) are agile but not manoeuvrable, while all manoeuvrable bats are also agile.

Straight Flight and Flight Speed

In level flight, the long axis of the body is kept almost horizontal (Norberg, 1976a). Wing and body movements of a specimen of *P. auritus* flying in a net cage 0.6 × 0.6 × 3.5 m were filmed by Norberg (1976a). At the beginning of the downstroke, the wings were extended at an angle of 49.4° above the horizontal and the tail and feet were held straight backwards. By the middle of the downstroke, the wing was twisted and the feet and tail began to move downwards, and in the latter part of the downstroke the wings were sharply cambered and the tail fully lowered. At the beginning of the upstroke, the elbows and wrists were slightly flexed and the camber still pronounced, but in the later part of the upstroke the feet were raised, which reduced the camber in the proximal part of the wings. The middle part of the wings was still cambered and the wingtips momentarily inverted before beginning the next downstroke.

In the above study, the bat was found to be flying slowly, at an estimated speed of 2.35 m s^{-1}. Norberg calculated that, with the bat's huge, drag-producing ears, the speed at which minimum power was required (i.e. the most energetically efficient speed) was slightly faster than this at 3.1 m s^{-1}. This is slow for a bat, but corresponds to the speeds at which *P. auritus* has frequently been observed flying while foraging around vegetation. Norberg (1976a) suggested that only bats which forage at slow speeds can afford to have large ears, since the coefficient of drag increases rapidly as flight speed increases.

However, *Plecotus* bats do not always fly so slowly. Baagøe (1987) used bat detectors, night vision equipment and multiple-flash photography involving two motor-driven cameras a fixed distance apart to measure flight speeds of 12 Scandinavian bat species. In straight or wide-turning flight, he estimated that *P. auritus* flew at an average speed of 4.5 m s^{-1}. This was almost identical to the flight speed (4.6 m s^{-1}) of *Myotis daubentonii*, a bat of similar size and wing loading of 7.0 N m^{-2}. *Nyctalus noctula*, a large bat with higher wing loading, flew faster at 8.0 m s^{-1}. *P. auritus* had the slowest speed of the 12 species, but not by much. Howard (1995) similarly found that *P. auritus* commuting between two fixed points along a route between roost and foraging areas flew at 5.9 m s^{-1}. Again, this speed is comparable with commuting speeds of similar sized species such as *Myotis nattereri* and *M. daubentonii*. Thus it appears that *P. auritus* can fly relatively fast and that it does so in straight flight when commuting. It probably does this in order to reduce the risk of being caught by predators, but pays a price because such rapid flight is more energetically expensive than slower flight. This could be one of the reasons why *P. auritus* forage close to their roosts and why most roosts are within 0.5 km of deciduous woodland (Entwistle *et al.*, 1997). Its minimum power speed is the slower one used during foraging.

Turning Flight

Rayner and Aldridge (1985) used a microcomputer to reconstruct a three-dimensional object from images taken by still or cine cameras and were able to illustrate a slow, powered turn by *P. auritus* in a flight chamber. The bat gained height as it slowed on approaching the turn and then decelerated during the turn from a straight flight speed of 1.5 m s^{-1} to a minimum of 0.55 m s^{-1}, when the curvature was steepest. The wings generated lift throughout the turn, but did not produce enough vertical force to support the bat's weight because the wings had to be banked to produce the lateral centripetal acceleration required to alter the direction of the flight path.

In another study, Aldridge (1987) investigated turning flight in six British bat species including *P. auritus* using Pennycuick's (1975) equation:

$$r = \frac{2W}{\rho \, C_{L} \, Sg \sin \theta}$$

where ρ is the air density, C_{L} is the lift coefficient, S is the wing area, g is the acceleration due to gravity, W is the weight of the bat and θ is the bank angle. From this equation, Aldridge deduced that the turning radius was proportional to wing loading and that bats with low wing loading would turn tightly and be manoeuvrable. The bats were trained to fly in a flight tunnel and then made to turn by a barrier being placed across their flight path. The turns made were photographed and curvature, speed and lateral and vertical accelera-tion calculated. The lift coefficient for each species was estimated from the equation above; these were the coefficients which would have developed if the bats had been performing gliding, rather than powered, turns. High values indicated that powered turns must have been used, and a C_{L} value of 1–2 was required to indicate that a bat was gliding. *P. auritus* was the only species with a C_{L} in this range (C_{L} = 1.57). Thus it was essentially performing an unpowered, or gliding, turn. The other bats, two *Rhinolophus* species, two *Myotis* species and *P. pipistrellus*, all performed powered turns and approached the turn at relatively high speeds. *P. auritus* can therefore make tight, powered turns or gliding turns and is able to do both at relatively low energetic cost because of its low wing loading. *Rhinolophus ferrume-quinum* was also found, in the study, to be able to make tight turns, but at higher energy cost. Low energy cost is thus a feature of twisting, turning flight in *P. auritus*.

Hovering

Hovering in *Plecotus* species has been investigated in a number of studies since it was first described by Eisentraut (1936). Norberg (1970a) filmed a hovering *P. auritus* in a flight tunnel and measured wingbeat frequency at 10.2–12.5 Hz. The mean speed of the wingtip was about 5.2 m s^{-1} averaged over an entire cycle. The greatest speed of the wingtip was reached in the upper half of the upstroke and in the middle of the downstroke. The wings swept downwards and forwards fully extended and with high camber and then turned upwards and slightly towards each other at the bottom of the stroke. The upstroke started with a slight flex of the elbow and wrist and rotation of the humerus, which increased the angle of attack. The forelimb rose upwards and backwards until the radius was inclined at 60–70° to the horizontal, at which point a simultaneous reversing rotation of the humerus caused the wing to flick backwards and upwards before the start of the next downstroke. During the cycle the uropatagium moved up and down as a result of leg movements; this had the effect of keeping a fairly constant angle of attack on the proximal part of the wing and also maintained the equilibrium of the body during the cycle. The long axis of the body was inclined at about 30° to the horizontal, and the body flexed and extended slightly during the cycle; it was most flexed during the first half of the upstroke. The lift coefficient obtained by *P. auritus* during hovering is 3.1 to 6.4 (Norberg, 1976b) and hovering is therefore more power-demanding than either straight or turning flight.

Norberg and Rayner (1987) classed *P. auritus* and *P. austriacus* as hover-gleaning bats, i.e. bats which glean from surfaces such as vegetation or tree trunks and which hover briefly beside these surfaces. They pointed out that, for energetic reasons, hovering bats should benefit from long wings but that, because hovering takes up relatively little of long-eared bats' time, selection has acted against the evolution of long wings because these would hamper non-hovering flight in cluttered situations. *Plecotus* therefore compromise with average-length wings, low wing loading and rounded wingtips, thus achieving good manoeuvrability at the cost of relatively expensive flight.

ECHOLOCATION

All microchiropteran species use ultrasound to navigate and to detect their prey and many also use either audible or ultrasound (or a combination) for social communication. The frequency range for navigation calls in European species is 18–120 kHz and many of them call at around 40–60 kHz. High-frequency sounds have short wavelengths, and the best sound for detecting an object is one whose wavelength is around the same length as that object. A sound with a frequency of 50 kHz has a wavelength of 6.8 mm (Altringham, 1996), which is an average length for an insect. This explains why so many bats call at around 50 kHz. Bats emit ultrasound in pulses, and it is the characteristics of these pulses which allow identification using bat detectors. The pulses may be frequency modulated (FM) or constant frequency (CF), or they may be a combination of the two. FM pulses sweep downwards through a range of frequencies (usually from around 65 to 25 kHz), while CF calls are at one frequency, often with a short FM component at the beginning or end. FM pulses are typically short – 0.5–5 ms – which allows the bat to finish emitting a pulse before the echo of that pulse comes back to it. From the time taken for the echo to return, the distance to a prey item can be estimated. As the bat approaches an insect, pulses become shorter, and in the terminal phase of an attack, the pulse rate increases rapidly until each pulse may be only a fraction of a millisecond long. This is the so-called 'feeding buzz' which can clearly be heard on bat detectors, although it sounds similar for all species and so cannot be used for identification.

The echolocation calls of both *P. auritus* and *P. austriacus* are characterized by their quietness combined with a very fast pulse rate (Catto, 1994). The call of *P. auritus* was analysed by Ahlén (1981), who described it as a faint and short FM sweep, about 2 ms long and with prominent second harmonics. There were several peaks in the frequency spectrum, the highest at 26, 42 and 59 kHz. The repetition rate was 20 pulses per second or more. Figure 2.9 shows a diagrammatic representation of this characteristic call. The call can most clearly be heard with the detector set at 45–50 kHz, but it is very faint and is only detectable if the bat is less than about 5 m away. This quietness (or absence of a call if the bat is further away but visible), combined with the fast repetition rate and the observed slow flight and large ears, is used to identify a long-eared bat in flight.

P. auritus is not always a whispering bat. Ahlén (1981) also identified a loud pulse, detectable at 40 m or more, 7.1 ms long and sliding in frequency from 42 kHz to 12 kHz, ending with a short (1 ms) CF component at 12 kHz and then a very short downward sweep (Figure 2.10). This call is heard on a detector as a soft but powerful smack, and the repetition rate is about 5.4 pulses per second. It may be emitted intermittently, usually when the bat is flying inside structures such as barns or mines, or more regularly when out in the open (Ahlén, 1981). Coles *et al.* (1989) noted that this loud long-sweep had its peak frequency at around 12 kHz, which is right in the middle of the most sensitive hearing range of *P. auritus* and speculated that it may well be a long-distance communication call, although its exact function is unknown.

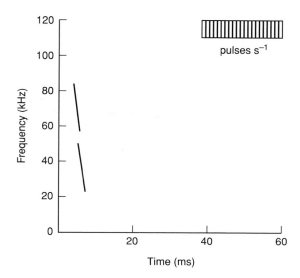

FIG 2.9 *Diagrammatic representation of the characteristic call of* P. auritus *(reproduced with permission from Catto, 1994).*

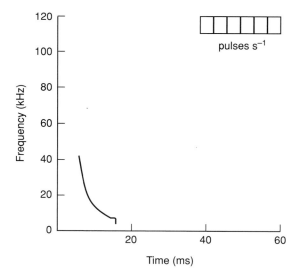

FIG 2.10 *Diagrammatic representation of the loud-long sweep (Ahlén, 1981) of* P. auritus.

The normal ultrasonic calls produced by long-eared bats are adapted to their foraging methods, whereby they fly in cluttered situations and glean prey from vegetation. In general, CF signals, which increase the range of target detection, are used by bats which hunt in open situations, while FM signals allow bats accurately to locate and identify obstacles and targets (Roverud, 1987) and are therefore suitable for use in cluttered environments. Gleaners, which must distinguish between echoes from potential prey and those from background vegetation, use low intensity, short (<1 ms), multiharmonic FM signals (Roverud, 1987). *Plecotus* bats do not have to detect prey at any great distance, and by using quiet calls they also avoid alerting insects which can hear them (see Chapter 3) for as long as possible.

The energetic cost of producing echolocation calls is relatively high in terrestrial mammals and resting bats, but in flying bats there is effectively no extra cost above that of flying because the calls are made by the same muscles which flap the wings (Speakman and Racey, 1991; Speakman, 1993). This was suggested by Speakman and Racey (1991) to be the reason why echolocation has not evolved in many groups of terrestrial mammals. Jones (1994) calculated that, in general, insectivorous bats produce about one call per wingbeat in the search phase of an insect chase, and thus the production of calls costs no more in energetic terms than would flapping without calling. However, about 12% of species (almost all gleaners) trade intensity for repetition rate and use each wingbeat to produce several very low-intensity calls instead of one loud one. Bats such as *Plecotus* species have thus adapted the method to suit their own foraging behaviour.

CHAPTER 3

Gleaning and Diet

THE relationship between bats and their insect prey is a complex one which evolves continuously. The present chapter reviews the response of insects to predation by bats and its implications for the way in which long-eared bats catch their prey. The hunting methods of the bats are considered, as is the effect these have on the composition of the diet.

INSECT RESPONSES TO ECHOLOCATION

Echolocating bats first appeared in the Eocene, by which time insects were long established (Sales and Pye, 1974), and groups such as moths (Lepidoptera) and lacewings (Neuroptera) then responded to the threat posed by the new predators by developing organs which could detect the bats' ultrasound. The presence of hearing organs in insects has been known for some time – as long ago as 1877, White suggested that moths might be able to avoid bats by listening to them squeaking. He was referring to the audible cries of the bats, since at that time echolocation was not understood, but the idea was later substantiated by the discovery that moths possess ears, or tympanic organs, which are sensitive to ultrasound in the frequency range produced by bats. The tympanic organs of noctuid moths were reviewed in detail by Roeder (1967) and since then similar organs have been described in five other lepidopteran families, as well as in green lacewings (Miller, 1970), some beetles (Forrest *et al.*, 1997), mantises, cicadas and water boatmen and one family of Diptera (Fullard and Yack, 1993).

Lepidoptera

The superfamily Noctuoidea includes moths of the families Noctuidae, Notodontidae and Arctiidae, all of which have similar hearing organs situated on the third thoracic segment, behind and below the attachment of the second pair of wings (Sales and Pye, 1974). Each organ lies within a deep, scale-free recess on the posterior wall of the third thoracic segment; the structure was described by Roeder and Treat (1957). A transparent tympanic membrane (equivalent to an eardrum) faces obliquely backwards and outwards into the recess. Anterior to the tympanic membrane is an air sac, an expanded part of the moth's respiratory system, across which sensory cells are suspended. There are two acoustic, or A, cells, which are modified bipolar neurones. These lie close together, suspended in a strand of tissue which runs from the centre of the tympanic membrane towards a skeletal support projecting into the air sac. The proximal nerve fibres from each A cell run in the tissue strand towards this support and are joined by a third nerve fibre from a large, non-acoustic B cell close to the support. The three fibres join to form the tympanic nerve which joins the main nervous system at the pterothoracic ganglion. The A cells are sensitive to vibration from the tympanic membrane and they generate nerve impulses which are transmitted along the tympanic nerve to the central nervous system.

When approached by a bat, noctuid moths will show a variety of responses including loops, spirals and changes of speed or direction. Roeder (1962) observed 402 encounters between bats and noctuid moths and found that when the moths reacted in this way, only 7% of them were caught, compared with 50% of those which did not respond. Roeder and Treat (1969) similarly estimated that insects which can hear have up to 40% less chance of being captured by bats than have those which cannot. A series of experiments by Agee (1967, 1969) studied the reaction of noctuid moths to pulsed ultrasound. At pulse rates of more than 15 s^{-1} and at sound pressure levels higher than 80 dB, the moths responded by looping or diving to the ground. Some resumed flight after 2–4 s, but others remained stationary on the ground for up to 10 min. If the sound pressure was lower than 80 dB, the moths made a directional turn away from the source of the sound. At pulse rates of less than 2 s^{-1}, they showed no directional response, but the flight pattern became erratic.

The tympanic organs of Notodontidae and Arctiidae are sensitive to sounds of 16–20 kHz, within the human hearing range, and also to those well into the ultrasonic range; they will respond to pulse rates of up to 45 s^{-1} (Haskell and Belton, 1956). Some arctiid species, besides being able to hear bats, are also able to 'jam' their calls. Dunning and Roeder (1965) showed that several arctiid moth species produced streams of clicks in response to bat calls. The dominant frequency of these was about 60 kHz, and if recordings of them were played to flying bats, the bats turned away from the sound. Achyra and Fenton (1992) proposed another function for these clicks. Many arctiid moths are unpalatable and have warning coloration. Achyra and Fenton suggested that the clicks are used as aposematic signals to warn the bats of the moth's unpleasant taste. A bat which has once heard the clicks and then tried to eat the moth is unlikely to repeat the experience. Such systems do not always work, however – Thompson (1982) found a garden tiger moth (*Arctia caja*), an unpalatable, warningly coloured arctiid, under a *P. auritus* feeding perch. It had been killed by the bat and then rejected whole. Obviously this particular bat had still to learn its lesson.

Moths of the superfamilies Pyraloidea and Geometroidea have tympanic organs on the abdomen, usually on the first segment (Fullard and Yack, 1993), whereas a few species of tropical Sphingoidea (hawk moths) have them on the labial palps. Recent work on species of geometrid moths which emerge in autumn and winter (Rydell *et al.*, 1997) showed that males had good hearing broadly tuned to 25–40 kHz, despite being preyed on less by bats than are moths which fly during summer. They responded to pulsed ultrasound by altering their flightpath or diving towards the ground. However, the females of these species, which are flightless and therefore not subjected to aerial predation, were found to have greatly reduced tympanic organs and to be virtually deaf.

Neuroptera

One family within the Neuroptera, the green lacewings (Chrysopidae), have a swelling near the base of each forewing. In the genus *Chrysopa* these swellings contain sensory cells resembling the tympanic ears of moths; they are sensitive to frequencies of up to 100 kHz (Miller, 1970). Miller (1971) reported that the response of green lacewings to artificial ultrasound pulses was a reaction of the flexor muscles of the forewing. This caused the insect to fold its wings. The behavioural response began 40 ms after stimulation (Miller, 1975), which enabled the lacewing to dive steeply out of the path of a hunting bat.

Coleoptera

Hearing organs have been described in some species of tiger beetles (Cicindelidae; Spangler, 1988) and dung beetles (Scarabaeidae; Forrest *et al.*, 1997). The organs differ in structure and placement between the two groups and have evolved quite separately; those in scarabaeids consist of a thin tympanic membrane backed by an air sac and are located behind the head (Forrest *et al.*, 1997), while those of tiger beetles are on the first abdominal segment (Spangler, 1988).

Other Groups

Other insects reported to possess hearing organs include some species of mantis (Yager and Hoy, 1986), field crickets (Pollack, 1994), Hemiptera such as some water boatmen (Corixidae) and cicadas (Cicadidae) and one family of cyclorrhaphan flies (Fullard and Yack, 1993). Insect ears are thus polyphyletic, having evolved many times in a number of different groups. This suggests that they are an important feature for nocturnal insects and that predation by bats exerts strong evolutionary pressure on such insects.

The ears of tympanic insects have their maximum sensitivity in the ultrasonic range used by most of the bats likely to prey on them (Fenton and Fullard, 1979). An interesting example occurs in Hawaii (Fullard, 1987), where *Lasiurus cinereus semotus* is the only bat species. The ears of moths on the islands were found by Fullard to be broadly tuned to 20–50 kHz but to be less sensitive than moths elsewhere to the higher end of this range. *L. c. semotus* uses orientation calls of 27.8 kHz, and the moths' maximum sensitivity was at around 30 kHz.

The range at which a hunting bat can be detected by an insect will strongly affect the chance that insect has to avoid capture and will vary with the intensity of the bat's call. At a distance of 10 cm from a bat's face, the intensity of calls ranges from more than 110 dB to 65 dB (Fenton and Fullard, 1981), and bats can detect insects at up to 20 m. Several species of moth can, however, detect bats at up to 40 m (Roeder, 1967). In general, therefore, it is likely that a moth should detect a hunting bat before it is 'spotted' by that bat. However, bats use a number of strategies to increase their chances of getting ahead.

BATS' RESPONSES TO INSECT HEARING ORGANS

Bats can increase the speed at which they fly. One example is *Euderma maculatum*, which is also an exception to the generalization that bats with big ears are gleaners. This species has enormous ears and feeds almost exclusively on moths (Ross, 1967), but Leonard and Fenton (1983), in a detailed study, found no evidence that it gleaned. Instead it flew at a height of about 10 m and caught moths in high-speed dives ending almost at ground level.

It appeared to be following the moths as they took evasive action having heard it coming. Possibly, by using these dives, *E. maculatum* is able to overcome the energetic expense of having to fly fast despite the drag caused by its big ears.

A second possible strategy by bats is to use higher echolocation call frequencies (Fullard, 1992). An African species, *Cloeotus percivali*, which uses the highest known frequency for any bat (212 kHz; Fenton and Bell, 1981), has been shown to feed exclusively on moths (Whitaker and Black, 1976). In Europe, greater and lesser horseshoe bats *Rhinolophus ferrumequinum* and *Rhinolophus hipposideros* also eat many moths (Beck, 1995; Jones *et al.*, 1995) and use higher frequencies (constant frequency components at 83 kHz for *R. ferrumequinum* and 113 kHz for *R. hipposideros*; Catto, 1994) than do vespertilionid species.

Bats may also use lower intensity calls. This is often associated with gleaning, as in *P. auritus*. Low-intensity ultrasound reduces the range at which bats can be detected by insects (Fullard, 1992); a combination of low intensity and high frequency is used in Africa by members of the families Nycteridae and Megadermatidae and there is evidence that moths are unable to detect the presence of these bats further away than about 2 m (Fenton and Fullard, 1979). In addition, because moths appear to be unable to differentiate between distant, loud bats and close-by, quiet ones (Faure *et al.*, 1993), they are less likely to take quick evasive action in response to low intensity calls. However, some bats which use low-intensity sound and which glean do not eat moths to any great extent (e.g. *Myotis nattereri* in Britain; Shiel *et al.*, 1991; Swift, 1997) and it is possible that the use of low intensity calls is primarily a strategy, not to reduce detection by insects, but to avoid the bats deafening themselves when flying in cluttered environments such as among foliage.

The fourth way in which bats can reduce detection by insects is to pick prey off foliage and other surfaces, i.e. to glean. Stationary or crawling moths, as well as flying ones, are able to detect and react to bat calls (Werner, 1981), but those with thoracic ears will be less sensitive in such situations because their tympanic organs are covered by their wings and so the sound will be muffled. Noctuid moths were found to be less good at detecting a gleaning bat, *Myotis septentrionalis*, than an aerial hunter, *Myotis lucifugus*, and were particularly poor at detecting the gleaner when their ears were covered (Faure *et al.*, 1993). Even when a resting moth does detect a bat, its escape possibilities are limited. It can 'freeze' (Werner, 1981) but is unlikely to have time to take flight and dive out of the way; once detected it is thus less likely to escape than is a flying moth. From available evidence, it appears that moths have not yet evolved a very efficient strategy for avoiding gleaners. Faure *et al.* (1993) suggested this may be because relatively few bat species worldwide (about 10%) are gleaners and thus evolutionary pressure on moths to counter the strategy has not been sufficiently strong. They viewed gleaners as predatory 'cheaters' in bat–moth interactions. However, this argument may not apply in Europe, where there are many gleaning bats (e.g. *Myotis myotis*, *M. blythii* and *M. nattereri*) and where *P. auritus* is one of the commonest species.

GLEANING

Gleaning is defined as capturing prey crawling or at rest on solid surfaces rather than in flight. Bats may glean from the ground (e.g. *Myotis myotis*; Arlettaz and Perrin, 1995; Arlettaz, 1996a) or grass (e.g. *Myotis nattereri*; Arlettaz, 1996b), or may switch between these substrates (Arlettaz and Perrin, 1995) depending on prey availability. They may glean from foliage, mainly trees and bushes, as does *P. auritus*, although this species is also known to take prey from grass and occasionally from the ground (Shiel *et al.*, 1991). Another form of gleaning is perch hunting, which is often practised by bats which feed on small mammals or very large tropical insects. An example is the African false vampire, *Cardioderma cor*, which eats large, ground-dwelling beetles and centipedes (Vaughan, 1976). This bat scans an area of ground from a perch and makes short (less than 5 s) flights to capture prey; it may alight on the ground for a second or two before returning to its perch.

Advantages of Gleaning

There are several advantages to bats of gleaning rather than aerial capture. One of these, as has been discussed above, is that it is a strategy against which moths have few defences. Moths are relatively large, soft-bodied insects and are therefore a profitable food source. In general, gleaning bats eat a higher proportion of moths than do aerial hunters. Gleaners are also able to fly later at night than are bats such as *Pipistrellus pipistrellus* which rely for most of their food on the dawn and dusk peaks of flying insects (see Chapter 4). This means that, particularly at high latitude, gleaners do not have to risk being seen and captured by predators on light evenings. They are less dependent on air temperature than are aerial hunters, and this is also a particular advantage in temperate regions where air temperature can vary from night to night. Numbers of flying insects have been shown to be significantly reduced on nights when dusk temperature falls below 10°C (Rydell, 1989a). By feeding on non-flying insects, gleaners are able to forage successfully on cooler nights.

A fourth advantage is that, by gleaning, bats are able to increase the size and also the range of insects which they can catch. Larger moths can be handled on vegetation than in flight and non-flying prey such as spiders, caterpillars and harvestmen can be included in the diet; these are obviously not available to aerial hunters. Barclay (1991) studied two *Myotis* species of similar size in an upland area in Canada, at 1350–2150 m above sea level and 51°N, where nights were cold in summer and the dusk insect peak short. He found that *M. lucifugus*, an aerial forager, did not produce young in the area, since no nursery colonies were found and all specimens caught were males. Females hibernated in the upland area but moved to lower altitude in summer. However, *M. evotis*, a gleaner, did form nursery colonies and rear young. He attributed the difference in reproductive behaviour to the foraging methods of the two species and suggested that, because *M. evotis* was able to glean some of its prey, it was able to meet the high energy demands of producing and rearing young in the cool, upland area.

Gleaning in P. auritus

Gleaning as a foraging technique by this species has been established by both observation and dietary studies. Millais (1904) observed a long-eared bat alighting on fresh cattle dung and eating the flies (yellow dung flies, *Scathophaga stercoraria*) which infested it. Barrett-Hamilton (1910) listed a number of observations of foliage gleaning, and Swift and Racey (1983) marked individual *P. auritus* with reflective rings and observed their foraging behaviour over a number of nights. The bats were seen to hover in flight, to turn frequently and to disappear among the tree foliage for about 20 s before reappearing.

Dietary studies, including those by Swift and Racey (1983), Rydell (1989b) and Shiel *et al.* (1991), confirm the presence in the diet of arthropods which do not fly and must therefore have been caught by gleaning. These include spiders (order Araneae), harvestmen (order Opiliones)and centipedes (class Chilopoda), and the diet also includes diurnal insects, such as brachyceran flies, which are unlikely to have been caught in flight at night. Both Rydell (1989b) and Shiel *et al.* (1991) estimated that approximately 40% of the diet was gleaned, even if it were assumed that all moths were caught in free flight. In fact, the proportion of the diet gleaned is almost certainly higher, as many moths are also caught in this way. Anderson and Racey (1991) found that, of the moths taken in a flight room by captive brown long-eared bats, approximately half were caught by gleaning and half by aerial capture.

Anderson and Racey (1991) described gleaning in their captive *P. auritus* in a flight room measuring 2.8 × 3.0 × 3.0 m, into which were released live moths of species known to be included in their natural diet (Thompson, 1982). Moths were caught by gleaning in 56% (*n*=53) of observations and in the air in 44% (*n*=41), and bats generally began hunting from a stationary position at a perch. Moths were gleaned mainly from vertical surfaces, but also from the ceiling and occasionally from the floor. Pursuits lasted from a few seconds to about half a minute, and flight was often twisting.

The bats in the above experiments were followed as closely as possible by a microphone attached to a cane manipulated by an observer. The microphone was connected to a QMC S200 bat detector in broadband mode; this monitored as accurately as possible echolocation calls produced during moth captures. Bats capturing moths in the air produced calls in 89% (*n*=23) of cases, but during gleaning calls were recorded in only 29% (*n*=8) of attacks. Furthermore, gleaning attacks were shown to be significantly more successful (*p*<0.001) when calls were absent, i.e. when echolocation was 'switched off' by the bat. Anderson and Racey (1991) believed it was unlikely that visual cues were being used during these non-echolocating attacks, since light levels in the experiments were very low. It was also obvious throughout the experiments that bats were only attracted to moving prey and that stationary moths were ignored, even at very short distances. The movements which alerted bats were fluttering, walking or flying, and bats which were alerted made characteristic listening movements of the head and ears. A second series of experiments with captive *P. auritus* (Anderson and Racey, 1993) showed that these bats were able to discriminate between fluttering and non-fluttering moths; they chose fluttering ones in 92.6% of trials when visual and ultrasonic cues were available and in 85.9% of trials when such cues were eliminated. The bats were clearly able to discriminate on the basis of the sounds produced by the fluttering moths. Many of these sounds have a frequency below 20 kHz, and this is the frequency at which *P. auritus* hearing is most sensitive (Coles *et al.*, 1989). Anderson and Racey (1993) therefore proposed that the bats used passive listening to prey-generated sounds to locate moths during most gleaning attacks. Although some noctuid moths produce ultrasound in flight as a result of the hindwings' margins rubbing together (Waters and Jones, 1994), most of these sounds have a frequency of around 46 kHz, which is well above the most sensitive hearing range of *P. auritus*. Thus they are not likely to be of much help to the bat in locating flying moths by passive listening (Waters and Jones, 1994) and therefore echolocation is used in most aerial attacks.

In Anderson and Racey's (1991, 1993) experiments, bats frequently hovered in front of fluttering moths for several seconds before gleaning them. While hovering in front of potential prey, they were more likely to remain silent than to produce echolocation pulses – echolocation calls were recorded in only 24% of sequences in which hovering occurred

(Anderson and Racey, 1993). The hovering distance (i.e. the distance from the prey to the place where the bat chose to hover) was relatively constant; it did not differ significantly between sequences with and without echolocation and it may have been related to the intensity of prey sounds. However, the mean duration of hovering was significantly longer ($p=0.04$) in sequences in which echolocation was not used. Anderson and Racey concluded that prey-generated fluttering sounds were sufficient to alert foraging *P. auritus* to the presence of moths. The bats mainly used passive listening to these low-frequency (below 20 kHz) sounds to locate prey, and hovered close to moths while listening to and locating them.

Gleaning by P. austriacus

The shortage of data on foraging in grey long-eared bats makes it difficult to establish the degree to which they glean their prey. They have been seen flying very slowly, hovering and turning frequently while flying among foliage and inside stables and sheepfolds (Barataud, 1990). This author reported that light-tagged *P. austriacus* captured insects inside farm buildings and he also observed them flying very close to tree foliage. A single radio-tagged individual was tracked by Fluckiger and Beck (1995), and this bat flew among the foliage of a chestnut tree; it was assumed to be gleaning while out of sight. Dietary studies indicate that, while *P. austriacus* undoubtedly does glean, it does so to a lesser extent than *P. auritus*. Beck (1995) found remains in faecal pellets of centipedes and spiders, as well as those of insects such as earwigs and booklice (Psocoptera) which rarely fly, but these were all present in very low proportions. The bats ate a high proportion of moths and beetles, but it is uncertain how many of them were gleaned. Bauerova (1982) considered that the diet of *P. austriacus* indicated it hunted mainly in free air space. A single laboratory study (I. Kaipf, K. Heblish and H.-U. Schnitzler, *unpublished*) reported that this species continued to emit echolocation calls while taking moths from leaves and thus appeared not to use passive listening. It may use a different gleaning method from *P. auritus*, but the whole question of gleaning in grey long-eared bats requires further investigation.

Aerial Capture

Anderson and Racey (1991) made detailed observations on the capture of moths by *P. auritus* in the air as well as by gleaning. In the majority of aerial captures in the flight room (72%; $n=23$), the moth was seized in the bat's mouth, but the uropatagium (13%; $n=4$) and wing membrane (6%; $n=2$) were also used. The uropatagium was used as a scoop to catch moths which were below the bat, and the wing tips were used to draw prey in laterally before transferring it to the mouth. On 9% of occasions, a somersault technique was used by the bat. During this manoeuvre, the bat was observed to roll forwards and downwards in the air, dropping briefly out of its flight path as it enveloped the moth with its body, wings and tail membrane. It resumed its flight once the moth had been transferred to the mouth.

DIET

The majority of insectivorous bat species have been shown to be opportunistic foragers rather than specialist predators on particular prey categories (Kunz, 1974; Fenton, 1995).

Findley (1993) reviewed much of the literature on the structure of bat communities and concluded that there was little evidence that such communities were organized by competition for resources; apparent overlap among species in a habitat was likely to be accounted for by behavioural flexibility among the bats. Arlettaz and Perrin (1995) agreed that most studies dealing with trophic ecology in insectivorous bats either showed them to be opportunistic or else failed to investigate food availability. Their own work on the sibling species *Myotis myotis* and *M. blythii* in Switzerland found that the two species, which occupy narrow trophic niches, showed no active prey selection within those niches. Selection has, however, been shown by greater horseshoe bats, *Rhinolophus ferrumequinum* in England (Jones, 1990). These bats preyed selectively on moths and large chafers, and avoided other insects when moths and chafers were abundant, although they took smaller, less profitable prey at other times. The sophisticated echolocation calls of horseshoe bats may allow them to discriminate between insects at a distance and so to select profitable prey items; vespertilionid bats, which use a different echolocation system, may not be able to do this so accurately and this may be one reason why most feed unselectively.

Fenton (1995) quoted *Plecotus* species as an example of the flexibility shown by vespertilionid bats during foraging – their ability either to exploit flying insects or to glean allows them to survive in cool, damp areas where insect numbers may be erratic. Although early dietary studies based on analyses of insect remains under feeding perches indicated that *P. auritus* was a moth specialist and ate little else, more recent investigations have shown that the species is flexible in its diet and takes a variety of prey. What it eats depends on what is available, which in turn depends on habitat, weather conditions, air temperature, time of year and even the time of night at which foraging takes place. It follows that any dietary studies which aim to establish selectivity must also consider what prey is available to the bats.

Diet Analysis Methods

Remains under feeding perches

Long-eared bats frequently carry their largest prey items to a feeding perch, or night roost, where they hang up in order to handle and consume them. They trim off hard or unpalatable parts of insects such as wings and legs and these then accumulate under the perch, from where they can be collected and analysed. Because the vast majority of remains are of large moths, analyses in the past led to the conclusion that these bats ate nothing else, since smaller prey items which were not taken to the perch were obviously missed. The method is therefore of limited use in diet analysis, but it also has advantages. Faecal analysis is unable to distinguish between different moth species, or even families, since few moth remains besides scales survive the passage through the bat's gut. Because remains under perches frequently include whole, or almost whole, wings, identification to species is possible. This provides valuable information on the size of prey taken, as well as on the probable habitat and time at which they were caught. By pairing wings, investigators are also able to assess the number of large moths which have been consumed.

Faecal analysis

This is the most widely used method for investigating bat diets. Because arthropods have an exoskeleton made of chitin, a substance only partially digestible by animals, pieces of exoskeleton survive passage through the gut in a recognizable form. They can be extracted from the faecal pellets and the arthropods they came from identified, usually to order and often to family or even species. Faecal pellets are relatively easy to collect, and the method has the advantage of not harming or disturbing the bat. Results are expressed as either percentage occurrence (the percentage of pellets which contain remains of a prey category) or percentage frequency (the number of fragments of a category ÷ the total number of recognizable fragments × 100). The method is fully described by McAney *et al.* (1991). The only other practical method, analysis of stomach contents, involves killing the bat and is therefore unacceptable since bat species are legally protected in Europe and all face conservation problems.

Faecal analysis is time-consuming and has been criticized as being inaccurate because bats chew their food thoroughly and tend to trim off the parts of insects which are most useful for identification. Also, hard-bodied insects such as beetles survive the passage through the gut better than do soft-bodied ones such as mayflies or very small ones such as midges. However, the above two points do cancel each other to some extent, since hard-bodied insects will tend to be trimmed more by bats than soft-bodied ones – a beetle will be trimmed more than a midge and therefore midges' legs, antennae and bits of wing are more likely to be found in pellets than are those of beetles.

In an attempt to evaluate the reliability of faecal analysis in determining food habits, Kunz and Whitaker (1983) fed various insects to captive bats and then its faecal pellets were analysed by a researcher who had no prior knowledge of the diet composition. The four commonest taxa in the diet were identified in the correct order of importance, thus demonstrating that the method was valid and could produce reliable results, although some limitations were revealed.

Insect Sampling Methods

Light traps

Light traps are easy to transport, inexpensive and easy to use in the field. They consist of a light, usually mercury vapour or ultraviolet, above a collecting tub. Their disadvantage is that they catch only phototactic, flying insects – they are efficient at sampling Lepidoptera, flying Coleoptera and Trichoptera, but catch few Nematocera and no non-flying arthropods.

Suction trap

A suction trap (Johnson, 1950; Johnson and Taylor, 1955) consists of a fan which draws air through a mesh cone, at the base of which is a collecting cylinder. Insects are drawn in with the air and trapped in the cylinder, where they are killed by a pyrethroid-type insecticide. The catch can be separated by discs which are dropped at intervals into the cylinder. Suction traps work well for small, airborne insects such as midges, but are less efficient for large or strong-flying ones such as beetles and large moths.

Malaise trap

This consists of an open-fronted tent made of dark-coloured netting (Southwood, 1966) (Figure 3.1). The roof slopes upwards to the innermost corners, where a small hole leads to a collecting tube. The trap is usually suspended between trees, and insects flying into the

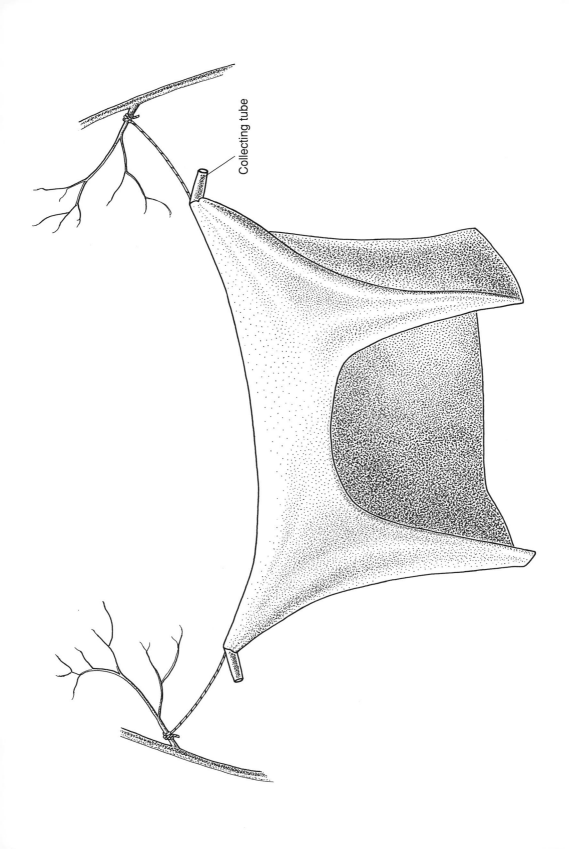

Collecting tube

netting crawl upwards and are collected in the tubes. This trap is less biased in its catch than most, but has the disadvantage of being of little use in windy conditions.

Sweep net
This is suitable for sampling insects from vegetation and thus for investigating the insects on which *Plecotus* bats may glean (Entwistle *et al.*, 1996). A hand net on a short handle is held in front of the body and swung a set number of times, if necessary sweeping the vegetation under investigation. The catch is then sprayed with insecticide and stored for later identification.

Diet of P. auritus

Early studies of remains from under *Plecotus* perches included one by Poulton (1929); remains were mainly of noctuid moths, with a few beetle elytra and wings of tipulids (crane-flies). More recently Thompson (1982) collected moth wings under a perch of *P. auritus* in Yorkshire and identified 13 species of Noctuidae, 1 of Arctiidae and 1 of Geometridae. The daily average number of moths eaten at the perch was 7.5 in July and 13.7 in August. The predominance of noctuid remains under perches was similarly emphasized in studies in Austria (Krauss, 1978; 92% Noctuidae), Denmark (Walhovd and Hoegh-Guildberg, 1984; 100% Noctuidae) and England (Robinson, 1990). Robinson identified the remains of 730 insects, of which 679 were moths (630 of them noctuids). The remaining 51 insects were beetles, flies, caddis flies, lacewings and 1 earwig. However, not all perches are used for the consumption of large moths. During a recent survey of a derelict mill site in Scotland (Swift, *unpublished*), I found a perch inside an open-fronted shed overgrown with ivy. Under the perch were bat droppings and 34 small, black beetle elytra. A bat flying out of the shed was identified as *P. auritus*. I suspect this bat had capitalized on a temporary high population of these beetles either in the shed or in the ivy covering it – a good example of opportunistic foraging by this species.

Detailed faecal analyses of the diet of brown long-eared bats have been made in Scotland (Swift and Racey, 1983), Sweden (Rydell, 1989b) and Ireland (Shiel *et al.*, 1991; Figure 3.2). These studies were conducted in different habitats; Swift and Racey's (1983) was in a steep-sided, flat-bottomed valley in a mountainous area at 57°05'N and at a height of 300 m above sea level. The roost was surrounded by deciduous woodland, coniferous plantations and well-established garden and parkland. Rydell (1989b) conducted his study at slightly higher latitude (57°45'N) and in a habitat consisting of a mixture of coniferous forest, deciduous woodland, lakes and farmland, whereas the Irish study took place in lowland (100 m above sea level) farmland constituted by grazing, hedgerows and mature trees. Only Swift and Racey sampled insect populations, and in none of the studies were the available non-flying arthropods investigated, but it seems likely that prey populations differed between the areas. Therefore, although the proportions of various arthropod groups eaten varied between studies, the diets overall showed notable similarity. All three studies showed that, while moths formed an important

FIG 3.1 *Malaise trap for sampling populations of flying insects. The trap is suspended across gaps between vegetation (e.g. woodland paths).*

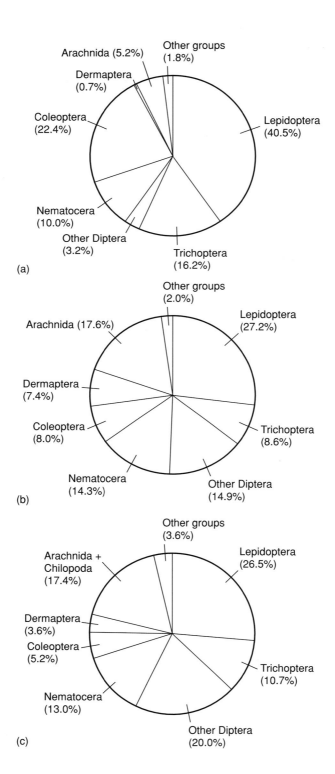

Arachnida (5.2%)

Other groups (1.8%)

Dermaptera (0.7%)

Coleoptera (22.4%)

Lepidoptera (40.5%)

Nematocera (10.0%)

Other Diptera (3.2%)

Trichoptera (16.2%)

(a)

Other groups (2.0%)

Lepidoptera (27.2%)

Arachnida (17.6%)

Dermaptera (7.4%)

Coleoptera (8.0%)

Trichoptera (8.6%)

Nematocera (14.3%)

Other Diptera (14.9%)

(b)

Other groups (3.6%)

Lepidoptera (26.5%)

Arachnida + Chilopoda (17.4%)

Dermaptera (3.6%)

Coleoptera (5.2%)

Trichoptera (10.7%)

Nematocera (13.0%)

Other Diptera (20.0%)

(c)

component of the diet, a variety of other arthropods was also eaten. The most important groups were found to be Lepidoptera (moths), Diptera (flies), Trichoptera (caddis flies), Coleoptera (beetles), Dermaptera (earwigs) and Arachnida, including Araneae (spiders) and Opiliones (harvestmen), as well as Chilopoda (centipedes) in Ireland. Other groups of less importance included Neuroptera (lacewings), Hymenoptera (sawflies and wasps) and Hemiptera (bugs). The proportion of moths in Scotland was higher than that in the other studies, but this may have been partly because the study was conducted from May to August, while the other two covered a longer period, from April to September. Because moths are most numerous in July and August, the diet was likely to contain more of them in midsummer. The proportion of moths in the diet in Ireland over the same period was a more comparable 35.5% (Shiel *et al.*, 1991). The proportion of moths in Scotland was considerably higher than their proportion in suction trap samples, indicating either that moths were selected by the bats or that many of them were gleaned, or both. Beetles were also more prevalent in the diet in Scotland than in the other two studies. A recent investigation (Swift, 1997) into gleaning in *Myotis nattereri* showed that, in a similar highland valley in Scotland, these gleaning bats ate a considerable number of small, vegetation-dwelling beetles, mainly leaf beetles (Chrysomelidae) and bark beetles (Scolytidae), both groups of which were abundant on trees in the area. It therefore seems likely that *P. auritus* were similarly feeding opportunistically on a local abundance of these small beetles. Opportunistic feeding was also shown by *P. auritus* in Ireland (Shiel *et al.*, 1991) in that 18% of the total number of insects eaten were yellow dung flies, *Scathophaga stercoraria*, which were abundant on cow pats in the pasture surrounding the roost. These flies are diurnal and rest on animal dung at night, and they must therefore have been gleaned by the bats. *P. auritus* normally glean from vegetation and not from the ground, but they were obviously able to adapt their behaviour in order to exploit a locally abundant resource.

In all three studies *P. auritus* ate very few small Nematocera, especially midges (Chironomidae and Ceratopogonidae), which were numerous in suction trap samples (Swift and Racey, 1983) and eaten in large numbers by other species in the same area in Sweden (Rydell, 1989b). Similarly, Taake (1992) found that this species ignored prey less than 3 mm in body length, although they were numerous in light trap samples. The bats are able to detect these small insects, since small numbers of them were eaten in the Scottish, Swedish and Irish studies, but they appear not to seek them actively. This may be because long-eared bats emerge from day roosts relatively late in the evening (see Chapter 4) and so miss most of the dusk peak of flying insects (Swift, 1980), or because, unlike 'aerial trawlers' such as pipistrelles, they do not forage in places where large swarms abound. The non-nematoceran Diptera eaten by *P. auritus* included strongly diurnal families such as Muscidae and Syrphidae, which were very likely to have been caught while at rest. The Trichoptera in the diet (Limnephilidae, Sericostomatidae and Hydropsychidae) were relatively large insects which sometimes move away from water. Caddis flies are weak fliers and

FIG 3.2   *Proportions of various arthropod orders in the diet of* P. auritus *from (a) Scotland (reproduced with permission from Swift and Racey, 1983), (b) Sweden (reproduced with permission from Rydell, 1989b) and (c) Ireland (reproduced with permission from Shiel* et al., *1991). Results were obtained by faecal analysis in all cases, and are expressed as percentage frequency.*

are frequently found at rest on vegetation when not over water. It is therefore probable that many of them were gleaned. Anderson and Racey's (1991) study showed that *P. auritus* in a flight room gleaned slightly more than half the moths they ate; it is likely that a similar proportion are gleaned in the wild. If we assume that the bats gleaned half the moths, most of the beetles, half the caddis flies and diurnal flies, all the earwigs, spiders, harvestmen and centipedes and none of the Nematocera, lacewings, Hymenoptera or Hemiptera in the diet, then the proportion gleaned was approximately 58% in the Scottish study, 58% in the Swedish one and 55% in the Irish one. The level of gleaning is thus remarkably consistent. It appears that when moths are plentiful (e.g. in July and August), the bats glean them preferentially, but at other times they can adapt to glean what is available, including diurnal flies and non-flying arthropods. Gleaning bats fly low over the substrate listening for prey-generated noise (R. Arlettaz, *pers. comm.*) and while doing so may disturb flies which then take off and are caught. Prey which make a noise as they move, such as earwigs, spiders and beetles, are probably detected by passive listening as they crawl on plants. Because long-eared bats are most sensitive to the low-frequency sounds made by fluttering moth wings, these are the preferred prey.

Studies of *P. auritus* in other areas show similar results. Lepidoptera were found to be the most important group in the diet by Taake (1992) and by Beck (1995). In this study, in Switzerland, Lepidoptera were present in 61% of faecal pellets, Diptera in 17% and Dermaptera in 17%. Apart from many of the moths, spiders, centipedes, hoverflies (Syrphidae), Empididae and lepidopteran larvae were also gleaned. Barataud (1990) observed *P. auritus* gleaning caterpillars in a highly opportunistic way from a willow tree which was heavily infested. The species is also opportunistic in that it feeds inside both day and night roosts. Overwintering moths were captured in a hibernaculum (Roer, 1969) and two species of diurnal moth were gleaned from a sheepfold used as a night roost (Barataud, 1990). Swift and Racey (1983) found faeces to contain remains of clothes moths (Tineidae), blowflies (Calliphoridae) and golden spider beetles (Ptinidae), a family which commonly scavenge in the nests of birds and mammals and which were present in the bats' roost. It seemed likely that all these were caught inside the roost.

Diet of P. austriacus

Analyses of remains under feeding perches have shown a high proportion of noctuid moths. Castor *et al.* (1993) analysed remains in Germany and identified 40 species of Noctuidae, 2 of Geometridae and 2 of Arctiidae (all Lepidoptera), as well as 1 species of lacewing (Neuroptera), 2 of caddis fly (Trichoptera) and 1 of cranefly (Tipulidae). Bauerova (1982) found a high proportion of noctuid remains under perches in the Czech Republic. Her analysis identified 137 species of moths from 11 families, including 98 Noctuidae, 14 Notodontidae, 13 Geometridae, 4 Arctiidae and 3 Sphingidae, as well as 3 species of beetle including 2 Scarabaeidae (chafers) and 1 Elateridae (click beetle). Bauerova (1982) also analysed 0.35 kg of faecal pellets and sampled flying insects in the area using a light trap. This analysis revealed more arthropod groups in the diet (Figure 3.3). Lepidoptera were by far the most important, followed by Coleoptera, including chafers and several families of much smaller beetles such as Carabidae and Cantharidae. During April and May, beetles were represented almost entirely by a single species of large chafer, *Rhizotragus aestivus*. Remains of Diptera appeared in the faeces early and late in

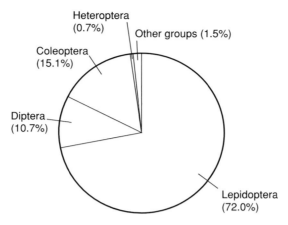

FIG 3.3 *Proportions of various arthropod orders in the diet of* P. austriacus *in the Czech Republic, calculated from data in Bauerova (1982). Results were obtained by faecal analysis and are expressed as percentage frequency.*

summer, particularly during April and October, i.e. at the time when fewest moths were available. The author did not state whether the dipteran remains were from Nematocera or from diurnal Brachycera and Cyclorrhapha. Remains of Hymenoptera, Neuroptera, Trichoptera and Hemiptera (true bugs, including Corixidae or water boatmen) were found in very small amounts.

Bauerova's (1982) analysis of perch remains indicated that *P. austriacus* was selecting larger moths than the average size available, although this may have been influenced by the bats' habit of taking only their largest prey to perches. Her observations of the species foraging round street lamps showed that the bats pursued large moths and ignored the numerous smaller ones around the lights. The perch remains also showed that *P. austriacus* fed mainly on moth species which typically fly high (at 2–5 m) and in free air space. It thus appears that this species catches more moths in flight than by gleaning. The large chafers also appear to have been caught in flight, since their elytra were intact and there were toothmarks on the abdomens, indicating the beetles had been flying when caught. The species of Hemiptera eaten likewise fly in free air space at a height of about 5 m. Barataud (1990) recorded the capture by a grey long-eared bat of two diurnal moths, thus confirming that the species does glean. However, it appears to do so much less than *P. auritus*. Beck (1995) agreed with this conclusion; analysis of faeces from bats in Switzerland found lepidopteran remains in 90% of pellets and moths were undoubtedly the main prey group. Diptera (in 43% of pellets) and Coleoptera (in 17%) were next in importance, again confirming Bauerova's results. Other arthropod groups, encountered only occasionally, were Neuroptera (in 4% of pellets), Hymenoptera (in 4%), Dermaptera (in 0.5%), Psocoptera (booklice; in 2%), Arachnida (in 1%) and Chilopoda (in 2%). Nemotocera and Brachycera/Cyclorrhapha were present in roughly equal quantities and the beetles consumed included large chafers such as *Melolontha* sp. Castor *et al.* (1993) in Germany and Whitaker *et al.* (1994) in Israel have also emphasized the dominance of moths in the diet of *P. austriacus*.

RESOURCE PARTITIONING AND INTERACTION BETWEEN SPECIES

It is generally agreed that species living in the same area must differ sufficiently in some aspects of their ecology to permit coexistence (McNab, 1971), and most of these aspects are associated with the partitioning of food resources. Resource partitioning (Husar, 1976) occurs when two very similar species live sympatrically and one or both alters an aspect of its foraging behaviour in order to avoid competition. The behaviour of at least one thus differs depending on whether the two are sympatric or allopatric. *P. auritus* and *P. austriacus* have been reported to share roosts (Stebbings, 1966) and to forage in the same habitats (Barataud, 1990; Fluckiger and Beck, 1995; Gaisler *et al.*, 1996); interactions between them are thus of interest. In addition, *Plecotus* species frequently forage in the same areas as other similar sized bats.

Interaction Between Plecotus *Species*

From the above sections, it can be seen that the diets of the two species are similar but by no means identical, the main difference being that *P. austriacus* gleans a smaller proportion of its food than does *P. auritus*. It relies mainly on large moths which it catches in free flight at heights of up to 5 m, and is less dependent than *P. auritus* on non-flying arthropods. *P. austriacus* appears to glean occasionally and opportunistically, while *P. auritus* gleans at least half its diet. *P. austriacus* can also handle larger and harder prey than can *P. auritus* (Beck, 1995). Freeman (1981) suggested that in the absence of dietary data, reasonable deductions could be made from the morphology of the jaws, teeth and skull, particularly the upper canines. It is possible that the slightly longer, stronger canines of *P. austriacus* (Corbet, 1964; Stebbings, 1967) allow it to tackle large beetles in flight. There is also some evidence that the two species may forage in different habitats when they are sympatric (Gaisler and Bauerova, 1985–6). While *P. auritus* forages mainly in deciduous woodland, *P. austriacus* relies less on woodland and more on gardens and parkland. This is further discussed in Chapter 4. It therefore seems that the two species differ sufficiently in foraging behaviour to coexist. Studies to compare diets in areas where they are sympatric and allopatric have, however, yet to be undertaken.

Interaction with Other Species

Long-eared bats which roost or forage in proximity to other vespertilionid species have been studied by Swift and Racey (1983), Rydell (1989b) and Shiel *et al.* (1991). In Scotland, *P. auritus* sharing a roost with Daubenton's bats (*Myotis daubentonii*), a similar sized species which usually forages over water, were found to interact little with them. The two species lived in different parts of the attic roost and foraged in different habitats and on different prey – the Daubenton's bats fed almost entirely on Chironomidae and Trichoptera which swarmed over water. Similarly, Rydell (1989b) found little overlap between the diets of *P. auritus* and *Eptesicus nilssonii* foraging in the same habitat in Sweden. *E. nilssonii* fed opportunistically on a broad range of flying insects and 47% of its diet consisted of small, swarming Nematocera. *P. auritus* also foraged in areas shared by *Myotis nattereri* (Shiel *et al.*, 1991), whose diet is much more similar. The two species are of equal size and both are gleaners. Some overlap was found in their diets, but both the above authors and Swift (1997) recorded that *M. nattereri* failed to exploit moths to anything like the same extent as *P. auritus* – in Ireland, moths made up only 5.4% of Natterer's bats' diet (Shiel *et al.*, 1991) and in Scotland they constituted 1.2% (Swift, 1997). If *M. nattereri* gleans by passive listening in the same way as *P. auritus*, then it is possible that its hearing is not sufficiently sensitive to low-frequency sounds to hear moths fluttering. Alternatively, if it uses echolocation, the moths may hear it coming and take evasive action. Research is needed; either way it appears that the two species differ sufficiently in their diets to avoid competing. To date, no studies on interactions between *Plecotus* bats and other gleaning species which take a lot of moths (e.g. *Myotis bechsteinii*; Stebbings, 1968) have been conducted.

DIGESTIVE EFFICIENCY

Once prey has been caught and eaten, it has to be digested. Different arthropods are likely to be absorbed with different efficiency, and as a first step towards quantifying such variation, Webb *et al.* (1993) conducted a laboratory study to determine the digestive efficiency of the biochemical components of mealworms (*Tenebrio* sp.) fed to captive *P. auritus*. They also compared the digestive efficiency of *P. auritus* with that of a similar sized species from the same area (*M. daubentonii*). Bats were weighed, fed a known weight of mealworms and then kept at constant temperature for 24 h and all the faeces produced were dried and weighed. Biochemical analyses were carried out on the faeces and on samples of mealworms. The mean apparent dry mass absorption efficiency by *P. auritus* was 0.853 and the mean apparent energy absorption efficiency 0.90; these values did not differ significantly from those for *M. daubentonii*. The first faeces were produced within 30 min of the bat finishing feeding, and an average of 50% of a total day's faeces were produced within 4 h.

Webb *et al.*'s (1993) data show that virtually all the lipid and protein in the mealworms was absorbed during digestion, but that there was an apparent negative absorption of carbohydrate, possibly indicating that some of the products of digestion of non-carbohydrates were lost as carbohydrate in the faeces. The authors also found a 58.8% apparent absorption of unidentified material by *P. auritus* and suggested this could be attributable to the partial digestion of chitin. Chitinase, an enzyme found in the gut of some insectivorous bats and other animals which feed on arthropods (Jeuniaux, 1961), is known partially to digest the chitin in insect exoskeletons. Webb *et al.* (1993) reported that chitinase has been found in the gut of *P. auritus* and suggested that, while the bat could not digest chitin nearly as efficiently as it could lipids and proteins, chitinase acted primarily to break up the pieces of exoskeleton, thus permitting easier access by digestive enzymes to the lipoproteins and carbohydrates embedded in them. Some of the high apparent digestive efficiency was due to partial digestion of chitin, but plenty of pieces of exoskeleton remained on which faecal analysis could be conducted.

WATER BALANCE

Because long-eared bats usually roost in places where drinking water is not available, they have access to water for only a few hours each night; water balance and the need to avoid dehydration are thus important aspects of their ecology. The main routes of water loss in bats are evaporation, faecal water loss and water loss in urine. The routes of water influx are free water in food, drinking and metabolic production of water.

Water Loss

Evaporation

Evaporative water loss is generally higher in bats than in other mammals of similar size, partly because evaporation is likely to be high from the large, unfurred wing membrane and partly because flight is energetically expensive (Speakman and Racey, 1991) and pulmonary evaporation is thus comparatively high. These factors are partly compensated for because blood flow to the wings can be reduced and oxygen extraction from the lungs is efficient (Webb, 1995). Webb *et al.* (1995) investigated evaporative water loss in captive bats of three Scottish species and calculated that the average rate of loss was 1.83 µl min^{-1} in *P. auritus*. This was significantly higher than the values for *M. daubentonii* or *P. pipistrellus*. It is possible that the relatively high rate in *P. auritus* was due to evaporation from its broader than average wings and big ears.

Faecal water loss

The water content of faeces from *P. auritus* fed on mealworms was found to be 73.3% (Webb *et al.*, 1993), which is a medium value for an insectivorous bat, while mealworms consist of, on average, 61.1% water. Webb *et al.* (1993) calculated that, since the apparent dry weight assimilation efficiency of mealworms by this species is 85.3%, this implies that 25% of the free water in food is lost in the faeces.

Loss in urine

Webb *et al.* (1994) found that, in captive *P. auritus* denied water for 11 h after feeding, urine production was positively and linearly dependent on food consumption and they predicted that urine loss at zero food consumption would be 0.048 µl min^{-1}. This is a medium value for a vespertilionid bat and considerably lower than that in *M. daubentonii*, which forages over water. These authors also found that, unlike *M. daubentonii*, long-eared bats denied water in the experiments lost only 6% of their body weight over 11 h and did not show signs of dehydration. They suggested that, because long-eared bats do not normally forage close to water, their relatively low rate of water loss in urine may be a physiological adaptation which compensates for their lack of easy access to drinking water.

A water budget model for wild *P. auritus* in summer was developed by Webb *et al.* (1994); this predicted that, if the bats did not drink, approximately 19% of water loss would be attributable to faecal water loss, 18–20% to urine loss and 59–62% to evaporation and losses due to reproduction.

Water Intake

Webb (1995) found the average free water taken in food by free-flying *P. auritus* to be 2.22 ± 0.64 g, assuming the water content of the food to be 61.1% of wet weight. Metabolic water production was estimated, from food consumption, to be 0.80 ± 0.25 g per day, and drinking water consumption to be 0.86 ± 0.27 g per day.

CHAPTER 4

Foraging Behaviour

THE diet of long-eared bats has implications for the times at which they emerge from day roosts to hunt their prey, and also for the habitats in which they hunt and their spatial and temporal use of foraging areas. Recent advances in the technology of wildlife telemetry have allowed miniaturization of radio transmitters to the extent that bats as small as *P. auritus* can now be tracked. This has made detailed investigations into foraging behaviour a realistic possibility; knowledge is accumulating with regard to what long-eared bats do all night, and is providing information essential for the promotion of their conservation.

METHODS FOR MARKING AND TRACKING FORAGING BATS

All methods of marking bats require individuals to be caught, and further stress is caused by the handling involved in fitting and removing tags. Licences are required for any procedure which involves disturbing bats in this way, and no study should be undertaken without sound reason and the expectation of meaningful results. However, for many research purposes, marking is essential, and the following methods are those which have been used with success in the field.

Reflective Rings

Aluminium-alloy bat rings (marketed by the Mammal Society; see p. 153) are covered with self-adhesive, brightly coloured, reflective tape (such as 'Scotchlite') and fitted to bats' forearms in the normal way; rings of 3.0 mm internal diameter are suitable for *Plecotus* sp. Various colour combinations can be used to mark individual bats. The advantage of this method is that the rings are inexpensive, quick to fit, cause little stress or potential damage to the bat beyond the usual risk of damage due to chewing, and last several months, although bats do eventually chew off the tape. They are useful for identifying individual animals inside roosts without having to catch them each time and for identifying foraging bats. However, since they can only be seen at short distances and in bright torchlight, they are of little use in trying to follow bats over any distance. They were used by Swift and Racey (1983) in a study to compare foraging habitats of *P. auritus* and *Myotis daubentonii*, and marked individuals of each species were able to be identified in the field.

51

Chemical Lights

These were described by Buchler (1976). They use a chemiluminescent liquid such as 'Cyalume' (American Cyanimid Company, New Jersey), and have recently become available in the form of fishing lures of various sizes; these can be bought in most field sports shops. The lures are easier to use than the capsules described by Buchler (1976) and, unlike capsules, they cannot be chewed through by the bats and so do not pose the same risk of poisoning them. The tag is glued to the bat's back mid-dorsally and gives off a bright light for several hours. Tags weigh less than 0.3 g and are removed by the bats' grooming after a few days. Light-tagged bats are visible at distances of up to about 200 m, and the method is useful for identifying foraging areas, although individual bats cannot be recognized. They last only one night and so can, in any case, provide limited information. Barataud (1990) used these tags to identify foraging areas of both *P. auritus* and *P. austriacus* in France, and they have also been used to find important habitats for endangered bats such as *Corynorhinus townsendii virginianus* in the USA (Adam *et al.*, 1994).

Radio Tracking

Telemetry was defined by Priede (1992) as any method of obtaining information on living free-ranging animals by remote means. It thus includes the use of instruments, such as ultrasonic bat detectors and night viewing devices, which do not involve attaching anything to bats; however, the method is usually associated with the use of radio tags. For many years after radio telemetry was used on larger animals, most vespertilionid bats were too small to carry even the lightest transmitters, but rapid advances in technology in the last 10 years have led to increasing miniaturization of components. The smallest transmitters currently available weigh 0.65 g (Holohil Systems, Ontario) and these have been used in two studies involving *P. auritus* and one involving *P. austriacus*, making them among the smallest bats so far tracked. Such small transmitters are inevitably rather simple, inefficient and have a limited range (Priede, 1992), but they have enabled previously unavailable data to be collected for long-eared bats and have greatly increased our knowledge of their foraging habits. Bats are located either by triangulation or by following (usually on foot since *Plecotus* forage close to roosts) and 'homing-in' on signals.

Studies

Fuhrmann and Seitz (1992) tracked eight *P. auritus* in a small pine forest in Germany. They successfully investigated activity patterns, use of foraging areas and the distance covered by bats in a night. *P. auritus* were also tracked by Entwistle *et al.* (1996) in a Scottish study involving 18 bats and investigating habitat use, distance travelled and the use of feeding sites. A single *P. austriacus* was radio-tracked for four nights by Fluckiger and Beck (1995) in Switzerland, and the method has also been used to find foraging sites in a conservation project on the endangered big-eared bat *C. t. virginianus* in America (Adam *et al.*, 1994).

Attachment methods

Transmitters are usually glued to small bats mid-dorsally using a surgical adhesive such as 'Skinbond'. Such adhesives are flexible when dry and will keep the transmitter in position for up to 2–3 weeks (Anderka and Angehrn, 1992); care should be taken to avoid adhesives with exothermic reactions. Glue has the advantage of causing least distress to the bat and adding very little weight to the package. The aerial, which is about 15 cm long, points backwards and trails behind the bat in flight (Figure 4.1). An alternative method of attachment, designed by Fuhrmann and Seitz (1992) for *P. auritus*, used a collar made from two layers of self-adhesive insulating tape. It incorporated a short piece of florist's raffia which naturally disintegrated after 6–10 days, thus ensuring that the transmitter would drop off if the bat could not be re-caught or if it slipped a forearm through the collar. The combined weight of a collar and transmitter was 0.8–0.9 g. Similar collars were used by Fluckiger and Beck (1995) on *P. austriacus*.

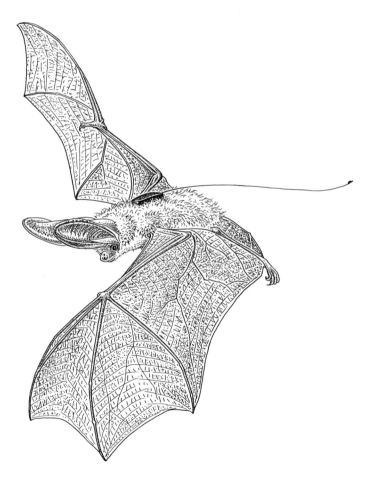

FIG 4.1   P. auritus *carrying a radio transmitter attached with glue, showing the position of the transmitter and aerial in flight.*

Effects of transmitters on bats

The behavioural effects due to disturbance caused by catching bats and attaching the transmitters appear to be minimal – Entwistle (1994) compared behaviour of *P. auritus* on the first night after attachment and on subsequent nights and found no difference. No tagged bats abandoned their roosts in her study. The main effect must be that of flying with a heavy weight attached and an aerial trailing behind. A generally assumed rule of radio tracking bats is that they should not carry more than 5% of their own bodyweight (Aldridge and Brigham, 1988). Entwistle *et al.* (1996) calculated that transmitter mass on their *P. auritus* ranged from 6.4 to 9.5% of body mass, and those of Fuhrmann and Seitz (1992) approached 10% in most cases. Adam *et al.* (1994) reported that transmitters were 7.5% of body weight for male *C. t. virginianus* and 8.5% for females (since males were slightly heavier than the post-lactating females in their study). They observed no effect of carrying transmitters on adults, but juveniles appeared stressed by them and tagged ones did not leave the roost to forage. Hughes and Rayner (1991) conducted a study on captive *P. auritus* in a flight room to investigate the effects of carrying artificial loads. They pointed out that wing loading on bats varies greatly under natural conditions and that factors such as pre-hibernation weight gain, pregnancy, weight of mammary tissue and the load of a full stomach of insects all have to be carried in flight. Also, since *P. auritus* has a low wing loading and broad, lift-producing wings, it should be capable of carrying heavier weights than other bats of similar size. Hughes and Rayner added fishing weights between the shoulder blades of their long-eared bats and observed the effects in flight. As loading increased, the bats flew more slowly and increased their wingbeat frequency. Since aerodynamic theory predicted that increased loading should have caused the bats to fly faster, this was unexpected. They concluded that carrying transmitters must have an effect on bats as small as *P. auritus*, but that further research was needed. Entwistle *et al.* (1996) could find no relationship between relative transmitter loading (transmitter mass/body mass) and either the furthest distance travelled or the time spent close to the roost and concluded that the transmitters caused no impediment to flight. Long-eared bats are thus certainly capable of foraging while carrying transmitters, and any marginal effects have yet to be shown.

ACTIVITY PATTERNS

Emergence

P. auritus emerge from day roosts late in the evening relative to many other vespertilionid species. Entwistle *et al.* (1996) found that the median time of emergence in north-east Scotland was 55 min after sunset and that emergence was strongly correlated with both time of sunset and time of civil twilight (defined as the period when the centre of the sun is between 0.8° and 6.0° below the horizon). In Britain, pipistrelles emerge 35 min after sunset (Swift, 1980) and large, fast-flying species such as serotines (*Eptesicus serotinus*; Catto *et al.*, 1995) and noctules (*Nyctalus noctula*; Racey, 1991) even earlier (see also Rydell *et al.*, 1996). Jones and Rydell (1994) calculated, from all available data from Europe, that the average median time of emergence was 44 min after sunset in *P. auritus*, compared with 33 min in *P. pipistrellus*, 8 min in *N. noctula* and 11 min in *E. serotinus*. The time of emergence of *Corynorhinus townsendii ingens*, a close American relative of *Plecotus* species, was found to be 45.5 min after sunset (Clark *et al.*, 1993). Activity patterns in insectivorous bats are generally considered to be controlled by an endogenous circadian rhythm synchronized to the daily light cycle by light-sampling behaviour (de Coursey and de Coursey, 1964), and individuals emerge within very narrow bands of light intensity (Erkert and Kracht, 1978). The high degree of correlation between time of emergence and the times of sunset and civil twilight indicate that *P. auritus* is no exception. The length of civil twilight increases with latitude in summer (Howard, 1995), and thus the time of emergence may be expected to be later relative to sunset further north in the bats' range. This does appear to be the case (Table 4.1); although the four studies listed in the table used slightly different methods to estimate when bats emerged, there is a strongly linear relationship between time of emergence and latitude ($r = 0.96$; $p<0.01$), indicating that long-eared bats emerge relatively later further north, where twilight lasts longer. Howard (1995) calculated that civil twilight lasts around 75 minutes at 58°N and around 45 minutes at 50°N in midsummer. *P. auritus* thus emerged 10–19 min before the end of civil twilight (Table 4.1), at which time light intensity is below about 3 lux (Swift, 1997). Mean light intensity at 57°N was measured at 0.7 lux 1 h after sunset (Rydell *et al.*, 1996).

The late emergence of brown long-eared bats is almost certainly connected with their habit of gleaning. Time of emergence in any insectivorous bat is likely to be a compromise between the need to go out and feed and the risk of predation at high light levels (Speakman, 1991a; Jones and Rydell, 1994). Predation by birds, mainly kestrels and tawny, barn and long-eared owls, has been estimated to account for about 11% of the annual mortality of British bats (Speakman, 1991a; see also Chapter 7). Speakman (1991a) concluded that, although bats comprise only a small proportion of the prey taken by their predators, the effect of the pressure this predation has on bat behaviour cannot be ignored. Species such as pipistrelles, which are aerial hunters and rely for most of their food on the dusk and dawn peaks of flying insects (Swift, 1980), have to emerge at relatively high light levels and risk being caught by predators but, because *P. auritus* gleans much of its prey, it relies far

TABLE 4.1   *Times of emergence of* P. auritus *at different latitudes in Europe.*

Study	Latitude	Average interval between sunset and emergence (min)	Note
Entwistle *et al.* (1996)	57°N	55	Median emergence; radio-tracked bats
Howard (1995)	51°23′N	40	Calculated average time of emergence from roost counts
Fuhrmann and Seitz (1992)	50°N	26	Average time of emergence of individual radio-tracked bats; range = 7–43 min
Barataud (1990)	46°N	15	Time of arrival of marked bats at feeding sites

less on this dusk peak. Non-flying prey are available all night, and a further reduction in the pressure for early emergence occurs because the peak activity of moths occurs around midnight (Rydell *et al.*, 1996). Early emergence would thus carry no benefits for long-eared bats and would increase their risk of predation, which in any case is high because they fly slowly. Late emergence is correlated with gleaning in many bat species in temperate regions (Jones and Rydell, 1994) and this may not only be because of food availability. It appears that gleaning itself is a dangerous occupation unless it is done in the dark, since gleaners have to fly slowly. Taake (1985) found that, of a sample of European bat species, those with pale coloured ventral fur emerged later in the evening and tended to be gleaners. Other European species which glean at least part of their diet also emerge late in the evening (e.g. *Myotis nattereri*; Swift, 1997), as do closely related American species such as *Corynorhinus townsendii* (Clark *et al.*, 1993).

Emergence Behaviour

In some vespertilionid species (e.g. *P. pipistrellus*; Swift, 1980; Bullock *et al.*, 1987), outburst, or clustering, behaviour has been described, in which periods when large numbers of bats emerge are interspersed with periods when few, if any, leave the roost. No detailed studies on the emergence of long-eared bats have been conducted, but anecdotal observations indicate that they do sometimes emerge in groups of two or three and that the emergence of one frequently seems to lead to the emergence of others. However, no definite clumping, or outburst behaviour, such as is obvious in pipistrelles, can be observed. Speakman *et al.* (1992) found that significant clustering was a feature only of larger (>150) colonies of pipistrelles and that at colony size of less than 100, emergence was random. They suggested that clustering may be due either to predator avoiding behaviour or to the effect of pressure on exit holes, and pointed out that, while predator avoidance may be an effect of clumped emergence in large colonies, it may not be the main reason for the behaviour. *P. auritus* form small colonies (Chapter 6), most of which number fewer than 80 individuals, and therefore they are probably never large enough for pressure on exit holes to become an issue. Thus, although the observed departure from the roost of small groups of bats may be a mild form of anti-predator, or 'safety in numbers' behaviour, proper clumped, or outburst, emergence does not occur. The time taken for a colony to emerge has been reported to be independent of colony size (Howard, 1995), again probably due to the formation of small colonies by this species and consequent lack of pressure on exit holes.

Light-sampling behaviour, whereby bats check the level of light intensity as a means of synchronizing their activity rhythm to the daily light cycle (de Coursey and de Coursey, 1964; Voûte *et al.*, 1974), has been observed inside *P. auritus* roosts (Swift, 1981). In the 10–15 min before emergence, bats flew inside the roost, and during flights they were seen to fly low over the exit hole, before alighting briefly on roof beams and then repeating the behaviour. Finally, they alighted beside the exit hole for a few seconds and then dropped through it.

Effects of Environmental Factors on Emergence

Rain during the expected period of emergence was found significantly to delay the time of emergence, but low air temperatures (<7°C) on dry nights did not prevent bats from emerging (Entwistle *et al.*, 1996). Heavy cloud cover resulted in earlier than normal emergence (Howard, 1995), but light cloud had little effect. The average time of emergence was found to vary significantly between roosts within an area and to be strongly correlated with the distance from the roost to the closest woodland (Entwistle *et al.*, 1996). Bats emerged earlier at roosts closer to woodland (Figure 4.2), a finding similar to that of Jones *et al.* (1995) for *Rhinolophus ferrumequinum*; these authors suggested that woodland located close to roosts may provide cover from aerial predators and so enable bats to emerge at relatively high light levels. The use of roosts close to woodland thus allows long-eared bats to extend their foraging period and is an important consideration for their conservation. It has been suggested as one of the reasons why *P. auritus* select roosts close to woodland (Entwistle *et al.*, 1997).

Emergence in P. austriacus

Data are sparse on times of emergence in this species. Bauerova (1982) reported it emerged around dusk (possibly around the end of civil twilight). Barataud (1990) observed that light-tagged specimens of both *P. auritus* and *P. austriacus* arrived at foraging areas approximately 15 min after sunset. A single individual radio-tracked by Fluckiger and Beck (1995) left the roost about half an hour after sunset. The time of emergence thus appears to be

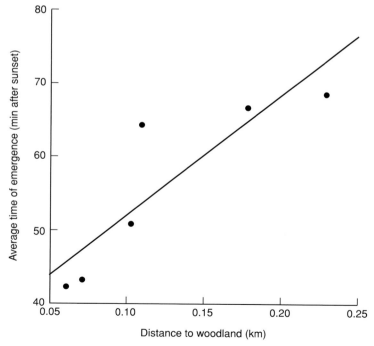

FIG 4.2 *Average time of emergence of radio-tracked* P. auritus *from six roosts, plotted against the distance from each roost to the nearest woodland (reproduced with permission from Entwistle* et al., *1996).* $r^2 = 0.79$; $p < 0.02$.

similar to that of *P. auritus* and in view of their broadly similar diets and foraging habits, this seems to be reasonable. The effects of environmental factors on emergence have not yet been documented.

Activity

In both *P. auritus* and *P. austriacus* (on which, again, limited data are available), the nightly activity pattern has been shown to be unimodal (Bauerova, 1982; Fuhrmann and Seitz, 1992; Fluckiger and Beck, 1995; Entwistle *et al.*, 1996). After emergence, bats remain active outside the roost all night. Entwistle *et al.* (1996) found that *P. auritus* in Scotland returned to the roost a median of 57 min before sunrise. Like emergence, the time of return was significantly related to both time of sunrise and time of civil twilight. In Germany, where the nights are longer in summer, the time of return to the roost of this species was earlier, at an average of 190 min before sunrise, and bats did not leave again before dawn (Fuhrmann and Seitz, 1992). In both studies, activity was characterized by periods of flight interspersed with short periods of inactivity which ranged from 1 to 65 min in duration. *P. austriacus* showed similar behaviour (Fluckiger and Beck, 1995); an individual was active for most of the night and remained stationary only occasionally.

The unimodal activity pattern of long-eared bats contrasts with those of many other temperate zone bat species, which are bimodal with peaks around dusk and dawn (Erkert, 1982). Such bimodal patterns are the commonest type of daily rhythms among animals (Aschoff, 1966), with the trough of activity occurring around midday or midnight, and with the second peak being lower and frequently reduced if environmental stimuli are removed. In some bat species (e.g. *P. pipistrellus*; Swift, 1980; Maier, 1992), the dawn peak may be suppressed at certain times of year and may only be obvious during lactation, when the high energy demands on females cause them to forage with maximum efficiency. At these times, the dusk and dawn peaks, which coincide with the peaks in activity shown by their flying insect prey, are separated by a period of night roosting, at which time the young are suckled.

The reason for the unusual unimodal pattern in long-eared bats is probably prey availability. Moths are unlike most flying insects in that they are active all night, with their activity peak around midnight (Rydell *et al.*, 1996); *Plecotus* are therefore able to keep foraging profitably at a time when non-moth feeders cannot do so. Non-flying arthropods, resting moths and diurnal insects are also equally available all night and thus gleaning, too, is profitable in the middle of the night. Long-eared bats emerge late and keep foraging until they have satisfied their energy requirements, after which they return to the roost and stay there. At high latitude, individuals may forage almost continuously during the hours of darkness (Entwistle *et al.*, 1996), while further south they have been found to return to their day roosts up to 573 min before sunrise and not to leave again.

Entwistle *et al.* (1996) found that the only bats which returned to the roost during the night were lactating females. When the young were newly born, mothers made several visits of short duration, while later in the summer they entered the roost less often but stayed longer. The reason for these returns was almost certainly to suckle infants. Unlike many rodents, which suckle their young infrequently, it appears that frequent suckling is the norm in insectivorous bats. Wilde *et al.* (1995) suggested that, because a mother's metabolic rate during flight is maximal, milk production is also rapid during foraging and accumulation of milk in the mammary glands means females have to feed their young several times per night. Frequent suckling also relieves autocrine feedback and allows maximal milk production during subsequent bouts of foraging. Two sub-species of *Corynorhinus townsendii*, *C. t. virginianus* and *C. t. ingens*, were both found to have activity patterns very similar to *P. auritus* (Bagley and Jacobs, 1985; Clark *et al.*, 1993). Both had unimodal patterns, with lactating females making up to three returns each night to the maternity roost. It seems that females of bat species with bimodal activity patterns combine a return to the roost to suckle infants with their activity trough in the middle of the night, but long-eared bats and their relatives have to incorporate visits to their infants into their main period of activity. Howard (1995) set up an automatic recording system based on an infrared beam to monitor activity inside a *P. auritus* roost. His results show that, while activity at night was highest during lactation, there was also some activity inside the roost at other times of year, indicating that some non-lactating bats did return during the night. He suggested that bats which foraged close to the roost may have returned for short resting periods. An alternative explanation is that the recorded activity was due to some bats curtailing their foraging early, as was established in Fuhrmann and Seitz's (1992) study.

Effects of Environmental Factors on Activity

Rain inhibited activity away from the roost as well as preventing emergence (Entwistle *et al.*, 1996); bats hung up and became inactive immediately rain started and there was a significant increase in hanging time during wet nights. These authors suggested that the apparent reluctance to fly in rain (shared by most bat species; Erkert, 1982) is most probably due to problems linked with thermoregulation – wet bats lose heat rapidly. Alternatively, they suggested, the sound of falling rain may interfere with the bats' system of passive listening for prey. Air temperatures as low as 3.5°C did not inhibit foraging by *P. auritus* (Entwistle *et al.*, 1996), unlike the situation in species which feed on flying insects – although low air temperatures may have inhibited insect flight, resting insects were still available for gleaning. Gleaning may also make mist and fog less of a problem for long-eared bats than for exclusively aerial foraging species. Mist droplets in the atmosphere absorb ultrasound (Sales and Pye, 1974) and so cause a reduction in the hunting efficiency of bats such as pipistrelles (Swift, 1980), but may not hamper passive listening to the same extent. However, radio-tagged *P. auritus* which emerged on foggy nights were found to show abnormal flight patterns and even sometimes to curtail foraging (A.C. Entwistle, *pers. comm.*), indicating that mist and fog do adversely affect their foraging to some degree. The effect of wind is likely to be similar to that on most bat species – on windy nights individuals forage more in sheltered areas such as woodland and behind hedges. Insects accumulate in such sheltered habitats under these conditions.

FORAGING

Flyways

Both *P. auritus* and *P. austriacus* consistently use landscape features such as hedges or tree-lines along which to fly between roosts and foraging areas and between feeding sites.

Features reported to be used are usually linear and, besides hedges and treelines, include overgrown banks, fences, forest rides, railway lines and streams with vegetation on the banks. Individual bats use the same flyways throughout the summer (Barataud, 1990), and flight along them is reported to be close to the ground and faster than normal foraging flight (Barataud, 1990; Entwistle *et al.*, 1996). Howard (1995) measured the speed at which *P. auritus* flew during commuting flights along a flyway and estimated their speed to be almost 6 m s^{-1}. This is considerably faster than their flight during foraging (Chapter 2) and comparable with that of other vespertilionid species of similar size. Howard's observations of *P. auritus* along flyways showed that they never crossed open spaces, even if using the flyways involved covering considerable extra distances. When commuting to a foraging area in a plantation 200 m from the roost across an open field, bats never flew over the field, but travelled about 300 m to the plantation by way of the hedge around the edge. Entwistle (1994) similarly reported that *P. auritus* covered extra distances because of their use of flyways.

Two possible reasons for the use of flyways are to reduce the risk of aerial predation or as navigational aids. Although both long-eared species do occasionally catch prey while flying along hedges (Barataud, 1990), the bats' fast, straight flight suggests this is not their main purpose. The possibility of predation by birds is probably a serious enough threat to prevent relatively slow-flying bats (even if they are flying at what is, for them, a fast speed) from flying in the open. Alternatively, it is possible that, because the echolocation calls of long-eared bats have very limited range, they have to rely on landscape features as navigational aids, as suggested by Howard (1995). Flyways are regularly used by other bats with low-intensity calls, such as *Myotis nattereri* (Swift, 1997), inferring that the navigation explanation is more likely. On the other hand, *M. nattereri* also flies slowly and must be as vulnerable as *Plecotus* to predation. *Myotis daubentonii* use flyways and never cross open ground, and their echolocation calls are much more intense. In any case, the two explanations are not mutually exclusive and it is quite probable that long-eared bats use flyways for both the above reasons. Eckman and de Jong (1996) found that *P. auritus* in Sweden avoided foraging in isolated patches of forest in an agricultural area or over forested islands in a shallow lake. They attributed this avoidance to the isolation rather than to insect abundance, which was actually higher in the open areas, and suggested that predation risk prevented bats from crossing open fields or water to reach productive foraging areas. This study emphasized the importance of flyways to *P. auritus* and the negative impact of habitat patchiness for this species.

Foraging Habitat

P. auritus

Historically, this species has always been described as a woodland forager and has been considered as a typical foliage gleaner in deciduous forests. However, just as it has been shown (Chapter 3) to be far more adaptable than this in its diet, so more recent studies have indicated that a variety of alternative habitats may also be used. Swift and Racey (1983) observed *P. auritus* marked with reflective rings foraging in deciduous woodland, birch scrub and a garden containing many mature coniferous and deciduous trees, and Barataud (1990) mist-netted individuals in village gardens, scattered woodlands, orchards and parkland among meadows. He also emphasized the importance of agricultural buildings as foraging sites – bats pursued insects into stables and sheepfolds through open doors and also gleaned moths at rest inside. They hunted extensively inside the buildings during wet weather, an opportunistic move which enabled them to keep foraging when conditions outside were unsuitable. Heise and Schmidt (1988) observed brown long-eared bats foraging in areas containing low bushes, as well as in forests. Two were caught in mist-nets only 50 cm above the ground, indicating that they were probably gleaning from these bushes. There is also evidence from insects consumed (Robinson, 1990; Shiel *et al.*, 1991) that the species may glean from grassland and pasture at times.

Quantitative data on the relative importance of various foraging habitats have been provided by two recent studies using radio tracking. The first of these was by Fuhrmann and Seitz (1992) in Germany. Six females (all non-reproductive or lactating) were tracked and they spent most of their time in woodland. Of the total foraging time recorded, 55.0% was spent in woodland with widely spaced trees (more than 2 m between trunks) and 29.3% in woodland with trees planted close together (less than 2 m between trunks). The remaining time (15.7%) was spent in gardens, parkland, orchards or along railway lines or motorway embankments. Entwistle *et al.* (1996) tracked 16 bats over a total of 65 nights in north-east Scotland. All of the 75 feeding sites located were associated either with woodland or with individual trees; 17% were in trees adjoining pasture and only 9% round trees close to water. Bats spent 42% of the total foraging time in mature deciduous woodland (excluding birch woodland), and when using non-native coniferous plantations (mainly spruce) they remained on the edge and did not use the inner woodland. The relative time spent in different types of woodland is shown in Figure 4.3.

To investigate whether bats used deciduous woodland preferentially, Entwistle *et al.* (1996) performed a utilization–availability test based on time budgets. They estimated the proportion of various types of woodland or groups of trees within foraging range of the roost from large-scale maps and then compared this with the time bats actually spent in each type by a Wilcoxon paired test. As shown by Figure 4.4, the bats spent significantly more time in mature deciduous woodland than would be expected if their use of all trees was random, i.e. they were selecting this type of woodland. Sweep net samples in foraging areas showed that, while there were no differences in the total numbers of insects available between woodland types, mature deciduous woodland did produce significantly higher numbers of moths. The authors suggested that this was the reason for the bats foraging preferentially there, since other factors important to the bats, the provision of surfaces from which insects could be gleaned and cover from aerial predation, were provided equally by all types of woodland. Moths are the preferred food of *P. auritus*, so they forage preferentially in the habitats in which most moths are to be found. Just as their diet is flexible, however, so bats of this species are also able to adapt their foraging behaviour to include other habitats containing trees and bushes.

P. austriacus

Foraging habitats of this species are reported to include woodland (Barataud, 1990), as well as open meadows (Bauerova, 1982) and pasture containing trees (D. Laffoley, *pers. comm.*). A single non-lactating female was radio tracked over four nights by Fluckiger and Beck (1995). This bat foraged in six distinct areas, including round a chestnut tree in a garden close to the roost, open meadows, a cherry orchard, forest edge and mixed woodland. It thus differs from *P. auritus* in hunting in open habitats such as meadows, and Fluckiger and Beck (1995) reported that it seemed to have two separate foraging strategies, one for

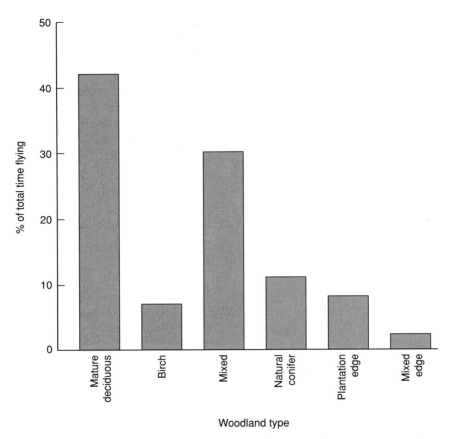

FIG 4.3   *The percentage of flight time of 16 radio-tracked* P. auritus *spent within different types of woodland in north-east Scotland.* n = 65 bat nights plus 7 half nights *(reproduced with permission from Entwistle* et al.*, 1996).*

cluttered environments which included gleaning and the other, involving faster flight, for open situations. This explains why there are fewer gleaned prey items in the diet of *P. austriacus* than in that of *P. auritus*. *P. austriacus* also differs from *P. auritus* in that it is reported to catch moths in flight round street lamps (see Chapter 9).

Use of Feeding Sites

Both brown and grey long-eared bats have been reported to use a series of feeding sites during a night's foraging, and to fly between sites quickly and directly, using flyways.

P. auritus

Flight within sites is slow and dipping (Entwistle *et al.*, 1996; Swift and Racey, 1983), and bats often fly among the branches of trees. The time spent in any one area is very variable

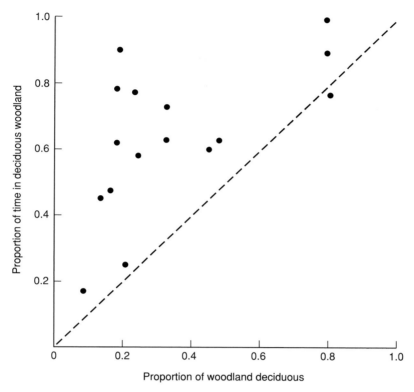

FIG 4.4   *Utilization–availability test to compare the time spent by individual radio-tracked* P. auritus *in deciduous woodland with the proportion of available woodland which was deciduous. The line represents the time each bat would spend in deciduous woodland if its use were random (reproduced with permission from Entwistle* et al., *1996).*

(Fuhrmann and Seitz, 1992), but stays of up to 30 min (Swift and Racey, 1983) and 35 min (Barataud, 1990) have been recorded. The average size of flight areas is also variable, and ranged from 0.3 to 10.5 ha in Fuhrmann and Seitz's study. Entwistle *et al.* (1996) recorded that individual bats used between 1 and 9 (median = 3) feeding sites per night and the number of flights between sites ranged from 1 to 16 (median = 6). They also found a high night-to-night predictability as to which sites a particular individual would use – each used a limited number at any time of year and of all sites, 77% were used by the same bat on more than one night. Females were significantly more likely to use the same site from night to night than were males, which thus appeared to be more opportunistic in their choice of sites. Sites to which females returned were those which had been used for longer the night before, indicating that bats remembered which sites were most productive and returned to them. Sites were frequently used by two or more bats at the same time (an observation also made by Fuhrmann and Seitz, 1992). Up to five bats were recorded feeding together, with no obvious interactions between them. Data showed that a bat was significantly more likely to use a site if another individual was also present. In some species, such behaviour is thought to be due to social facilitation (Wilkinson, 1995), whereby bats are attracted to rich food patches by the echolocation calls of conspecifics. In this way, they benefit from the foraging success of other individuals. However, because of the very short range of *Plecotus* calls, Entwistle *et al.* (1996) considered it unlikely that this was the case in their study, and it was more probable that individuals found productive feeding sites independently. They found no evidence of aggressive interactions between *P. auritus* foraging together – a similar situation to that reported by Racey and Swift (1985) for pipistrelles in rich food patches.

P. austriacus

Fluckiger and Beck (1995) found that this species similarly used sites on successive nights and also re-visited a site on the same night on occasions. Castor *et al.* (1993) reported that grey long-eared bats used feeding sites opportunistically, varying sites according to weather conditions and food availability, and Bauerova (1982) also found them to be opportunistic in their use of street lamps. Individuals flew fast and straight under a line of street lamps, pursuing large moths which had been attracted to the light. Fast, straight flight was also used when hunting above meadows, but in gardens and woodland, flight was slow and fluttering, much more like that of *P. auritus* (Fluckiger and Beck, 1995).

Distance Travelled from the Roost

A constant feature of the behaviour of both *Plecotus* species is that they forage close to roosts. Barataud (1990) mist-netted both species, and only ever caught bats in nets which were set up close to human dwellings. Castor *et al.* (1993) always observed *P. austriacus* foraging close to roosts, and Fluckiger and Beck (1995) reported that this species moved a maximum of 1.4 km from their nursery roost during radio tracking.

Swift and Racey (1983) sighted marked *P. auritus* a maximum of 1.1 km from a nursery roost during July and August (the lactation period) and Fuhrmann and Seitz (1992) found radio-tracked bats of this species moved a comparable 1.5 km from the roost during lactation, although they foraged up to 3.3 km from the roost in September and October. This may, however, have been due to a shortage of available food close to the roost late in summer, since Entwistle *et al.* (1996) found no reduction in the foraging distance of females due to lactation.

Entwistle *et al.*'s extensive study found that the furthest feeding site was 2.8 km from the main roost site. This site was used by a male; the furthest site used by a female was 2.2 km from the roost. Overall, bats spent 92% of their foraging time within 1.5 km of the roost (Figure 4.5) and significantly more of their time within 0.5 km of the roost than further away. When data for males and females were analysed separately, it was shown that, while females spent most of their time within 0.5 km of home, males showed a more equal distribution of their time between distance bands. This is obvious in Figure 4.6, which shows data for pairs of male and female bats tracked simultaneously. A significant positive relationship was found between the time spent within 0.5 km of the roost by female *P. auritus* and the area of deciduous woodland within that distance. Thus, it appears that it is important to the bats to have woodland available close to the roost, a conclusion which reinforces the finding of Entwistle *et al.* (1997) that *P. auritus* select roosts which have deciduous woodland within 0.5 km, rather than choosing buildings at random.

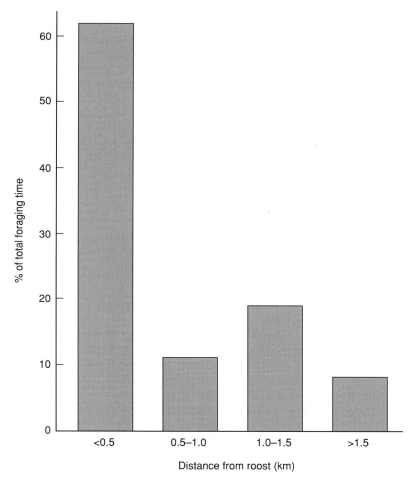

FIG 4.5 *The percentage of total flying time spent by 16 radio-tracked* P. auritus *from roosts in north-east Scotland in distance bands progressively further from roosts.* n = 65 *bat nights plus 7 half nights (reproduced with permission from Entwistle* et al., *1996).*

The reasons why female *P. auritus* forage closer to roosts than males are not clear. It is possible that females are restricted because they have to make energetically expensive flights back to the roost to suckle their infants. Although this explanation is at variance with the finding of Entwistle *et al.* (1996) that there was no difference between the distances travelled by lactating and non-reproductive females, it is possible that patterns involving foraging close to the roost may become intrinsic in females and may prevail even in years when they do not give birth. Alternative explanations suggested by these authors are that either males may be aggressively excluded from close-by foraging areas or that they may benefit from reduced intraspecific competition if they move further from the roost.

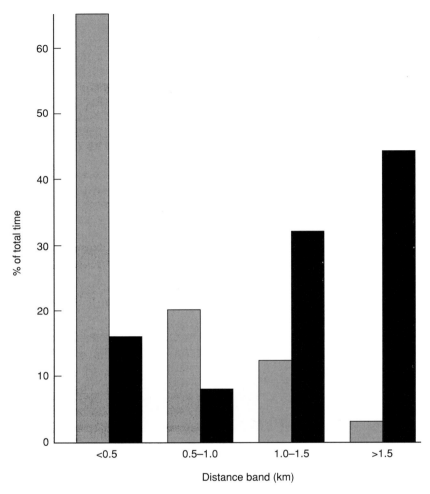

FIG 4.6   *The percentage of total flying time spent by male and female* P. auritus *of simultaneously tracked pairs in distance bands progressively further from roosts. Light bars, female bats; dark bars, male bats (reproduced with permission from Entwistle et al., 1996).*

Feeding Rate and Duration of Foraging

Insectivorous bats feed rapidly, particularly in the first hour or two of foraging, when they are very hungry and insect availability is generally high. Kovtun and Zhukova (1994) estimated that most species consume approximately 25% of their own body weight in insects per night. This, for a *P. auritus* weighing on average around 8 g, means it eats about 2 g of insects, mostly in the first 2 h of foraging. Since large craneflies weigh about 50 mg, small beetles about 75 mg and noctuid moths an average of around 100 mg, this means that a long-eared bat would have to eat somewhere around 40 craneflies, 27 small beetles (such as leaf or bark beetles) or 20 noctuid moths in a night.

Rydell (1993) suggested that, at high latitudes, insectivorous bats may act primarily as energy maximizers rather than as time minimizers, which would mean they would forage during all the time available if it were energetically profitable to do so. If they were time minimizers, the duration of foraging would reflect the changing energy demands of reproduction, i.e. foraging time would increase slowly during pregnancy and then rapidly as lactation proceeded. No evidence was found by Entwistle *et al.* (1996) to indicate that this was the case in *P. auritus* – lactating and non-reproductive females and males all had foraging durations which did not differ significantly from each other. The total median foraging time for females was 235.7 min and that for males was 271.9 min. These were comparable to the average foraging duration of females in Germany (353.6 min; Fuhrmann and Seitz, 1992). It therefore appears that, at high latitude, shortness of darkness precludes *P. auritus* from being a time minimizer. Instead, it is an energy maximizer, foraging for as long as darkness permits. There is evidence that this species makes extensive use of daily torpor during lactation (Speakman and Racey, 1987; see also Chapter 5) to make up for the energy shortfall caused by the demands of rearing an infant.

CHAPTER 5

Reproduction

BATS are placental mammals, and they share the reproductive characteristics of this group. Mating and fertilization are followed by a period of gestation, during which the growing embryo is nourished by the placenta. After the young is born, it is cared for and fed on milk by its mother until weaning. However, bats' reproductive cycles are far from typical of small mammals – instead of being short-lived and producing many offspring, like mice, bats live long lives and produce relatively few, large offspring in which they invest a high degree of maternal care. Bats such as *Plecotus* species which live in temperate zones have seasonal cycles which are adapted to incorporate a period of hibernation and to ensure that the young are born and weaned at times of year which maximize their chances of survival. To this end, they show a number of highly specialized reproductive adaptations.

SEASONAL CYCLE

Like all bats living in temperate zones, long-eared bats undergo only one reproductive cycle per year. They have a relatively long gestation period and the young must be born as early as possible in summer to ensure they have a sufficient period after weaning in which to accumulate enough fat to survive their first winter. In addition, females need an adequate supply of insect food to sustain pregnancy and lactation. Summers in temperate zones, particularly at high latitude, are not long enough to incorporate mating, pregnancy, weaning and pre-hibernal fat accumulation. The monoestrous cycle is therefore extended over winter, with mating beginning in autumn and ovulation and pregnancy delayed until spring (Figure 5.1). The process of spermatogenesis begins in late spring, after males have emerged from hibernation, and continues through summer. Spermatozoa are produced late in summer, after which the testes regress in September and October. Mating begins in October and continues sporadically through winter and, in *P. auritus* but probably not in *P. austriacus* (Stebbings, 1970), in early spring. Spermatozoa are stored in the uteri of females and in the epididymides of males over winter. Females ovulate in late April or May, after hibernation ends, and the ovum is fertilized by sperm stored in the uterus. Pregnant bats move into nursery roosts during spring and parturition takes place here, usually in early to mid July. Mothers and young remain in nursery roosts during lactation in July and August and may stay on there into autumn. There is some evidence that mating may occur in nursery roosts in *Plecotus* colonies.

The reproductive cycle is therefore long for a small mammal – spermatozoa produced

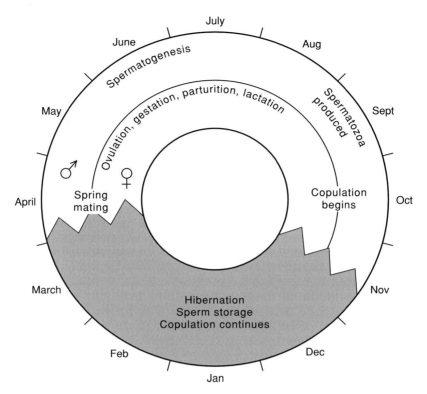

FIG 5.1 *Schematic representation of the annual reproductive cycle of long-eared bats (adapted from Racey, 1974a).*

one summer do not result in live young until the next. Since the vast majority of *Plecotus* females produce a single infant, the reproductive rate is thus very low. Because of the length and complexity of the cycle, a female which does not become pregnant, which aborts a fetus or whose infant dies, loses its chance to reproduce for a whole year. A number of adaptations in the reproductive cycle have evolved which minimize the chances of such failures. These ensure that a high proportion of adult females, estimated at 70% (Entwistle, 1994) to 97% (Benzal, 1991), do produce young each year and that the infants have the best possible chance of survival.

MALE REPRODUCTION

Reproductive Organs

The anatomy of male long-eared bats is typical of vespertilionid bats except that there are two pairs of Cowper's glands (Figure 5.2) instead of one. The possession of two pairs of these glands appears to be shared only by *Plecotus* and *Corynorhinus*, a closely related North

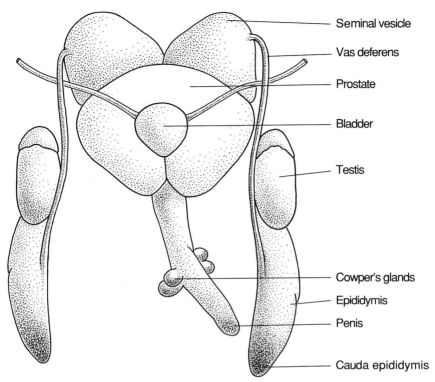

FIG 5.2   *Diagram of the male reproductive organs of a long-eared bat.*

American genus (Pearson *et al.*, 1952). The testes, which produce spermatozoa, consist of tightly coiled seminiferous tubules surrounded by interstitial cells which produce the hormones responsible for aggression and libido. The testes are abdominal before birth but descend around the time of birth to occupy a position in the upper thigh, level with the penis. The duct system includes the vasa efferentia and epididymis, which empties into the vas deferens and then the urethra. The accessory glands include the ampullary, prostate and Cowper's glands. All of these contribute constituents to the semen, including essential nutrients, fructose and various electrolytes which aid in maintaining the pH of the seminal fluid at around 7 (Hill and Smith, 1984). The size and activity levels of the accessory glands are controlled by hormones secreted by the interstitial cells in the testes and vary throughout the annual cycle. The penis is the copulatory organ and its erection is controlled by engorgement of the corpora cavernosa with blood. *Plecotus* also have a baculum, a small bone which caps the end of the corpora cavernosa.

Hormonal Control of the Reproductive Cycle

Testosterone, secreted by the testes, controls the process of spermatogenesis and maintains the secretory activity of the accessory glands. The reproductive cycle of male long-eared bats and of all other bat species which hibernate are characterized by an asynchronous, annual recrudescence of the testes and accessory organs, and this asynchrony results in cycles in both which are out of phase with each other (Gustafson and Damassa, 1987). Although the total plasma testosterone level increases at the same time as testicular activity begins in spring, the accessory organs do not begin to increase in mass or show other signs of seasonal activity until some time later, when plasma testosterone levels are at a maximum. This delayed response by the accessory organs suggests that there is some form of androgen resistance, which appears to be due to variations in androgen availability rather than to changes in the sensitivity of the target organs. Gustafson and Damassa (1987) suggested that the levels of plasma testosterone are controlled by a sex steroid-binding hormone (SBP) which has been found in the blood of several vespertilionid species and which binds plasma testosterone, rendering it effectively unavailable for physiological action. They proposed that only when non SBP-bound levels of testosterone increase later in summer does enough free testosterone circulate to cause the accessory organs to become active.

Age of Maturity

Stebbings (1966), in a population study of *Plecotus*, found that two out of three males born one summer underwent spermatogenesis the following summer and were thus sexually mature (defined by the production of sperm) in their second autumn. A third showed no signs of maturity at this age and presumably did not undergo spermatogenesis until it was 2 years old. Speakman and Racey (1986) reported that 3 out of 57 *P. auritus* males captured in north-east Scotland (i.e. about 5%) showed signs of sexual maturity in the autumn of their birth, when they were about 3 months old, and Entwistle *et al.* (in press) also found that a few showed limited testicular development at 3 months, although most underwent spermatogenesis for the first time in the summer of the year following their birth. Entwistle *et al.* (in press) pointed out that the degree of testicular development in the 3 month old males in their study was much less than that in adults caught at the same time, and that they may not have been fertile. Sexual maturity in an individual's second summer thus appears to be normal in this species, as in most other vespertilionids. A similar situation exists in *C. townsendii*, in which a few males mature in their first autumn and most in their second summer or autumn (Pearson *et al.*, 1952), and in *Corynorhinus rafinesquii*, in which males mature in their second autumn (Jones and Suttkus, 1975). It seems that a few *P. auritus* may not mature until at least their third year (Stebbings, 1966), an unusual situation among vespertilionid bats.

Factors influencing attainment of sexual maturity

Speakman and Racey (1986) found there was a strong direct relationship between the age at which male *P. auritus* become mature and their body condition, measured by means of an index (body weight/forearm length). They suggested that long-eared bats had to attain a target weight before they attained puberty and that only those in very good body condition would mature in their first summer. Entwistle *et al.* (in press) similarly found that bats which showed signs of testicular growth and epididymal development at 3 months had significantly higher relative body condition than did those which remained immature. Benzal (1991), in a study in central Spain, found that juvenile male *P. auritus* gained less weight than did juvenile females in the period before their first hibernation. He suggested that most males were not heavy enough to attain sexual maturity before they went into hibernation. The factors influencing age of maturity are thus likely to be time of birth (late births in a colony will result in very few becoming mature before winter), weather conditions, food availability and foraging ability in individual bats.

Methods of assessing maturity

Because the testes regress seasonally in temperate zone bat species, it is not always obvious which males of adult size are actually sexually mature. Racey (1974b) showed that in *Pipistrellus pipistrellus* assessment could be made by external examination of the caudae epididymides. The tunica vaginalis, a sheath of peritoneum covering the testes and epididymides, appears black through the skin due to the presence of pigment-bearing cells, or melanocytes. As the caudae epididymides become distended with sperm, the sheath stretches and the melanocytes separate so that the colour becomes mottled, and the tunica vaginalis remains mottled after the sperm have been voided; it does not regain its jet black colour in adults. Although the method has been used to determine sexual maturity in *P. auritus* (Speakman and Racey, 1986; Boyd and Stebbings, 1989) and other species, until recently its efficacy has not been tested. However, Entwistle *et al.* (in press) have now reported that 26% of *P. auritus* males were wrongly assessed by the method; in their study, a few males known to be juveniles had completely white, unpigmented caudae epididymides. They found that the relative size and shape of the caudae epididymides was a more reliable indicator in *P. auritus* – those of immature animals were small and nodular, while those of adults were larger and dorso-ventrally flattened.

Spermatogenesis

The process is initiated in late spring or early summer in most European species, and continues through summer. At the end of summer, spermatozoa are released from the testes into the epididymides and the testes regress. Testicular growth was first observed in *P. auritus* in Scotland in early July (Entwistle *et al.*, in press) and reached a peak in mid August. Changes in testicular size indicated that spermatogenesis was complete and spermatozoa were released into the epididymides around the end of August. The testes then regressed, but the caudae epididymides remained large for some months, before gradually shrinking during the hibernation period. The testes remained quiescent throughout hibernation.

The factors controlling the onset of spermatogenesis are not fully understood. Racey (1978) reported that premature arousal of *P. pipistrellus* from hibernation, associated with both food availability and temperature, was shown to result in premature initiation of spermatogenesis. Light also had some effect, since the process was inhibited in pipistrelles kept in total darkness, but there was no evidence that increasing photoperiod was necessary to stimulate testicular development. Speakman and Racey (1986) found that a few juvenile *P. auritus* showed signs of sexual maturity in their first autumn and pointed out that they did this at a time when daylength was becoming shorter.

Entwistle *et al.* (in press) assessed the use of torpor by male *P. auritus* in summer by recording the proportion of torpid males caught in roosts and investigated the relationship between the use of torpor and testosterone levels. They found that the use of torpor was lowest in July and August, when spermatogenesis was at its peak, and highest in May and September. Use of torpor was almost completely suspended at the time when the initial distension of the caudae epididymides was recorded, and this was also accompanied by a drop in body mass and a tendency for male bats to increase their use of warm nursery roosts. They concluded that torpor and peak spermatogenesis may be incompatible in this species, either because endothermy is a prerequisite for spermatogenesis or because bats' ability to enter torpor is reduced when testosterone level is very high. The two explanations are not mutually exclusive. After spermatogenesis is complete, testosterone level drops and the accessory organs are maintained by much lower levels. It appears that this lower level does not inhibit hibernation, since a moderate level is maintained all winter. Entwistle *et al.* (in press) suggested that levels of testosterone may briefly be elevated during periodic arousals from hibernation in order to maintain secondary reproductive processes.

Sperm Storage by Males

Sperm stored in the caudae epididymides over winter are capable of fertilization in a number of species of hibernating bats. Strelkov (1962) showed that an increasing proportion of females of four vespertilionid species, including *P. auritus*, were inseminated as hibernation progressed. Racey (1972) conducted experiments on captive noctules (*Nyctalus noctula*), in which females were not allowed to mate in autumn, but were introduced to males at various times during winter and then became pregnant the following spring. The minimum storage time by a male was taken as being the interval between the date of distension of the caudae epididymides and the date when the female was introduced. In this way, Racey showed that sperm remained capable of fertilization for at least 5 months and up to 7 months. A histological study of reproductive tracts taken from hibernating bats (Racey, 1975) revealed no differences between noctules and a variety of other British species including *P. auritus* in the storage sites or appearance of stored sperm, so it is likely that the viability of sperm of all these species is similar. In all of them, spermatozoa were orientated towards the epithelial cells of the vas deferens, and it is probable that their survival was in some way connected with these cells.

Mating

Strelkov (1962) caught female *P. auritus* in hibernacula in artificial caves during winter. He extracted the uteri, washed out the contents and examined them microscopically for stored spermatozoa. In November, shortly after their arrival at the cave, only 14% of females were inseminated. In December, this had risen to 63%, in January–March to 81%, and by April 100% were inseminated. He concluded that in this species mating occurred throughout winter, either through males arousing and copulating with dormant females or during periodic arousals and moves to different parts of the cave by groups of bats. Copulation by males with torpid females has also been recorded in *C. townsendii* by Pearson *et al.* (1952). Strelkov's data indicate that the main mating season for *P. auritus* is winter and early spring, rather than autumn as is the case in most vespertilionid species. Stebbings (1970) observed matings in *P. auritus* in September–October and in April with equal frequency, but reported that *P. austriacus* from the same roost mated only in autumn. Horacek (1975) similarly reported differences in the mating behaviour of the two species. In *P. auritus*, mating mainly occurred in winter-type roosts and activity in transitory roosts (Chapter 6) was high, particularly in spring, while in *P. austriacus* it occurred mainly in summer roosts and transitory roosts were not used. *P. austriacus* thus do not appear to mate in spring, although their behaviour has not been documented well enough to draw conclusions regarding winter mating.

Entwistle (1994) recorded that the proportion of male *P. auritus* found in nursery roosts increased through summer and that the proportion of females decreased after lactation was complete, followed by a decline in the number of juveniles. By October, nursery colonies were dominated by males. Brown long-eared bats remain in nursery roosts longer than do most species in autumn and Entwistle suggested that, by moving into roosts in this way, males increased their chances of gaining access to mates. On balance, she considered that *P. auritus* most probably have an unstructured, promiscuous mating system with no continuing bond between individuals once mating is over. Because *P. auritus* mate throughout winter, the energy expenditure involved in males defending females would not guarantee them reproductive success, since the females could not be defended all winter. Mating systems in both species of long-eared bats are discussed further in Chapter 6.

FEMALE REPRODUCTION

Reproductive Organs

The primary sex organs are the paired ovaries, and there is also a pair of oviducts, a bicornuate uterus, as in all vespertilionid species, and a vagina with an opening between the anus and the urethra. There are two uterine horns of equal length, with a shorter common uterine canal between them and the vagina. The ovary has several functions. It produces the mature gamete, or ovum, which develops in the follicle, a structure within the ovary. The development of the follicle is controlled by pituitary hormones, and specialized cells which make up the outer layer of the developing follicle are also involved in producing the female sex hormones, or oestrogens. Oestrogens are produced throughout oogenesis and travel in the bloodstream to the uterus, where they cause the uterine lining to proliferate in preparation for the arrival of the fertilized ovum (Hill and Smith, 1984). At ovulation, the ovum is released from the follicle into the open end of the oviduct, through which it travels to the uterus. It may implant in either of the two uterine horns after fertilization. After ovulation, granulosa cells remaining in the follicle hypertrophy and luteinize to form the corpus luteum, which secretes progesterone throughout pregnancy. Racey and Swift (1981) showed that the plasma progesterone level in *P. pipistrellus* increased to a peak level of 38 nmol l^{-1} about 6 days before parturition and then fell sharply. The corpus luteum volume showed a similar peak, but the rise to the maximum level was more gradual, indicating a lag between hypertrophy of the luteal cells and their increased functional capacity. Progesterone levels in *Plecotus* have not been investigated.

Age of Maturity

Stebbings (1966), during a study of a mixed colony of *P. auritus* and *P. austriacus*, recaptured four females of known age over several years. None of the four had produced an infant in its second summer when it was 1 year old. Three gave birth when they were 2 years old and must therefore have mated for the first time during their second autumn or winter. The fourth was not captured when it was 2 years old, but gave birth the next year. It thus seems to be the norm in *Plecotus* bats for females to give birth for the first time at 24 months of age, although some may not do so until they are 36 months old. Entwistle (1994) analysed data collected in a ringing study of *P. auritus* in north-east Scotland over a number of years. Like Stebbings, she found that females produced their first young when they were 2–3 years old. In this respect, long-eared bats differ from their American relative *C. townsendii*, females of which mated in their first autumn (Pearson *et al.*, 1952) and from most European vespertilionid species (e.g. *P. pipistrellus*, *N. noctula* and *Myotis* species) in all of which at least some females mate for the first time during their first autumn (Racey, 1974b).

Method of assessing sexual maturity
Sexual maturity cannot be ascertained externally in female bats, but the condition of the nipple can be used to indicate whether or not one has previously suckled an infant (Racey, 1974b). A parous female is defined as one which has given birth, and it may at the time of examination be inseminated, not inseminated, pregnant or lactating. A nulliparous female is one which has not given birth, and it may be immature, mature but not inseminated, inseminated or pregnant for the first time. A female which is mature but which has never given birth would be classed as nulliparous; however, because in practice almost all females which are mature do give birth, the system produces few misclassifications of this sort. Another problem could arise with a female whose first infant was stillborn; in this case, because the infant had never suckled, the mother would be classified as nulliparous although she had, in fact, given birth. In practice, such cases are probably rare and almost all nulliparous females are those which are too young to have given birth, although the term 'immature' cannot be applied to them. Sexual maturity in females can only be established by histological examination of the uterus (Racey, 1974b). The nipples of nulliparous females are rudimentary and give rise to long hairs which are dark with light coloured tips. Those of parous females are larger, with a dark, keratinized area and short, light coloured, wavy hair.

Sperm Storage by Females

Spermatozoa produced in summer and inseminated into females during autumn or winter matings are stored within their reproductive tracts until ovulation in spring. Storage thus takes place in both males and females for periods of several months. In horseshoe bats (Rhinolophidae), sperm are stored in the oviducts, but in all Vespertilionidae so far studied the storage site is the uterus. In pipistrelles (*P. pipistrellus*) and noctules (*N. noctula*), the two British species in which sperm storage has been most studied, histological sections showed that the uterus was distended with spermatozoa (Racey, 1975). These were orientated parallel to each other and with their heads towards the uterine epithelial cells, particularly at the upper end of the uterus where it gives rise to the oviduct (the utero-tubal junction). Electron microscopy further showed that contact was established between the epithelial microvilli and the plasma membrane of adjacent spermatozoa (Racey, 1975). There is an abundance of glycogen in the uterine epithelium of the pipistrelle during the period of storage, and the occurrence of fructose in the uterine plasma suggests that epithelial cells may secrete nutrients which are taken up by the stored sperm. The mechanism of sperm storage has not been studied in long-eared bats; it is probably similar to that in other vespertilionid species, although it is clear that the uterus does not become distended with semen. Because *P. auritus* mate throughout winter and spring, it is likely that storage by females plays a less important part in the reproductive cycle than it does in species, such as *P. pipistrellus* and *N. noctula*, in which most mating occurs in autumn; in *P. auritus* storage appears to be more equally shared between males and females. However, sperm from autumn matings is stored by females and it has not so far been shown to be infertile by spring. In *P. austriacus*, which appears to mate mostly in autumn, sperm storage in the uterus is likely to be an important aspect of the reproductive cycle, but no data are available.

Ovulation

The factors controlling ovulation have not been studied in *Plecotus*, but Pearson *et al.* (1952) examined reproductive tracts of the related species *C. townsendii* and found that the follicle developed very little until January; most growth occurred between January and April. Ovulation was not easily induced in these bats by increasing ambient temperature before February, although after then ovulation could be advanced by moving individuals to a warm room. Racey (1976) reported that ovulation could be induced in pipistrelles by warming them up and feeding them. He proposed that they ovulated in the wild in response to increases in air temperature and food supply, and that the result was the impressive synchrony of births which occurs in a colony. The flight from hibernacula to summer roosts, which also occurs in response to temperature rises, may be a contributing factor. Ovulation can also be induced by injecting bats with gonadotrophins, the substances thought naturally to trigger the process (Racey, 1976); these have been isolated in the pituitary glands of a number of vespertilionid species (Anthony, 1987). The follicle responds to gonadotrophins with increasing sensitivity as winter proceeds.

In *C. townsendii*, both ovaries were found to be equally active (Pearson *et al.*, 1952) – of a sample of 34 bats, 19 ovulated from the right ovary and 15 from the left. There was therefore no evidence of asynchrony of ovarian function in this species.

Gestation

Eisentraut (1937) first noted that the rate of fetal development in bats was affected by environmental temperature. He observed that single pregnant mouse-eared bats, *Myotis myotis*, became torpid in cold conditions and that the torpidity could continue for several days. Furthermore, periods of torpor reduced the size of the fetus a female was carrying. Kolb (1950) similarly correlated a 3 week delay relative to the previous summer in the first births in a colony of *Rhinolophus hipposideros* with a 3 week spell of cold weather in May. Racey (1969) showed that the mean length of gestation in *P. pipistrellus* could be extended by the induction of torpor at different stages during pregnancy and that the extension corresponded to the length of the period of torpor. His finding questioned the generally accepted concept of a fixed gestation period for heterothermic mammals, and in a further series of experiments (Racey, 1973), he showed that parturition could be delayed in groups of pregnant pipistrelles which were deprived of food and maintained at temperatures of between 5 and 10°C for up to 14 days. Gestation rate was slowed in bats fed ad lib at a temperature of 5°C and accelerated in those at 30 and 35°C. Racey and Swift (1981) showed that delayed gestation was not confined to the extreme conditions set up in laboratories, but also occurred in the wild. They recorded that gestation length in a colony of pipistrelles varied by 10 days in two consecutive years when weather conditions during early pregnancy differed appreciably, and that the delay in the second year occurred concurrently with a spell of cold, wet weather when very little insect food was available.

Delayed gestation appears to be universal among heterothermic bats and is clearly an adaptation which allows them to overcome the problem of periodic cold weather and reduced food availability in temperate regions. Particularly at high latitudes, such conditions are common in mid to late spring. Unlike other small mammals such as rodents, in this situation bats are not able to abort or reabsorb their embryos and then remate, but by 'shutting down' pregnancy for a few days or even weeks they are able to remain pregnant and so still produce the year's infant. Fetal growth rates in bats are among the lowest of all mammals (Kihlstrom, 1972), and it may be that this slow rate was a prerequisite for the evolution of delayed gestation.

Parturition in long-eared bats in Britain occurs in late June and July. Births in a mixed colony of *P. auritus* and *P. austriacus* were recorded during July (Stebbings, 1966, 1970). Boyd and Stebbings (1989) reported that parturition in *P. auritus* in southern England took place in late June and during July, and Speakman and Racey (1987) found births reached a peak in *P. auritus* colonies in north-east Scotland during the first week in July. Swift (1981), working in the same study area in Scotland, recorded that first births occurred between 30 June and 15 July, and Entwistle (1994) also stated that long-eared bats in the area gave birth in July. She found that births were spread over about a month, both within and between colonies, and Howard (1995) reported that births in an English colony were spread over about 3 weeks in most years.

Because ovulation does not follow mating immediately, the start of gestation is difficult to measure but, from data on numerous species, it is generally assumed that ovulation coincides with the time at which females first move into nursery roosts. Speakman and Racey (1987) first observed *P. auritus* around nursery roosts in the first week of May, and noted that most moved into these roosts about a week later. Swift (1981) recorded very similar timing in the same area, and the time of ovulation was thus most probably between 28 April and 7 May. Length of gestation was calculated by Swift (1981) to vary between 60 and 65 days over 3 years and Speakman and Racey (1987) estimated it to be 60–70 days. Gestation length varies with the size of bat species, and thus *Plecotus* might be expected to be in the middle of the range for British bats. This appears to be the case – its gestation is longer than that of the pipistrelle (41–51 days; Racey and Swift, 1981) which is smaller, and slightly shorter than that of the noctule (70–73 days; Racey, 1991) which is larger. Gestation in the related species *C. townsendii* in America was found to vary between 56 and 100 days (Pearson *et al.*, 1952).

Fecundity

In Stebbings' (1966) mixed colony of *Plecotus* species, some females regularly recaptured were found to give birth every year while others gave birth every other year. Entwistle (1994) estimated that, in Scotland, the proportion of females which gave birth in any year was 70%, compared with a level of 63% in Stebbings' study. Both were lower than in Spain, where fecundity was estimated at 97% (Benzal, 1991). Entwistle suggested that the reason for the varying levels may have been a relatively high degree of reabsorption or spontaneous abortion among this species in some areas.

BIRTH AND LITTER SIZE

Parturition

Births of bats are difficult to observe under natural conditions, where roosts are dark and crowded and females easily disturbed. Descriptions of parturition therefore usually rely on captive bats, although it is possible that behaviour in captive colonies may be abnormal. However, Ransome (1990) used an image intensifier to watch births in *Rhinolophus ferrumequinum* in a nursery roost, and his observations indicate that recorded data on captive bats are probably reliable. Kleiman (1969) kept captive colonies of four British species, including *P. auritus*, and females of all these gave birth. All births took place during daylight hours and all females assumed the same position in which to give birth. They hung with their heads upward and gripped with their thumbs and widely spread feet. The tail membrane was curved ventrally and, together with the wings, formed a net to catch the infant as it was born. The position of the wings made it difficult to see the birth presentation of the baby, but Kleiman (1969) reported that a head-first presentation was commonest in noctules, although most vespertilionid infants are born in the breech position. Presentation has not been documented in *Plecotus*, but in a single birth observed in *C. townsendii* (Pearson *et al.*, 1952), the infant was born in the breech position. Infants are very active immediately and grip their mother's fur with their teeth and thumbs. They move towards the thoracic nipples and attach themselves firmly. They are then thoroughly licked by the mother. The placenta is reported to be eaten by noctules, pipistrelles and serotines (Kleiman, 1969) and by *C. townsendii* (Pearson *et al.*, 1952). In captive *P. auritus* which I have kept (Swift, *unpublished*), no placentae were ever found on the floor of the cage following births, so it is assumed that this species also does the same.

Baby bats are relatively large at birth compared with the young of many other mammals. A literature survey (Kurta and Kunz, 1987) revealed that, at birth, bats typically weighed 20–30% (average = 22%) of adult mass, compared with a range in other similarly sized mammals of 5–10% (average = 8%). Newborn *P. auritus* have been found to weigh an average of 1.76 g (de Fanis and Jones, 1995a), which is 22% of an average adult mass of 8 g. As in all bat species, the pubic ligament expands to up to 30 times its normal length during birth, under the influence of the hormone relaxin. This allows the birth of such large infants to take place.

Litter Size

Although bats have large babies, they have relatively few of them. The vast majority of species produce a single infant, and Vespertilionidae are the only family in which multiple births occur with any frequency. Twins occur occasionally in a number of species, but only eight species are known regularly to produce more than two infants (Tuttle and Stevenson, 1982). In the European species studied, twins occur occasionally, and triplets very rarely, in both the noctule (*N. noctula*; Racey, 1991) and the pipistrelle (*P. pipistrellus*; Racey, 1972), but twins appear to be rare in other species including *P. auritus* (Schober and Grimmberger, 1989) and have not been recorded to date in *P. austriacus*. The twinning rate varies with maternal age and geographical distribution – there is evidence that older females have twins more often than younger ones, and twin births occur rarely in England (Racey, 1982) but more frequently in northern Scotland (Swift, 1981) and Russia (Rakhmatulina, 1972), indicating that more twins are born at high latitude. These factors may affect twinning in *P. auritus*, but so far there are insufficient data to draw conclusions.

Constraints on Litter Size

Because bats are the only mammals capable of sustained flight, it seems reasonable to connect their small litter size with this ability. Pregnant females have to fly, feed and negotiate roost entrances while carrying a heavy load. However, the total weight of embryos at full term does not differ between bats and similarly sized terrestrial mammals – in both cases the weight they carry is about 25% of the adult mass. The difference is that bats carry one large embryo and terrestrial mammals several smaller ones. Barclay (1995) suggested that the reason for small litter size is connected with flight, but for post-natal, and not pre-natal, reasons. Terrestrial mammals are weaned at around 37% of adult weight and bats at an average of 70.9%; weaning in *P. auritus* does not take place until juveniles have a mass of 60–70%, and a forearm length of 97.6%, of adult values. This constraint seems to be connected with flight, since young birds similarly do not fly until they are almost fully grown, and it is likely that wings must be fully calcified before they are able to withstand the forces placed on them in flight. Rearing an infant to this large size is costly to a female, but Barclay (1995) argued that, although the energy demands on female bats are very high during lactation, the limiting factor may be calcium and not energy. All of the calcium required to produce the skeleton of a volant juvenile bat has to come from the mother's milk, and arthropods are a very poor source of this mineral. Birds and terrestrial mammals are able to supplement their diet, and that of their offspring, with other calcium-rich foods such as snail shells or vertebrate bones, but bats do not have this option. There is evidence that bats of some species deplete their own calcium stores in order to meet the demands of their offspring, resulting in a decline in the specific gravity of their long bones such as the humerus and an increased risk of wing bone fractures (Barclay, 1995). It therefore seems likely that the heavy demand of rearing young to independence, and particularly of providing enough calcium to do this, is the main factor which limits the number of infants produced.

POST-NATAL GROWTH AND DEVELOPMENT

Long-eared bats are born hairless, pink in colour and with their eyes closed. Their feet are disproportionately large and well-developed to enable them to cling to beams in the roost, a feature shared by all newborn bats (Ransome, 1990). In common with other vespertilionid species, they are born with their milk teeth present and with the incisors specialized by having hooked tips to enable them to grip the mother's nipple securely. This allows an infant to cling to the nipple even when the mother is in flight. Although infants are not carried on normal foraging flights, they are transported inside the roost (Swift, 1981) and on flights outside if the colony moves roosts during the pre-flight period. The skeleton of a newborn long-eared bat is soft and flexible, consisting mainly of cartilage. The ears are closed and hang downwards over the face. Their appearance is similar to the description given by Pearson *et al.* (1952) of infant *C. townsendii.* These authors also recorded that when infant *C. townsendii* were 7 days old their ears became erect and a few days later their eyes opened. By 4 days old they had a covering of hair and by 30 days they had almost reached adult size.

Swift (1981) observed *P. auritus* under natural conditions inside a nursery roost during summer. Individual mothers and their babies were marked (the mothers with reflective rings and the babies with coloured ink spots), so that the ages of the infants were known. Babies less than 1 week old were found attached to their mothers' nipples at all times except when the adults left the roost to forage, at which time the infants huddled closely together in a crèche. The rate of emission of audible isolation calls, or i-calls (Gould, 1971) was initially high (around 1 s^{-1}) just after the adults had left, and then fell to about 0.1 s^{-1}. It increased again as the mothers began to return and search for their babies. After 7 days, huddling behaviour in crèches was much less obvious and few i-calls were recorded. From 12 days of age, infants were never found attached to their mothers except when suckling between foraging trips made by the mother. They groomed themselves from this age and no grooming by mothers was observed. Juveniles first left the roost at around 30 days of age and they made practice flights in the roost for several days before this. Howard (1995) similarly recorded first flights outside the roost at around 30 days, and also observed juveniles flying inside the roost for 7–10 days before this, as well as practising landing on vertical surfaces.

De Fanis and Jones (1995a) caught 15 *P. auritus* at a nursery roost during late pregnancy and brought them into captivity, where they taught them to feed on mealworms and where the bats were able to fly. Five babies were born, and the growth and development of these was studied for 40 days before the bats were released. Detailed observations from this study are similar to those of Swift (1981) under natural conditions. During the first week of life, babies were always found attached to their own mother's nipple; which nipple they chose was found to be random. When isolated from their mothers, babies remained quite still and emitted i-calls; mothers actively sought their offspring when they heard these calls. By 5–6 days of age, the babies' eyes had opened and they began to crawl around actively. They were no longer attached to the nipple all day and they began to play a more active part in reunions with their mothers after separation. By 10–12 days, babies began to groom themselves and mothers no longer groomed them. They also began to flap their wings. After 20 days, they began to make trial flights in the roost, and from day 33–35, they flew actively. McLean and Speakman (1996) similarly found that captive infant *P. auritus* spent progressively less time attached to their mothers' nipples after 5 days of age.

From the limited data available, growth and development in *P. austriacus* appears to be similar to that in *P. auritus*, and weaning in both species is completed about 6 weeks after birth.

Growth

Bats are unique among mammals in that they provide their young with milk until they achieve at least 90% of adult skeletal size and at least 70% of adult body mass (Kunz and Stern, 1995). Because the young cannot fly until their wings have reached adult size, they are dependent on their mothers for longer than are the young of most mammals. Post-natal growth is strongly influenced by the quality and quantity of milk with which infants are provided. In most species studied, growth rates (usually measured by mass or forearm length) are initially linear and then slow down. The asymptotic mass (i.e. the mass at which infants stop growing) is usually less than the adult mass because it does not include accretionary growth after the first year, nor variations such as autumn fat deposits. For all temperate zone species, there is a negative correlation between post-natal growth rate and asymptotic body mass, i.e. the smaller the species, the faster it grows. Growth rate is also affected by climate (Kunz and Stern, 1995), and temperate zone bats grow faster than tropical ones. High growth rates are achieved in highly seasonal environments. A species such as *P. auritus*, which lives at high latitude, might therefore be expected to grow rapidly. Measurements recorded by de Fanis and Jones (1995a) show this to be the case. However it should be noted that, in general, growth rates in studies using captive bats tend to be high, since adults have access to unlimited food and so are able to provide infants with a constant milk supply. In the wild, unfavourable weather conditions may cause a shortage of insects, leading to extensive use of torpor by mothers and subsequent curtailment of milk supply. This will slow growth rates considerably. No data on growth rates under natural conditions are currently available for either *Plecotus* species for comparison.

The average body mass of newborn infant *P. auritus* was 1.76 ± 0.29 g (de Fanis and Jones, 1995a). Mass increased linearly for the first 15 days (Figure 5.3) and then stabilized from 15–25 days before showing a slight decrease over days 20–25, when juveniles used up energy during their initial practice flights. After day 30, it rose again, stabilizing at between 60 and 70% of adult mass. Forearm length also showed a linear increase for the first 15–16

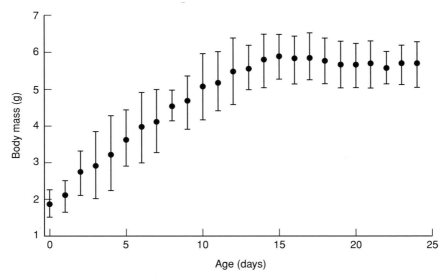

FIG 5.3 *Rate of post-natal weight increase in infant* P. auritus *in captivity (reproduced with permission from de Fanis and Jones, 1995a). Values shown are mean ± S.D. (n = 5).*

days (Figure 5.4), after which the rate of increase slowed considerably. On the day the bats were released (around day 40), the forearm length averaged 36.40 ± 1.18 mm ($n=5$), while the mean length for adults was 37.28 ± 1.47 mm ($n=10$). This meant that on day 40 juvenile forearm length was 97.6% of that of adults. The rate of forearm growth in de Fanis and Jones' study was 1.2 mm per day during the linear phase – the same rate as was recorded in the closely related species *C. townsendii* under natural conditions (Pearson *et al.*, 1952). The growth pattern in *C. townsendii* was very similar to that in *P. auritus* – forearm growth was found to be linear to about 16 days and then to slow down. By 4 weeks, forearm length was almost equal to that of adults.

Wing Morphology

De Fanis and Jones (1995a) found that the wingspan of *P. auritus* infants increased linearly until the age of 25 days and then slowed down, and they also showed that there was a difference in the rate of development of different parts of the wing. The hand–wing area (the area of membrane between digits 2 and 5, referred to as the dactylopatagium in Figure 2.8 on p. 26) increased rapidly until day 20–21 and then slowed considerably, while the area of the arm–wing (the membrane between the body and digit 5, referred to as the plagiopatagium in Figure 2.8) increased rapidly until day 15–16, after which it similarly slowed. The hand–wing was thus the less developed area at birth and the tip area ratio (hand–wing area/arm–wing area) increased gradually until day 15–16, when it reached a value which presumably enabled the hand–wing to produce the necessary thrust to make practice flights. Aspect ratio increased until day 15, after which it decreased sharply and then stabilized. Wing loading showed a negative correlation with age (Figure 5.5), i.e. as the bat grew, the wing area increased faster than the wingspan and so wing loading decreased. A wing loading value similar to that of adults was achieved after 30 days, at the same time as juveniles began to make sustained flights.

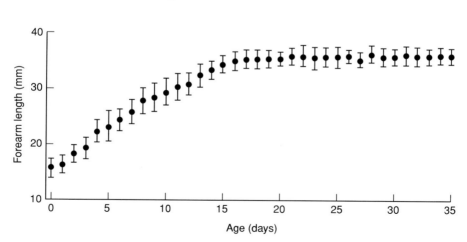

FIG 5.4 *Rate of post-natal growth, measured by forearm length, in captive* P. auritus *(reproduced with permission from de Fanis and Jones, 1995a). Values shown are means ± S.D.* (n = 5).

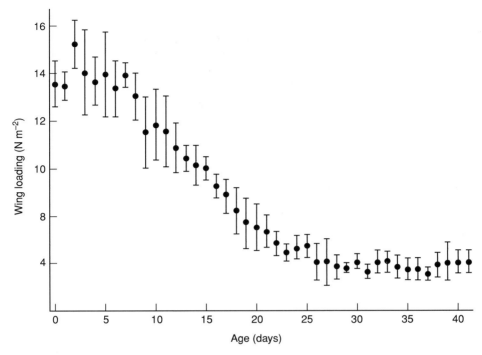

FIG 5.5   *Changes in wing-loading values in five captive* P. auritus *from birth to weaning (reproduced with permission from de Fanis and Jones, 1995a). Values are mean ± S.D.*

Vocalizations

All newborn vespertilionid bats emit isolation calls (i-calls). These are used for communication and to alert the mother to the baby's whereabouts. They have audible and ultrasonic components, consist of a rapid 'slide' upwards in frequency and have a duration of 20–50 ms (Gould, 1971); their function is further discussed in Chapter 6. De Fanis and Jones (1995a) found that i-calls were emitted by newborn *P. auritus* and that they stimulated a mother's response and helped her to locate her baby. The characteristics of the calls changed as the babies grew in de Fanis and Jones' study. As a baby matured, the calls increased in frequency and shortened in duration and their harmonic content decreased. As well as being communication calls, i-calls also acted as precursors of orientation calls. Calls resembling orientation pulses were first recorded 12–14 days after birth, and these appeared to be derived from shortened i-calls. After 7 days, the structure of i-calls changed as they became divided into two segments separated by a gap. The duration of the gap first increased and then decreased, before disappearing by day 20. As the infant grew, the section of the call before the gap became shorter, while the section after it disappeared. At around 20 days, i-calls were replaced almost completely by echolocation calls, although bats older than this were still able to produce long-duration calls resembling i-calls if they were distressed. I-calls were clearly emitted orally, unlike most echolocation calls in *P. auritus*, which are made through the nose.

The i-calls recorded by de Fanis and Jones (1995a) in *P. auritus* were similar in structure to those of other species. However in some species (e.g. *Eptesicus fuscus*; Moss, 1988), they are considered to have different ontogenetic origins from orientation calls, while in others i-calls are considered to be precursors of sonar signals in the same way as in *P. auritus* (Gould, 1971; Matsumura, 1979; Brown and Grinnell, 1980).

Thermoregulation

Infant *P. auritus*, like young of all insectivorous bats, are heterothermic in the early post-natal period and rely on close physical contact with their mothers to keep them warm. Nursery roosts are usually in warm places and thus heat loss is minimized and rapid growth promoted. Ontogeny of thermoregulation occurs rapidly in most species and its timing is thought to be related to the accumulation of insulating fat and to the completion of hair growth (Kunz, 1987). In *P. auritus*, babies cease to be continually attached to their mothers at around 6 days old (de Fanis and Jones, 1995a) and by the same age they have grown a complete covering of hair. It seems probable that they begin to thermoregulate around this time, although the exact age of onset is not known. Even after the infants thermoregulate, poor weather can affect the amount of food their mothers receive and therefore the amount of milk produced. Growth can thus be slowed at any time during lactation, just as it can be speeded up at high roost temperature.

Post-Flight Development

Weight loss during the early flight and weaning period such as was recorded by de Fanis and Jones (1995a) in *P. auritus* is common in bats (Kunz, 1987; Kleiman, 1969) and is due to the mobilization of fat stored during the pre-flight period. This fat provides a buffer to compensate for the high energetic cost of learning to fly and allows the juvenile time to improve its foraging ability. The ability develops rapidly in long-eared bats, since flights begin at around 30 days and weaning is complete by 40–42 days (Swift, 1991). The method by which juveniles learn to catch insects and to find their way around their habitat is not precisely known, but observations by Howard (1995) suggest that they do not follow their mothers on foraging flights. Instead, they explore on their own and gradually find their way around. A radio tracking study on *Rhinolophus ferrumequinum* (Jones *et al.*, 1995) showed that juveniles of this species similarly foraged independently of adults and gradually moved further from their roost, as did *Myotis myotis* in another radio tracking study (Audet, 1990).

Post-flight mortality is difficult to assess in wild populations of bats, since corpses are rarely found and not all juveniles which disappear from a roost will have died. Juvenile *Plecotus*, which practise flying inside the roost, are likely to be less at risk at this time than are the young of many other species because they are relatively adept at flying by the time they leave the roost and so are less vulnerable to predation, stranding or injury. Humphrey and Kunz (1976) estimated a 4% post-flight mortality in *C. townsendii*, which also fly inside nursery roosts, compared with 6.5% before flight began. Figures for *Plecotus* are not available.

ENERGETICS OF REPRODUCTION

All mammals are subjected to increased energy demands during reproduction and meeting this extra requirement is likely to be an important constraint on their behaviour. Estimates of respiratory costs associated with milk production in small terrestrial mammals, as well as in insectivorous bats, suggest that lactation is much more costly than pregnancy (Speakman and Racey, 1987) and that energy expenditure by the mother is likely to rise to a maximum late in lactation. Studier *et al.* (1973) showed, from experiments on *Myotis lucifugus* using bomb calorimetry, that lactation involved the expenditure of up to four times as much energy as did pregnancy, and Kurta *et al.* (1990) calculated the average requirement for assimilated energy to be 48.9 kJ day^{-1} in pregnancy and 105.1 kJ day^{-1} in lactation in free-ranging *Eptesicus fuscus*. About 2% of the total energy required during pregnancy went into fetal tissue, while milk production accounted for 28% of the energy assimilated during lactation. The latter study used the doubly labelled water (DLW) technique (briefly described below), a method which allows energy expenditure to be calculated in free-living animals and thus under natural conditions. Methods such as calorimetry are confined to captive animals in the laboratory.

Speakman and Racey (1987) used the DLW technique to calculate energy expenditure by *P. auritus* at roosts in north-east Scotland. Their results showed that total energy expenditure by females increased through pregnancy and that approximately 3% of the total respiratory cost was invested in fetal production. After parturition, total energy expenditure rose sharply and a significant proportion of the new level (20–40%) was allocated to milk production. Energy production continued to rise throughout lactation, reaching a peak just before weaning, a pattern common to all bat species and to other small mammals.

DLW Technique

This is a non-invasive method for measuring energy expenditure directly in free-living animals (Speakman and Racey, 1988a). The principle of the technique is that if a label of oxygen (e.g. the stable, non-radioactive heavy isotope ^{18}oxygen) is introduced into the water in an animal's body, it rapidly pervades the body water pool and will then decline exponentially as the pool is turned over, i.e. as the label is eliminated from the body and replaced by unlabelled water derived from inspired water and from eating or drinking. The rate of decline depends mainly on the rate of elimination of labelled water and labelled respiratory carbon dioxide. If a label of hydrogen (e.g. deuterium, ^{2}hydrogen) is introduced into the body, however, its rate of decline will depend only on the rate of elimination of water and replacement with unlabelled water. Therefore, if both labels are introduced together (hence the term doubly labelled), the difference in the rate of decline of the two labels will depend on the rate of elimination of carbon dioxide. DLW thus provides a method of indirect calorimetry which avoids the necessity of connecting animals to laboratory equipment (Speakman and Racey, 1988a). It makes a number of assumptions, e.g. that the rates of production of water and carbon dioxide are constant and that the size of the body water pool does not change over time. These assumptions are not realistic, and the result is that the technique has certain inaccuracies. Speakman and Racey (1988b) measured carbon dioxide production by *P. auritus* using DLW and indirect calorimetry under laboratory conditions. The two methods were employed simultaneously on the same bats, and calorimetry was assumed to give the 'correct' measurement. They found that DLW consistently overestimated carbon dioxide production by about 14% and concluded that there was a systematic bias in the technique. This was offset by the fact that DLW provided invaluable data which could not be collected in the field in any other way. In addition, for the purpose of comparing energy expenditure at different stages of reproduction, bias is not a serious problem provided it is constant.

Strategies for Accommodating Energy Demand

There are three ways in which animals are known to respond to the increased energy demand of pregnancy and lactation:

- they may utilize stored fat or food hoards
- they may increase food intake
- they may reduce expenditure on some component of their energy budget not concerned with reproduction; this is referred to as compensation.

No bat species is known to hoard food and storage as fat is mainly confined to large mammals, although some species of small ones do deposit fat which is used in lactation. In bats, fat accumulation has the problem that carrying extra weight on foraging flights involves extra energy expenditure. There is, in any case, a limit to their carrying capacity and they already have to transport a fetus or, on occasions, a large infant. There is evidence (Speakman and Racey, 1987) that *P. auritus* do increase their fat reserves during pregnancy, but it was established that the stored fat could provide, at most, 2–3 days' worth of extra energy. Speakman and Racey suggested that fat deposition in this species is more likely to be an insurance against sudden, serious shortfalls in energy supply than a prolonged subsidy for reproductive requirements.

Increased food consumption to compensate for high energy demand has been widely demonstrated in small terrestrial mammals, but there are a number of reasons why it is less likely to be used by bats. The time available for foraging is limited by short nights, especially at high latitude, and there are also temporal limitations on food availability – insect numbers fall at certain times during the night (Chapter 3). The high energetic cost of bat flight, estimated at 21 times the basal metabolic rate for *P. auritus* by Racey and Speakman (1987), means that extending the foraging period would only be an efficient method of assimilating extra energy if prey levels were reasonably high. Finally, the amount of food a bat can eat is limited by the handling time, which is the time taken to track down, catch and consume a prey item. Swift (1980) and Maier (1992) found changes in the activity patterns of *P. pipistrellus* in pregnancy and lactation, but no increase in the total time these bats spent foraging in a night. In *P. auritus*, Entwistle *et al.* (1996) found that neither the time spent foraging nor the distance individuals moved from the roost differed between lactating and non-reproductive females. There was thus no evidence of increased food consumption during lactation.

Because insectivorous bats in temperate regions are heterothermic, they can use torpor to reduce energy demand as a form of compensation – an option open to few small terrestrial mammals. There is evidence from a number of studies that the use of torpor is widespread among insectivorous bats. Speakman and Racey (1987) used the DLW technique to

Plate 1 A brown long-eared bat (*Plecotus auritus*) in flight. The large, erect ears can be seen in torchlight. Photo: Frank Greenaway.

Plate 2 Grey long-eared bat (*Plecotus austriacus*). The tragus shape, dark brown facial colouring and short thumbs identify this individual. Photo: Frank Greenaway.

Plate 3 (*below*) A brown long-eared bat at roost with ears in the 'ram's horn' position. The transverse folds in the conch close in a fan-like action as the ear relaxes. Photo: John Haddow.

Plate 4 Because long-eared bats fly inside roosts, their droppings become scattered around attics and may cover furniture or other possessions stored there.

Plate 5 *(below)* *P. auritus* flying close to vegetation. During foliage gleaning, brown long-eared bats frequently stop echolocating and search for prey by passive listening. Photo: Frank Greenaway.

Plate 6 Insect remains accumulate beneath feeding perches. Clearly, the bat that used this perch had been hunting large yellow underwing moths. Photo: Frank Greenaway.

Plate 7 Flyways are consistently used by long-eared bats to avoid crossing open spaces while commuting between roosts and foraging areas. They fly close to vegetation along landscape features such as overgrown streams.

Plate 8 A group of brown long-eared bats in their normal roosting position in an attic. They were photographed from below and are huddled between the ridge beam and the sarking, in the angle formed by a rafter.

Plate 9 A female brown long-eared bat with a newborn infant. Babies are continuously attached to their mother's nipple during their first week of life. Photo: Frank Greenaway.

Plate 10 *(below)* Brown long-eared bats have been found to select older houses with complex roof spaces. A colony of 80 roosted in this Victorian house and frequently moved between roof compartments.

Plate 11 *(above)* Long-eared bat roosts are likely to be situated in wooded valleys. Well-maintained fishing rivers are an important feature of the ecology of the species.

Plate 12 *(below)* *P. auritus* select houses which have woodland within 0.5 km. This roost is surrounded by mature deciduous and coniferous trees.

Plate 13 A hibernating brown long-eared bat with folded ears. The tragi hang down, superficially resembling the ears of other species. Photo: Frank Greenaway.

measure energy expenditure in free-living *P. auritus* throughout the summer in north-east Scotland. Bats were captured in nursery roosts, weighed and measured and their reproductive state ascertained. They were then injected peritoneally with water containing labelled oxygen and hydrogen. After allowing the [18]oxygen 90 min to reach equilibrium, a blood sample was taken from each bat and they were then released in the roost. Twenty-four hours later they were recaptured, reweighed and a second series of blood samples obtained. The study found that the body mass of females was higher (mean=9.2 g) at the start of lactation than at the start of pregnancy (mean=7.3 g), indicating that a significant increase had occurred during pregnancy and that this was not attributable to the mass of the fetus and accessory structures. It was partly due to enlargement of the mammary glands, but this explained only 10% of the increase. The authors suggested that the rest may have been fat, to be used as an emergency supply which could tide the bat over in the event of a 2–3 day serious food shortage. Speakman and Racey next predicted the energetic costs in pregnancy and lactation of a bat which remained continuously endothermic, predictions being made from results of laboratory respirometry combined with microclimate measurements in the field and allometric predictions of flight cost. These were compared with the field results from the study (Figure 5.6). In early pregnancy, the observed expenditure was about 50% of the predicted value for an endothermic bat, suggesting that daily torpor was being used. The observed energy expenditure then increased rapidly, until by parturition it exceeded the predicted rate for an endothermic bat. This suggested that bats shifted strategy during late pregnancy to become continuously endothermic. Immediately after giving birth, energy expenditure dropped again to a much lower than expected level, suggesting that they compensated for high energy demand by extensive use of torpor. The strategy used by long-eared bats is thus complex. The continuously endothermic period in late pregnancy suggests the possibility that torpor at this stage may be incompatible with fetal development (Speakman and Racey, 1987), or possibly the delay in gestation which would result from torpor would mean that the young would be born too late in the year to have a realistic chance of accumulating enough fat to survive their first winter. There does not appear to be a comparable period of endothermy during lactation, so milk production must be compatible with daily torpor.

Effect of Torpor on Milk Production

The disadvantage to a female bat of saving energy by heterothermy is the non-specificity of torpor. Mammary metabolism is slowed down, as is that of other body tissues and the result would be a decrease in milk secretion unless the gland were protected in some way. Wilde *et al.* (1995) investigated lactation in *P. pipistrellus* and found that milk production was tailored to the intermittent suckling pattern of the species by local mechanisms within the mammary gland, which responded to the frequency and completeness of milk removal. Reduced body heat did decrease the rate of milk synthesis and therefore milk production was reduced while bats were torpid. However, the response of the mammary gland to frequent or intermittent suckling was an acute one, unlike that in most other mammals, in which it is a long-term response. This means that, in pipistrelles, milk synthesis is increased by frequent returns to the roost to suckle infants. If a similar situation exists in *Plecotus* species, then this would explain why females return to their nursery roosts several times per night (Entwistle *et al.*, 1996; see Chapter 4) during the lactation period. After each visit, the

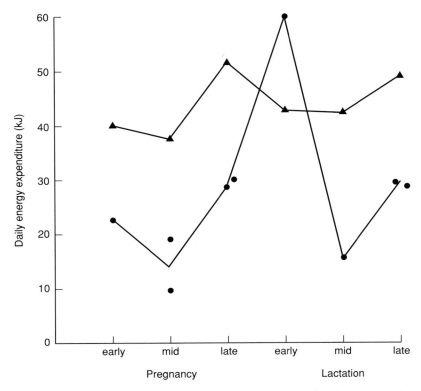

FIG 5.6   *Variations in daily energy expenditure in free-living female* P. auritus *during pregnancy and lactation, compared with predicted values for a continuously endothermic bat (see text). Measurements were made using the DLW technique, and each point represents a single individual (reproduced with permission from Speakman and Racey, 1987). ●—●, free-living bats measured by DLW; ▲—▲, predicted values for a continuously endothermic bat.*

acute response of the mammary gland to suckling probably causes rapid milk production during the next bout of foraging. In this way, an infant could receive most of its daily supply of milk in two or three feeds and milk production could then be greatly reduced while the mother is torpid.

CHAPTER 6

Social Organization and Behaviour

R OOSTS are an important aspect of the ecology of long-eared bats. They provide shelter from the weather, protection from predators and a warm environment in which to produce and rear young. How roosts are selected, how bats use them and whether and why they move between roosts in an area are all questions which have been investigated recently. This chapter also looks at the structure of nursery colonies, at where males live during summer and how this affects mating behaviour and at behavioural interactions between mothers and their offspring.

ROOSTING BEHAVIOUR

Roost Sites

In common with most bat species, *Plecotus* do not excavate or build places to live, but rely for shelter on existing structures. In prehistoric times these structures were natural ones such as caves, tree holes and rock crevices, but sinanthropic (artificial) roosts have become very important to many bats. Some species, such as *P. pipistrellus*, have become so well adapted to living in sinanthropic roosts that they are rarely found anywhere else. *P. auritus* in Britain also seem to rely heavily on such roosts, since they are one of the British species most closely associated with attics. Sinanthropic roosts have replaced many natural structures; they include roof spaces replacing tree cavities; cracks in buildings, bridges and expansion joints replacing rock crevices; and mines, tunnels and culverts replacing caves.

P. auritus *Roosts*

The natural roosts of this species are thought to be tree holes (Horacek, 1975), and in central Europe there is evidence that they are still used extensively as summer roosts (Bauer, 1960; Hanak, 1969). *P. auritus* is one of the European species most likely to use bat boxes (Chapter 9), particularly in coniferous forests where there are few buildings and natural tree holes are scarce. Bat boxes resemble tree holes and so they are used as substitutes. In Switzerland, *P. auritus* are more often found in tree holes than in houses (Fluckiger and Beck, 1995), and Stutz (1989) reported that they tended also to roost at high altitude away from centres of human population. However, in other areas (e.g. central Bohemia; Horacek, 1975), brown long-eared bats form nursery colonies almost entirely in houses, despite the fact that there are plenty of available tree holes. Harmata (1973) also found them mainly in old buildings in the Czech Republic. In Scotland, Entwistle (1994) found that nursery roosts were almost all in houses and that tree holes, together with farm buildings, were used only as temporary roosts at times when food was in short supply and bats became torpid to save energy. It is possible that sinanthropic roosts are used more by this species at high latitude because the warmth they provide is critical to the bats' ability to produce and rear young in cool, short summers. Attics also have an advantage over tree holes in that they provide space for young bats to practise flying before they have to go outside for the first time.

Church lofts have been reported to be used as roost sites in the Netherlands (Daan, 1980) and *P. auritus* also make use of churches and church porches in England. One such porch was used as a day roost for a colony and another only as a night roost (Brown *et al.*, 1983). Such roost sites are usually in the porch roof, against the main wall of the church and south-facing.

P. austriacus *Roosts*

Unlike their congenerics, grey long-eared bats almost always use sinanthropic roosts during summer and generally live in closer proximity to human settlements than do *P. auritus* (Hanak, 1969). The use of tree holes by nursery colonies of this species is unknown and bats live only in attics (Horacek, 1975; Gaisler *et al.*, 1990; Fluckiger and Beck, 1995). These are always warm and in old buildings (Harmata, 1973); colonies have been reported to use church lofts which they frequently share with colonies of *P. auritus* (Daan, 1980). These findings support the theory of Horacek (1975) that *P. austriacus* is a recent inhabitant of Europe which spread across the continent only in historical times as warm, sinanthropic roosts became available.

Position of Bats within Roosts

Brown and grey long-eared bats differ in the positions in which they are most commonly found in roosts (Horacek, 1975). *P. auritus* was described by Gaisler (1966) as a fissure rooster which usually maintains contact with roof beams on two sides. The commonest place to find them is in the apex of the roof, in the angle between the ridge beam and the rafters (the diagonal beams which project downwards from either side of the ridge towards the sides of the attic). They are also sometimes found at gable ends between stone walls and beams (Figure 6.1).

P. austriacus, on the other hand, has been described as a space roosting species (Gaisler, 1966) which roosts in contact with wood on one side only. Horacek (1975) maintained that they are most frequently found in the apex of the roof, on the ridge beam between joints with rafters and not in their angles (Figure 6.1). Less frequently they are found in the angles of the rafters. This difference supports the theory (Horacek, 1975) that the two species had different origins and different pre-sinanthropic roosts: *P. auritus* used tree holes, but *P. austriacus* probably roosted in large caves.

Roost Selection

Long-eared bats rely heavily on their roosts to provide both warmth and protection and thus the characteristics of the roost may exert an important influence on the survival of a

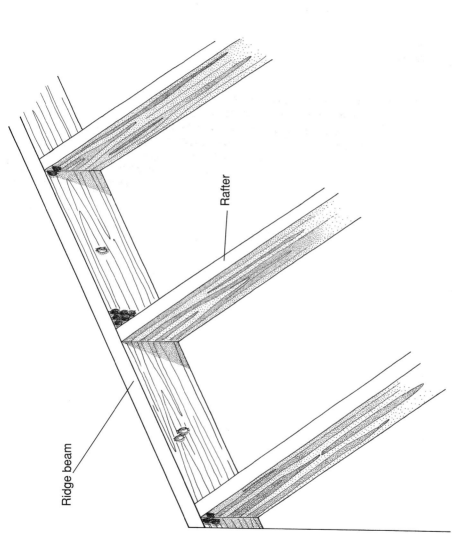

Ridge beam

Rafter

FIG 6.1   *Diagram of ridge beam and rafters in an attic, showing the most commonly used roosting positions of long-eared bats.* ●, *positions occupied by* P. auritus; ○, *positions occupied by* P. austriacus.

colony. Some buildings may provide more suitable conditions than others and it seems likely that colonies select the buildings in which they roost. Entwistle *et al.* (1997) set up a study to investigate this. They located a total of 54 *P. auritus* roosts in their study area in north-east Scotland and then compared characteristics of these roosts with those of other buildings randomly selected from a telephone directory of the area. The study found that the use of houses as roost sites was not random; roost selection was occurring and bats appeared to select houses both for their location and surrounding habitat and for specific physical features of the building.

Habitat

More roosts than expected were situated in river valleys and, compared with the randomly picked buildings, roosts were significantly closer to woodland and to open water. The median distance to the nearest woodland was 60 m ($n=48$) for roosts and 215 m ($n=16$) for random houses. Furthermore, there were significantly greater areas of both deciduous and coniferous woodland within 0.5 km of roosts than within this distance of random houses. Woodland close to roosts is very important (Chapter 4), both because *P. auritus* spend most of their foraging time in woodland less than 0.5 km from the roost and because such close-by woodland provides protection from predators and allows bats to emerge to forage relatively early in the evening. Roosts may have been mainly in river valleys because, in Scotland, this is where most woodland is concentrated. Well-maintained salmon fishing rivers (such as the Dee and the Spey, both of which are in the study area) usually have trees along their banks, with especially high concentrations of deciduous woodland. In contrast, much of the countryside away from rivers is pasture or moorland with few trees. Similarly, the finding that roosts were closer to open water than were randomly picked houses may have been due to the situation of roosts in wooded river valleys. The median distance from roosts to the nearest open water was 215 m ($n=48$) and that from random houses was 450 m ($n=16$).

Roosts were found to be associated with villages, probably reflecting the distribution of buildings – areas containing more houses presented more roosting opportunities. However, no roosts were located within Aberdeen city, probably because the lack of woodland in a city would make it unsuitable for brown long-eared bats. Hanak (1969), Gaisler (1979) and Gaisler and Bauerova (1985–6) all similarly reported that *P. auritus* avoided urban areas.

Physical features of the building

Compared with adjacent houses not used as roosts, Entwistle *et al.* (1997) reported that those used as roosts were older and contained larger roof spaces which were more likely to be divided into a number of compartments. Seventy-three percent of attics used as roosts had more than one compartment (range = 1–8), which gave bats a range of roost sites, and thus a range of roost temperatures from which to select a site. Roosts were also more likely to be lined with rough wood and to contain sarking (boards which cover the rafters and on which the roof slates rest). They were less likely to contain glass fibre insulation material than were adjacent houses. These features were probably concerned with warmth, since attics with sarking and without insulation will maintain a relatively high temperature, although it is possible that rough wood lining was also chosen by the bats because it resembled their natural roost sites in trees. Large roof spaces may have been chosen because *P. auritus* need enough space to fly in the roost, although this feature was not significant when controlled for by location of the roost (Entwistle, 1994). Wooden lining and large roof spaces with several compartments are generally features of older houses, which explains the study's finding that *P. auritus* selected houses that were, on average, about 100 years old (Entwistle, 1994). This contrasts with houses in which pipistrelles roost, which are an average of 15.4 years old (Wardhaugh, 1992). Pipistrelles have different roosting requirements, which are fulfilled by modern house design.

P. auritus roost in the darkest available parts of attics (Entwistle, 1994), although they do tolerate some degree of illumination, normally from small skylight windows. Such low level light may even be beneficial to them by allowing them to monitor when it is dark enough to go out and forage. The absence of cobwebs generally associated with *Plecotus* roosts (Chapter 2) is probably due to them being removed either by air currents created by the bats' flight or by physical contact with their wings, since Entwistle (1994) found no evidence that attics with many cobwebs were avoided. There was also no evidence that bats deserted roosts as the volume of their droppings increased, although Entwistle (1994) pointed out that, since *P. auritus* generally form small colonies, the volume of guano in their roosts is small compared with that of, for example, pipistrelles. A high level of disturbance by humans inside roosts probably causes abandonment, but in general *P. auritus* is more tolerant of disturbance than many other species which live in houses, e.g. *Myotis daubentonii* and *Myotis nattereri* (Swift, *unpublished*). At some roosts, long-eared bats have been found to return following extensive renovations to the house, reflecting their loyalty to traditional, long-used sites.

The temperature of roof spaces was found to be important in roost selection by *P. auritus* (Entwistle *et al.*, 1997). Bats selected warmer buildings – the mean average daily temperature in the apex of roosts was 17.9°C, while the mean average daily temperature in randomly picked houses was 16.7°C. There was evidence that bats were selecting not only warmer buildings but also buildings which had a greater capacity to trap heat. The presence of sarking may be connected with this, since it improves insulation and so reduces temperature variation.

How bats seek and find suitable roosts is not clear. Because most are close to deciduous woodland, it is probable that buildings are found and investigated during foraging flights. Smell or echolocation may be used (Entwistle, 1994), or it is possible that bats may be attracted by the presence of conspecifics. What is clear, however, is that long-eared bats gain a number of ecological advantages by selecting the buildings in which they roost. Bats from warm roosts surrounded by large areas of deciduous woodland have been found to grow faster, achieve better body condition and have higher survival rates than do those from less favoured roosts (Entwistle, 1994).

THERMOREGULATION IN ROOSTS

The previous chapter has shown that thermoregulatory behaviour by reproducing *P. auritus* is complex. Bats may become torpid in response to short-term, occasional adverse weather conditions and they may also use daily torpor on a more regular basis to balance high energy demand at certain times during summer, although there is evidence that torpor is incompatible with certain stages in the reproductive cycle, e.g. peak spermatogenesis in males and late pregnancy in females. By selecting warm roof spaces as roosts and adjusting their behaviour to minimize heat loss and energy expenditure during times of high demand, long-eared bats are able to balance their energy budget and still complete their reproductive cycle within the time available.

Roost Temperature

The difference in temperature recorded between *P. auritus* roosts and randomly picked houses (Entwistle *et al.*, 1997) was not due to heating of the space by the bats – the authors reported that temperature probes placed close to and away from roosting bats showed no differences. The bats actively selected warmer houses in which to roost. The average daily temperature of nursery roosts in Scotland ranged from 10.5°C to 26.6°C, while the mean hourly temperature ranged from 6.3°C to 40.6°C (Entwistle, 1994). Daily variation in temperature was similar between roosts and throughout summer. Entwistle recorded that minimum roost temperature occurred between 0500 and 0700 hours, and roosts then heated rapidly to a maximum temperature in mid afternoon (1200–1500 hours) before declining through the late afternoon and evening. Roost temperature was influenced by the air temperature outside, the amount of solar radiation in a day and the wind speed. Bats used different compartments within the roost space to select the optimum microclimate at any time and frequently changed compartments through the summer. Cooler areas were generally selected in June and October (consistent with more use of torpor at these times) and warmer areas in July and August, when reproductive demands on bats resulted in less use of torpor. Individuals were likely to resort to torpor to conserve energy at a wide range of roost temperatures below about 22°C (Entwistle, 1994).

Clustering

The formation of dense groups, or huddles, by individuals may be used instead of torpor to conserve energy, or both may be used together. Clustering is particularly common during the lactation period in many species, at a time when energy demand is high and juveniles have to maintain a relatively high body temperature in order to grow. Trune and Slobodchikoff (1978) found that pallid bats (*Antrozous pallidus*) formed clusters at normal roost temperatures, which allowed them to reduce oxygen consumption and energy expenditure. Juveniles were found at the centre (the warmest part) of the cluster more often than would have been expected had their position been random, and the authors proposed that the adults were displaying a form of reciprocal altruism by mutually allowing each other's offspring access to a beneficial position. *C. townsendii* also formed densely packed clusters on the ceilings of the caves where they roosted during the lactation period (Humphrey and Kunz, 1976).

Clustering was found by Entwistle (1994) to be effective in reducing heat loss in *P. auritus* – laboratory experiments showed that a cluster of bats in a small space raised the ambient temperature by around 3°C. In roosts, both clustering and torpor were found to be used during the study, together resulting in significant savings in energy expenditure by the bats.

There is some evidence that *P. austriacus* makes less use of clustering behaviour than does its congeneric. Stebbings (1970) observed that *P. austriacus* did not form clusters during summer months, while *P. auritus* in the same attic did, and Horacek (1975) found that solitary individuals in a roost were much more likely to occur among *P. austriacus*. This difference may be connected with the high level of intraspecific aggression reported in grey long-eared bats (Stebbings, 1970), and may be a further reason why this species seeks warmer attics than does *P. auritus* (Jooris, 1980) and why its distribution is restricted to warm, lowland regions.

Reaction to Low Temperature

Normal daily fluctuations in temperature may be compensated for by the use of torpor and clustering within the roost, but there are times during spring and summer when serious energy shortfalls are caused by adverse weather conditions. Extended cold spells or very wet weather cause shortages in insect availability and may mean that foraging is unproductive or even impossible. At such times, *P. auritus* react by temporarily abandoning their nursery roosts and moving to alternative roosts in the area (Entwistle, 1994). Such roosts are normally in tree holes or farm buildings and have cooler microclimates than main roosts. A radio tracking study (Entwistle, 1994) showed that there was a strong correlation between the occurrence of cold nights and the use of cool alternative roosts by *P. auritus*. Using these roosts allowed bats to drop their body temperature further than they could in the warmer main roosts and so conserve more energy until conditions improved.

Reaction to High Temperature

Stebbings (1966) reported that *Plecotus* bats altered their roosting behaviour when the air temperature in the roost exceeded about 40°C, when they hung from the rafters with their wings partly spread. During an exceptionally hot spell of weather in Scotland during August 1995, I visited four *P. auritus* roosts known to have been occupied within the previous week. Three of them were found to be empty, despite the presence of fresh droppings. In the fourth I found only two bats (out of a colony counted the previous week at 20) and both of these were hanging from rafters with their wings slightly spread, in the position shown in Figure 6.2. The temperature at the roof apex was 39°C at 1430 hours British Summer Time and this particular roof had only two compartments, both of which were equally hot. It therefore appears that roosts can become too hot for long-eared bats. In an attempt to lose heat, they may roost away from the apex and hang in open air space (Figure 6.2), but if they still overheat it appears they have to abandon the attic. I suspect the colonies from the roosts I visited had temporarily moved to cooler alternative roosts.

TEMPORARY AND TRANSITORY ROOSTS

Temporary Roosts

Sometimes termed alternative roosts, these are used by colonies for short periods when conditions in main nursery roosts are unsuitable, as described above. Entwistle (1994) found little evidence that they are used for any reasons other than thermoregulatory ones. No correlation was found between their use and degree of disturbance at the main roost, nor between their occupation and changing use by the bats of foraging sites. There was also no large-scale change from main to temporary roosts such as might have been expected if the

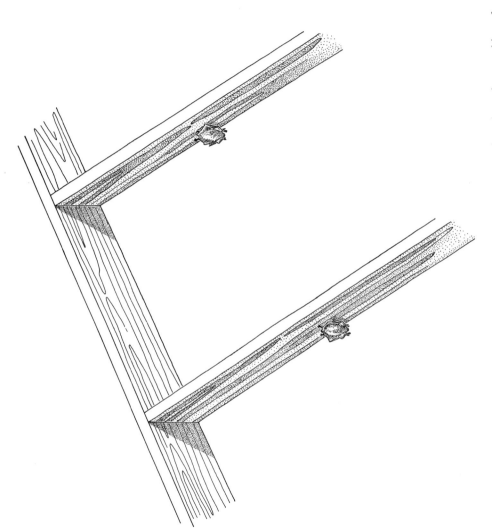

FIG 6.2   *Roosting positions adopted by* P. auritus *at high roost temperature. Bats move away from the roof apex and hang from rafters with wings slightly spread.*

purpose of their use was for predator avoidance, as suggested by Taake and Hildenhagen (1989). However, long-eared bats may also switch roosts to reduce levels of infestation by ectoparasites (see Chapter 7) and this was not investigated in Entwistle's (1994) study. Bauerova and Zima (1988) agreed that alternative roosts were used for thermoregulatory reasons. They mist-netted both *P. auritus* and *P. austriacus* at a cave entrance in the Czech Republic during summer. This cave was not used as a nursery roost and few long-eared bats hibernated there. The highest intensity of visits was recorded in late summer, and there was also a peak of activity at the cave in April–May. These are the two times in summer when torpor is used most by the bats, making it very likely that the cool cave was used for periods of torpor to save energy. Gaisler and Hanak (1969) found that temporary roosts were used equally by both *P. auritus* and *P. austriacus* in summer, confirming that, in this behavioural aspect, there is no difference between the two species.

Available evidence seems to indicate that although short-term use is made of cool roosts by long-eared bats, they are generally faithful to one main nursery roost all summer. In this respect they differ from some vespertilionid specis (e.g. *Nyctalus noctula*), which change roosts frequently (Sluiter and van Heerdt, 1966).

Transitory Roosts

These are roosts used during movements between hibernacula and summer roosts and back. They are occupied sporadically and for short periods, mainly in spring and autumn, although males may also use them in summer (Horacek, 1975). Heise and Schmidt (1988) maintained that after the break-up of nursery colonies in autumn and between the end of hibernation and the flight to nursery roosts in spring, *P. auritus* live largely independently of one another and seek shelter in a variety of roosts including, if the weather is severe, cellars, caves and mine shafts normally used as hibernacula. Tree holes and bat boxes are also used. There seems to be no colony cohesion within these roosts. As well as sheltering bats, transitory roosts are used in connection with mating behaviour. *P. auritus* netted at entrances of hibernacula during late July and August were all found to be adult or immature males (Horacek, 1975), and females had all departed from nursery roosts by late August or early September. In contrast, *P. austriacus* were never netted at hibernacula during summer and bats were found in nursery roosts as late as October. Horacek (1975) suggested that male *P. auritus* visited the caves as potential mating sites and were then joined there by females for mating in autumn, while *P. austriacus* mated in summer roosts and so did not visit hibernacula at this time. Similarly in spring, *P. auritus* were active around cave entrances in March and were probably using the entrance region for mating; they did not move into summer roosts until late April. *P. austriacus*, which are not thought to mate in spring, did not display these spring flights around cave entrances.

NURSERY COLONIES

Colony Size

Long-eared bat colonies are typically small compared with those of many other species. Those of *P. auritus* mostly number from 10–20 adults (Speakman *et al.*, 1991a; Entwistle,

1994), although the range of colony size is much larger than this. Horacek (1975) reported that, of 12 colonies studied in the Czech Republic, 11 numbered 5–10 individuals, none contained 10–20, one colony had 20–30 members and none was larger than this. Heise and Schmidt (1988), working in Germany, found colonies of 22 and 25 adults in bat boxes in a forest, and colonies in southern England numbered 20 (Stebbings, 1970) and 25–35 (Howard, 1995). Several colonies of over 50 have been recorded in south Wales (Morgan, 1989) and Swift and Racey (1983) studied a colony of 83 in northern Scotland. The largest colony recorded, in north-west England, numbered over 150 (Billington, 1993), although it is not clear whether this included the year's juveniles. Most colonies are much smaller, although they tend to be less noticeable and so overlooked. Speakman *et al.* (1991a) and Entwistle (1994) conducted large-scale searches for as many roosts as possible in an area. Speakman *et al.* (1991a) found 34 colonies of *P. auritus* in a 3200 km^2 area in north-east Scotland; most contained 10–20 individuals, the largest numbered 55–60 and the mean colony size from roost counts was 16.8. Entwistle (1994), in a similar area, reported that the range of colony size, as measured by roost counts, was 1–74 and the mean was 15 (n=56 colonies). Most colonies contained 10–20 individuals, although Entwistle claimed that the number of bats found on each roost visit was probably only about half the total colony size, since many bats moved into inaccessible parts of attics and so were not in evidence. Recapture rates of marked bats in her study indicated that actual colony size was 30–120 (average=48). My own field notes, from wooded valleys in central Scotland, indicate that *P. auritus* colony size from roost counts in this area ranged from 3 to 47, with an average of 20 (n=18).

Latitude might be expected to exert an influence on colony size, since it is possible that larger colonies might conserve more heat through clustering and therefore colonies further north might be larger. This does not seem to be the case – the range of colony size in Germany and the Czech Republic, at around 50–52°N (5–25 adults; Horacek, 1975; Heise and Schmidt, 1988), is very similar to that in Sweden at 57–58°N (2–25 adults; Rydell, 1989b). Colony size is correlated with the area of woodland within 0.5 km of the roost (Entwistle, 1994) and it seems probable that this is the factor which keeps *P. auritus* colonies small. They forage close to roosts and rely heavily on trees, particularly deciduous woodland, as foraging habitat. Areas such as river valleys in Scotland and lakeland areas of north-west England are associated with large areas of deciduous woodland, which accounts for the occasional large colonies recorded in these regions, but there are also plenty of small colonies associated with small areas of woodland.

P. austriacus colonies are similar in size to those of *P. auritus*. Horacek (1975) found a difference in the average size of colonies of the two species in the Czech Republic (of 20 colonies of *P. austriacus*, two numbered 5–10, 14 numbered 10–20, three numbered 20–30 and one numbered 30–40; most thus numbered 10–20 as opposed to 5–10 in *P. auritus*), but since 10–20 appears to be the average size for *P. auritus* colonies elsewhere, there is no real difference. Stebbings (1970) studied a *P. austriacus* colony which contained a maximum of 22 adults, and Schober and Grimmberger (1989) reported that colonies of up to 30 have been recorded. This species relies less on woodland than does *P. auritus* and thus there may be fewer very small colonies. The average size of a colony from roost counts (10.4; Gaisler *et al.*, 1990), however, is very little different from that recorded by Speakman *et al.* (1991a) and Entwistle (1994) for *P. auritus*. Both are small in comparison with most house-dwelling bat species, including *P. pipistrellus*, in which average colony size is 117 bats (Speakman *et al.*, 1991a) and colonies of as many as 2000 individuals are known.

Colony Composition

Entwistle (1994) found that the proportion of male and female *P. auritus* in nursery colonies changed through the summer. In May, the bats in the colony were nearly all female, but the number of males increased from early June to a peak after the young were weaned in late August–September. At this time, the number of females decreased, followed by a decrease in the number of juveniles as weaning was completed. By October, the colonies were dominated by males. The behaviour of males is discussed below, but it is clear that over the summer the proportion of males in nursery colonies, estimated at 30% in one study (Speakman *et al.*, 1991a) and 18–20% in another (Heise and Schmidt, 1988), is high relative to that in other species such as *P. pipistrellus* (1.2%; Speakman *et al.*, 1991a). Table 6.1 shows the composition of a sample of *P. auritus* caught at roosts in north-east Scotland in early summer (Speakman *et al.*, 1991a). The composition was very variable between roosts, and one colony consisted entirely of mature and immature males. It should be noted that the criterion for assessing male maturity (Racey, 1974b) used in this study has since been found to be unreliable for *P. auritus* (see Chapter 5).

Both Entwistle (1994) and Heise and Schmidt (1988) recorded that group composition among female *P. auritus* in nursery colonies was stable, although less stable sub-groups existed within these groups. Heise and Schmidt (1988) conducted a long-term ringing study of colonies occupying bat boxes in a forest in eastern Germany. Recapture of ringed bats over a number of years showed the existence of totally isolated colonies of females; even colonies which lived in close proximity to each other did not mix. A colony thus consisted of a closed society, which may indicate that members were closely related, although no such relationship could be proved. Immigration and emigration were not found to occur during the study and thus females born into a colony remained in it for life. Colonies sometimes split temporarily into two or three smaller groups which occupied different boxes for short

TABLE 6.1 *Composition of a sample of brown long-eared bats captured from 12 roosts in north-east Scotland during early summer (from Speakman* et al.*, 1991a).*

| Roost | Females | | Males | |
	Parous	Nulliparous	Adult	Immature
A	12	0	1	6
B	19	1	4	5
C	26	5	3	8
D	10	1	0	6
E	8	1	0	0
F	16	9	3	9
G	5	0	0	0
H	14	6	7	15
I	0	0	3	2
J	18	5	2	15
K	22	2	0	0
L	8	2	0	4
Total	158	32	23	70
(%)	57.9	11.7	8.4	25.6

periods before reassembling. The authors suggested that occasionally one of these smaller groups might have moved away to become totally dissociated from the rest of the colony and that this may have been how new colonies were formed. In another bat box study of social groups in forests, Park *et al.* (in press) similarly found that composition of female groups of *P. auritus* was constant. Ringed females were frequently recaptured in the same group with the same smaller group of other females.

Roost Fidelity

Female *P. auritus* are strongly faithful to roosts as well as to colonies. In a ringing programme conducted from 1980 to 1991, Entwistle (1994) never recorded a female moving from one roost to another or a bat being recaptured anywhere other than in the roost where it was ringed. Bats ringed as juveniles were still associated with their natal roost when they were a year old, although among juveniles, males were found to be more likely to move away from natal roosts than were females. Similar strong roost fidelity in this species was recorded by Benzal (1991) in Spain.

Pipistrelles have been shown to be able to recognize members of their own colony by means of scent cues (de Fanis and Jones, 1995b) and to differentiate between odours of colony mates and those of strangers, and it is probable that *P. auritus* can do the same. Smell is therefore one method by which colony cohesion could be maintained and communication established between members. *P. auritus* also produce a loud, long call (Chapter 2) which is quite different from normal orientation calls and is thought to be produced for communication purposes. These calls can be detected from bats flying in the open and inside roosts (Ahlén, 1981), and their purpose may well be connected with colony cohesion. Many loud, long calls can be detected during pre-dawn swarming outside roosts, some on emergence and a few during foraging (A.C. Entwistle, *pers. comm.*).

Little is known of the composition or roosting behaviour of *P. austriacus* colonies. Stebbings (1970) found, from recapture rates of ringed bats of both species in a mixed *Plecotus* colony, that individual *P. austriacus* were less likely to be found in this nursery roost over a long period of time than were *P. auritus*, but he attributed this to lower survival rates among *P. austriacus* and not to unstable colonies. He found no evidence of immigration or emigration of females from the colony. It is probable that *P. austriacus* has a similar social structure to *P. auritus*, i.e. that colonies consist of small, stable groups of females which may be related to each other and which are philopatric, but more data are needed to confirm this.

BEHAVIOUR OF MALES IN SUMMER

In Heise and Schmidt's (1988) study, males behaved differently from females in that they did not remain in the colony of their birth. Juvenile males returned to their natal colony in the spring following their birth, as did those in Entwistle's (1994) study. They thus returned to a roost they knew and to foraging areas with which they were familiar, which increased their chances of surviving at a time when they still had to reach full adult weight. However, during the summer they dispersed from the colony and most of them were never recaptured. The authors suggested that by leaving the area the males ensured genetic exchange occurred between colonies. Because all females in an area were probably related, the males had to move considerable distances to find unrelated ones. They appeared to live a vagabond-like life, associating with different nursery colonies each year; this behaviour, the authors proposed, explained the appearance every year of unringed adult males in previously thoroughly ringed colonies.

Park *et al.* (in press) disagreed with Heise and Schmidt; in their ringing study in England, male *P. auritus* were frequently recaptured at the same site, although they were not quite as faithful to one site as were females. Entwistle (1994) also found high site fidelity among males, although they were slightly more likely to move away from a roost than were females. There seems thus to be uncertainty as to exactly how males behave. They move into nursery roosts in the middle of summer (Entwistle, 1994), probably to take advantage of the warm conditions and the availability of clustering to allow them to remain endothermic and so maintain spermatogenesis. The assumption that they enter nursery roosts for warmth is supported by the finding of Entwistle (1994) that males are more numerous in nursery colonies at high latitude than they are further south. Earlier in the year, it is possible that they do live a nomadic existence as suggested by Heise and Schmidt (1988) and that at these times they live in cooler roosts where they can use torpor. In this way, they may find their way round a greater area of habitat than do females, which may explain why they forage further from the roost (Entwistle *et al.*, 1996). When they need warmth, they seem more likely to return to their natal roost than to any other. The existence of roosts which appear to contain only males (Speakman *et al.*, 1991a; Table 6.1) suggests that males may form these aggregations when they do not need warm roost conditions and then move into nursery colonies as their requirements alter.

Stebbings (1970) found that the number of *P. austriacus* males in a nursery colony increased through June, July and August to a peak in September, in much the same way as *P. auritus* did in Entwistle's (1994) study. Unlike *P. auritus*, however, they were not found in clusters within the roost; only one male was recorded in each roof section at a time, which Stebbings interpreted as territoriality. This species showed a much higher level of intraspecific aggression than did *P. auritus*. Horacek (1975) found that males made up approximately 50% of *P. austriacus* nursery colonies, but that most males roosted solitarily within the attic space. Because this species roost only in roof spaces, males obviously entered nursery roosts in summer seeking warmth, but they did not use clustering to conserve heat in the same way as did *P. auritus*.

MOTHER–YOUNG INTERACTION

Selective Nursing

P. auritus females are able to recognize their own infant and they only suckle and care for their own. In this they resemble the majority of bat species, although there have been reports that bats which live in very large colonies (e.g. *Miniopterus schreibersii*; Brosset, 1966; *Tadarida brasiliensis*; Davis *et al.*, 1962) may suckle indiscriminately. All European species investigated (e.g. *P. pipistrellus*; Swift, 1981; Hughes *et al.*, 1989) reject all babies except their own. Mothers appear to have no difficulty in recognizing their infants on returning after foraging trips, despite roosts being dark, crowded and noisy.

Swift (1981) observed a nursery colony of *P. auritus* inside the roost, using night vision equipment. By marking individual mothers and infants, it was established that a female was always associated with the same infant, which was presumed to be her own. A reunion was observed between an infant aged approximately 4–5 days and a female which returned from foraging. The female alighted on a rafter close to where the cluster of infants was situated and remained motionless for about 10 s with its ears erect. The rate of emission of i-calls from the babies increased and the mother moved towards the cluster, emitting short, audible calls. She approached one infant, sniffed and licked it and then raised herself on her knuckles and feet and guided the baby underneath her body, allowing it to attach to a nipple. She suckled the infant for about 10 min before leaving it in the cluster again and departing the roost.

Among captive long-eared bats, there is conclusive evidence that females suckle only their own young. McLean and Speakman (1996) made 152 observations by infra-red video of mothers and babies in roost boxes inside a flight enclosure, and in none of these was an infant attached to a female other than its own mother. De Fanis and Jones (1995a) used a video camera to monitor mother–young interactions in a captive colony of *P. auritus* in a flight room. Recordings revealed that mothers never approached babies other than their own and that after the first few days recognition between them appeared to be mutual. In the first few days, before the youngsters' eyes had opened, babies remained still on separation, emitting only i-calls, and the mothers appeared to do all the selecting. They were always observed to smell an infant before accepting it. After the babies' eyes had opened, at around 5–6 days, they played a more active part in reunions, and mothers showed less interest in locating them after this time.

Recognition Between Mothers and Offspring

All insectivorous bat species so far investigated use both acoustic and olfactory cues in mother–young recognition, and de Fanis and Jones (1995a) assessed the importance of these cues in *P. auritus* using dual choice experiments which involved bats having to choose between the smell or call of their own offspring or mother and those of a different infant or mother. Vocalizations of each infant were recorded daily using an ultrasonic bat detector with a time-expansion facility (Pettersson Electronics, Sweden). Infants were recorded in isolation and during reunions with their mothers. Odours were obtained by stroking the bats (particularly their muzzles round the facial glands) with cotton wool swabs. Dual choice experiments to investigate use of smell involved a circular arena with a radius of 12.5 cm to test the babies' responses and a wooden Y-maze to test those of the mothers. Bats were considered to make a choice if they approached a swab, sniffed it and stayed close to it for at least 1 min. For acoustic choice tests, recorded calls from infants or mothers were played into the Y-maze from two channels of the instrumentation recorder and broadcast through ultrasound loudspeakers. Bats were considered to make a choice if they moved into one of the branches of the maze and stayed there for at least 2 min. The experiments showed that mothers were able to identify their own baby by scent cue alone and also by acoustic cue alone. In all experiments, all females ($n=5$) made the correct choice at their first attempt. They were also able to 'upgrade' their memory of their own infants' i-calls, since in all cases mothers were able to distinguish between the i-calls of their offspring recorded the same day as the experiment (new calls) and those recorded the previous day (old calls). In all cases, mothers chose their infants' new calls. Infants aged 7–15 days were shown to be able to distinguish the scents of their own mothers from those of other lactating females and to distinguish the calls of their mothers from those of others. Like the mothers, all infants made the correct choice at their first attempt. Recognition between mothers and young was thus mutual after the first week of life, and neither mothers nor infants appeared to have any difficulty in recognizing their respective baby or mother.

During late summer, female *P. auritus* which have given birth are characterized by an oily secretion which stains fur and membranes orange-brown and which appears to come from the facial glands (Stebbings, 1966). The secretion has a strong, somewhat sweet smell and stains particularly the ventral fur of the bat. Stebbings suggested that it may be used in individual mother–young recognition in this species, although it may also be connected with marking roosts and finding conspecifics with which to mate (see below). Similar secretions have been described in a number of other vespertilionid species, e.g. *Eptesicus serotinus* (Kleiman, 1969). The secretion from the facial glands of *Eptesicus fuscus* was analysed by Dapson *et al.* (1977) and found to contain short-chain, unsaturated fatty acids which have relatively strong odours.

The main function of i-calls is to elicit a response in a mother when her infant is separated from her and to aid her in locating and recognizing it. They are most important in the first 5 days of the life of a baby, before it can see and move around and before it begins to take an active part in recognition behaviour. As the infant begins to recognize and search for its mother after separation, it makes fewer i-calls and the structure of the calls begins to change until, by around 12 days, they have given way to orientation calls.

Retrieval of Infants

Infant long-eared bats are not carried by their mothers on normal foraging flights but are occasionally carried in flight if the mother is disturbed or if the colony moves roost during the period before the young can fly. On such flights, babies may occasionally be dropped away from the roost. Inside the roost, they may fall from beams or may stray from the normal roost site. In such circumstances, mothers retrieve their babies and return them to the colony. Bats of many species are known to do this and there is a wealth of anecdotal evidence of infants being 'rescued' in this way from many different places. A *P. auritus* infant of about 2 weeks old was successfully retrieved after it was found in an apartment and placed outside (Schaffler, 1993), and Howard (1995) recorded that very young babies of this species commonly fall from the roof apex where they roost and are retrieved. Older infants attempt to crawl back to the roost site on their own, but the youngest wait to be found by their mothers. In long-eared bats, as in most species, the most important proximal cues a mother uses in searching for her lost offspring are probably smell and her memory of where she left it (Kunz, 1973; Brown, 1976), but the i-calls produced by the infant are the most important distal cue and the signal which triggers a response in her to search for it.

MATING BEHAVIOUR

The three commonest types of mating system among temperate zone bats (Altringham, 1996) are:

- resource defence polygyny
- female defence polygyny
- random, promiscuous mating.

Monogamous behaviour, usually shown by species in which the male is needed to help rear the offspring, is relatively rare in bats and is confined to tropical species such as *Lavia frons* (Wickler and Uhrig, 1969). Resource defence polygyny involves the defence by males of mating territories which are visited by females. In a few tropical species (Bradbury, 1977a, b), a form is seen in which males display by gathering and vocalizing at a central display site, or lek, which females visit to choose a mate. Defence of mating territories is shown by European species such as *P. pipistrellus* (Gerrell and Lundberg, 1985) and *N. noctula* (Sluiter and van Heerdt, 1966). In both these species males occupy a territory (often a bat box or a tree) which they defend from other males and to which they attract females using songflight (Lundberg and Gerrell, 1986). Park *et al.* (in press) suggested that male defence of territory is most likely to have evolved in species, such as pipistrelles, in which female groups are unstable and therefore difficult to defend. Because female groups in *P. auritus* are stable, they considered that this species is more likely to have a system involving defence of females. However, defence of females is not possible during winter, and intermittent mating throughout winter has been shown to occur in *P. auritus* (Strelkov, 1962). Groups of males are common in nursery roosts late in summer (Entwistle, 1994) and no signs of aggression have been recorded, either between males within a group or between groups within a roost. Park *et al.* proposed that, due to the relatively large size of female groups, they may be defended by groups of males and not solitary ones. However, Entwistle (1994) considered that, on the available evidence, the most likely mating system in *P. auritus* is a random, promiscuous one in which swarming occurs and females mate with many males. Since brown long-eared behaviour includes mating by males with torpid females and mating in early spring when there is no evidence of the formation of any groups, this system appears to be the most likely.

There is, however, more evidence of female defence polygyny among grey long-eared bats. In this species, males do show signs of aggressiveness towards other males (Stebbings, 1970) and could well be defending groups of females in late summer and autumn. There is no evidence so far of winter or spring mating (Horacek, 1975) and so the problem of males being unable to defend females during hibernation does not arise. More research is needed into the mating behaviour of this species, but it does appear to be one area in which there are clear-cut differences between them and *P. auritus*.

Another difference between grey and brown long-eared bats recorded by Horacek (1975) is that the brown, odourous secretion produced by the facial glands of *P. auritus* (Stebbings, 1966) does not appear to be produced by *P. austriacus*, at least in autumn. Horacek (1975) considered that the main purpose of the secretion in *P. auritus* was to mark potential mating roosts, and he connected high activity of bats of this species at transitory roosts in autumn and spring with marking roosts and searching for mates. If the mating system is a promiscuous, swarming one, then brown long-eared bats should visit as many roosts as possible in order to maximize their chances of mating; by marking roosts in this way, they advertise their presence. Horacek (1975) never recorded any activity of the facial glands in *P. austriacus*, nor was activity at transitory roosts observed. He proposed that this species used a different system for finding mates and observed that mating appeared to be confined to summer roosts. This behaviour could be explained if grey long-eared bats used a female defence mating system. Males gather and defend groups of females in nursery roosts during late summer and mating occurs there. There appears to be no swarming and no need to find and mark additional mating roosts.

CHAPTER 7

Population Biology

A NUMBER of long-term ringing studies have been undertaken on long-eared bats during the last 40 years and these have begun to provide information regarding how long the bats live and how the composition of their colonies varies over time, as well as allowing estimates to be made of population density. Ringing studies have also been used to investigate the distances covered by *Plecotus* during movements between roosts and hibernacula. Other aspects of their biology connected with colonial behaviour include predation and its effect on bat populations and parasite infections and their relationship with colony size.

LIFE EXPECTANCY AND SURVIVAL RATE

Boyd and Stebbings (1989) used data from a 10 year study of *P. auritus* in a 10 000 ha coniferous forest to estimate survival rates in the population. An extensive system of bat boxes was established in the plantation, which consisted mainly of mature Corsican (*Pinus nigra*) and Scots (*Pinus sylvestris*) pine. Bats were caught in the boxes 2–4 times during each year of the study. Survival rates were estimated by two methods, the first of which involved ringed cohorts of known age, i.e. bats which had been ringed as juveniles. Distributions for both males and females gave good fits to a negative exponential curve (Figure 7.1), suggesting a constant annual survival rate. This rate was calculated to be 0.602 for males and 0.861 for females, after the female rate had been corrected for the rate of increase and skewness of age distribution. Boyd and Stebbings (1989) also estimated survival using a method involving bats of unknown age, as described by Cormack (1964). This provided an estimate of survival based on the probability that a bat alive one year would also be alive the next; overall annual survival was estimated from the geometric mean of the annual survival estimates and gave values of 0.623 ± 0.076 (SEM) for males and 0.780 ± 0.035 (SEM) for females. Variation in survival between years was greater for males than for females; this variation was emphasized in a study in north-east Scotland (Entwistle *et al.*, 1994), in which survival in males (0.76) was found to be similar to that in females.

An earlier study by Stebbings (1970) used the same method involving bats of unknown age and gave similar survival rates for *P. auritus*. This study involved a mixed colony of *P. auritus* and *P. austriacus* in the attic of a research station, and for the whole colony annual survival rate was estimated to be 0.750, which gave an estimated life span of 16 years for *Plecotus* bats (Stebbings, 1970). The population was stable and hence increment was equal to mortality, since there was no evidence that immigration or emigration took place to any

106

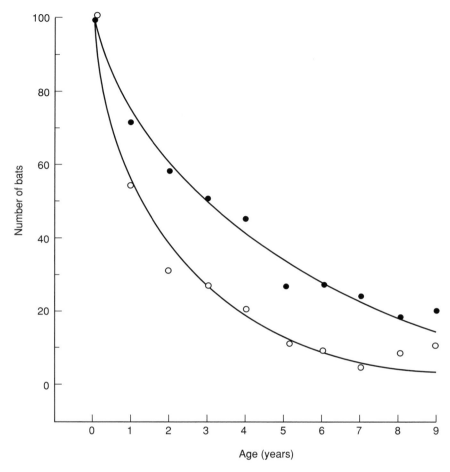

FIG 7.1   *The number of male and female* P. auritus *alive in successive age classes, starting with 100 bats of each sex. Age of individual bats was known, since bats were ringed as juveniles. Exponential curves were fitted by least-squares regression (reproduced with permission from Boyd and Stebbings, 1989).* ●, *female bats;* ○, *male bats.*

extent. By 1970, the presence of the two species had been established and survival rates were calculated for each separately (Stebbings, 1970). In *P. auritus*, annual survival rate was calculated at 0.542 for males, 0.758 for females and 0.743 for both sexes combined. Life span was estimated to be 7 years for males, 16 years for females and 15 years for the sexes combined. The population of *P. austriacus* suffered a sharp decline during the study, which Stebbings attributed to the severe winter in southern England in 1962–63. There was a large drop in the number of bats caught following this winter and this affected the estimated survival rates, which over the whole study were calculated to be 0.452 for males and 0.621 for females. Life span was estimated to be 5 years for males, 9 years for females and 7 years for both sexes combined. At this roost, therefore, the survival rate in *P. austriacus* was considerably lower than that in *P. auritus*. In southern England, *P. austriacus* is at the extreme northern limit of its range. It is known to be susceptible to poor weather conditions, and Stebbings' study shows how marginal is its hold in the area.

Climate is the most important single factor affecting mortality in all bat species (Ransome, 1990). Cold, late springs cause delays in gestation and subsequently juveniles cannot gain enough weight after they have finished growing to survive their first winter. Poor weather during lactation also causes delays in growth, as well as high mortality, among unweaned infants. For all species, including long-eared bats, there is ample anecdotal evidence that females may abandon babies during extended spells of cold, wet weather in the lactation period. Roer (1973) showed that the mortality rate among juvenile *Myotis myotis* was high in years when the summer was cold but very low (2.2%) during a warm summer. Juveniles appear to be more affected than adults by poor weather, but mortality rate also rises among adults in very bad summers.

Longevity

The life spans calculated by Stebbings (1966, 1970) for long-eared bats are average values and some individuals live much longer, just as some die much earlier. Bats as a group live long lives (Herreid, 1964) and the maximum ages which they attain are difficult to assess for this reason – it is noticeable that in many ringing studies the maximum age recorded is the same as the length of the study. Large-scale ringing studies on *P. auritus* began in the late 1950s and the ages recorded have increased progressively since then. The maximum age of brown long-eared bats in the Netherlands was reported to be 12.5 years (Heerdt and Sluiter, 1958) and then 22 years (Heerdt and Sluiter, 1961). Similarly in Switzerland, ages of 18 years (Jenni, 1978), 20 years (Jenni, 1981), 22 years (Aellen, 1983–4) and 30 years (Lehmann *et al.*, 1992) have been recorded. There are thus several records of brown long-eared bats living to ages of more than 20 years. Lehmann *et al.* (1992) reported that, in a ringing study which has been ongoing since 1957 in the Swiss Alps, one female had been captured seven times, the last 30 years after it was ringed. Since its age was not known at the time of ringing, 30 must be considered the minimum age of this bat. When it was most recently caught in 1990, the authors recorded that it showed only slight signs of ageing. Its dorsal fur was rusty brown instead of greyish brown and was slightly thinner that that of other bats, especially round the shoulder blades. Its nipples were not exposed or lactating (capture was in mid August) and thus it had probably not produced an infant that year. However, its teeth showed only moderate signs of wear and its body condition was generally good, indicating that it may not have been near the natural end of its life.

There are few records of longevity in *P. austriacus*. The oldest age recorded is 11.75 years (Gaisler and Hanak, 1969) in the Czech Republic. However, it is unlikely that the lives of bats of this species are so much shorter than those of *P. auritus*, and the recorded life span is almost certain to increase as more long-term studies are carried out.

POPULATION SIZE

It is difficult to measure population size in bats since they are nocturnal, small and dispersed over a large area. Traditionally, numbers have been estimated by counting individuals on emergence from roosts. However, this method takes account only of bats in known roosts and ignores those in others. It also does not allow for roost changing by colonies, nor for those males not in the nursery roost at the time, since the vast majority of known roosts are in houses. More recently, surveys of foraging areas using ultrasonic bat detectors have been undertaken to monitor changes in bat populations. These are not suitable for *Plecotus* bats, however, because of the low intensity of their orientation calls and the consequent difficulty in detecting them ultrasonically. It is also difficult to count long-eared bats on emergence because they leave the roost to forage late in the evening when it is almost dark (Chapter 4). Counts of bats in roosts are therefore the only practical way to monitor *Plecotus* populations, although they frequently underestimate actual colony size (Entwistle, 1994; see Chapter 6). Because these species roost in apices of attics they are relatively easy to find and thus colonies are likely to be reported by roost owners. For this reason, poster campaigns asking the public to report roosting bats tend to produce relatively high numbers of long-eared roosts (Speakman *et al.*, 1991a; Swift, *unpublished*). If searches are sufficiently thorough in an area, most roosts in houses will be found, although the problem of temporary, alternative roosts such as those in tree holes will not be solved.

An intensive poster campaign was used by Speakman *et al.* (1991a) to find roosts of *P. auritus* in north-east Scotland, and this was supplemented by advertisements in a local newspaper in an attempt to find as many roosts as possible. The campaign lasted 4 years and probably located most *P. auritus* roosts, since a subsequent study in the same area (Entwistle, 1994) found no more new ones. In contrast, the rate of discovery of new *P. pipistrellus* roosts showed no sign of slowing towards the end of the project (Speakman *et al.*, 1991a). A total of 34 *P. auritus* roosts was found in an area of 3200 km^2; they contained a total of 706 bats, which gave an estimated population density in the area of 0.0166 bats ha^{-1}. Since colony size in the species is around 20 (see Chapter 6), this equated to about one roost in each 10×10 km square. However, since roosts were confined to wooded river valleys, the population was locally much higher than this and the maximum number of long-eared bats recorded in a 1 km square was about 90 (J. Speakman, *pers. comm.*). By comparing their findings with historical records of the area, Speakman *et al.* (1991a) concluded that brown long-eared bats are not as common in north-east Scotland as they were 100 years ago. They attributed the decline mainly to contraction of the range of river valleys because of destruction of woodland elsewhere in the area, and to increasing urbanization round Aberdeen making large parts unsuitable for these bats.

Boyd and Stebbings (1989) estimated the population density of *P. auritus* in their study area of coniferous forest in England. In this area, the bat boxes provided were the only suitable roost sites for the bats, and these were relatively easy to monitor over a number of years. The population increased steadily as young were recruited; over the 10 years of the study the total population increased from 73 to 140, giving an approximate doubling time of 10 years. Since the total area of the forest was 10000 ha, this gave a population density of 0.014 bats ha^{-1} – a figure very similar to that estimated by Speakman *et al.* (1991a) in Scotland.

From the above figures, Speakman (1991a) calculated the population density of *P. auritus* to be about one tenth that of Britain's commonest bat, *P. pipistrellus*, and, since the geographic range of *P. auritus* covers about 80% of that of *P. pipistrellus*, he estimated the total British population of *P. auritus* to be about 8% of that of the pipistrelle. There are approximately 4.63 million pipistrelles in Britain (Walsh *et al.*, 1987) and therefore the total population size of *P. auritus* was estimated to be about 370 400 (Speakman, 1991a). The total British population of *P. austriacus* has been counted at about 1500 (Stebbings and Griffiths, 1986) and is confined to an area of around 1400 km². This gives a population density for the species of about 0.001 bats ha⁻¹, or one colony of 20 bats in every 15 10×10 km squares — a density of about one-fifteenth that of *P. auritus* in the small area of Britain in which *P. austriacus* occurs.

SEX RATIO

Benzal (1991) studied a population of *P. auritus* living in boxes in a pine plantation in central Spain. Overall, the number of males in the boxes, which housed mainly nursery colonies, was high and the sex ratio did not differ significantly from 1:1 (96 males:101 females). However, among adult bats, the ratio was biased towards females (49 adult males:75 adult females). Conversely, among juveniles, females were always less numerous than males (47 juvenile males:26 juvenile females). In this population, therefore, it appeared that there was either a higher proportion of males at birth or a higher survival among males in infancy. This may have compensated for what appeared to be higher mortality in males than in females among adult bats. Benzal (1991) found that juvenile males were significantly lighter than juvenile females in autumn and suggested that this implied a higher mortality among males during their first winter, which may have been compensated for by more males than females being born. Boyd and Stebbings (1989) found that, in the first 5 years of their study, there were significantly more male than female juveniles in the population (59 males:39 females), but that in the second 5 years the ratio did not differ significantly from 1:1 (93 males:95 females). The overall sex ratio also varied over the course of the study — the proportion of males increased during the first 5 years and then decreased. In any year, a greater proportion of males than females were juveniles, but the ratio of juvenile males:juvenile females did not vary significantly from 1:1 in any one year. Their findings thus differed from those of Benzal (1991) and the situation regarding the sex ratio at birth is not clear. The recent finding by Entwistle *et al.* (in press; see Chapter 5), that the normally accepted criterion for assessing maturity in male bats is unreliable for *P. auritus*, may explain this confusion. Among adults there does appear to be a constant bias towards females (Stebbings, 1970; Boyd and Stebbings, 1989; Benzal, 1991), suggesting that intersexual differences in the ecology and behaviour of the species cause a higher death rate among males than females.

FLIGHT DISTANCES

Both *P. auritus* and *P. austriacus* are considered to be stationary species which do not move long distances between summer and winter roosts (Strelkov, 1969; Gaisler and Hanak, 1969); *P. auritus* is known to occupy the same roosts all year round in some areas (Strelkov, 1969). Recorded flights of marked individuals have all been short. Harmata (1987) noted that both species moved only about 500 m between roosts in woodland, and Park *et al.* (in press) similarly recorded only short movements (up to 1.75 km) by *P. auritus* between bat

boxes in a forest area. Gaisler and Hanak (1969) investigated flight distances of ringed individuals of both long-eared species over 20 years, and the longest flights recorded were
42 km for *P. auritus* and 62 km for *P. austriacus*; these were distances between summer and
winter roosts. Long-eared bats do, however, occasionally fly further than this. A group of *P.
auritus*, apparently flying south-west, landed on a ship 70 km from the Yorkshire coast in
1948 and another was found dead on a lightship 50 km east of Norfolk in October 1968,
coincident with an influx of birds from Scandinavia (Corbet, 1970). In September 1995, a
brown long-eared bat was found on an oil platform in the North Sea 150 miles from the
Scottish coast (Hutson, 1996). One specimen of *P. austriacus* was found on a lightship 18
km off the Sussex coast in 1969, followed by one found dead on the coast 11 days later
(Corbet, 1971). These events may indicate that both species undertake long-distance flights
occasionally, but they are more likely to have been caused by bats being accidentally blown
out to sea by strong winds. There is no evidence that long-eared bats of either species make
organized, regular migratory flights of any great distance, unlike, for example, *N. noctula*,
ringed individuals of which have been recorded migrating up to 2400 km in Europe
(Hanak, 1966).

In being essentially stationary species, long-eared bats resemble others in the plecotine
group. *C. townsendii* is also a relatively sedentary species which was found to fly an average
distance of only 11.6 km from nursery roosts to hibernacula (Humphrey and Kunz, 1976).
These authors, in an extensive study, found that 80% of ringed bats returned to the same
hibernacula year after year and that 85.5% of ringed bats made flights of less than 1.6 km;
only two flights exceeded 8 km.

Homing

The ability of bats to return to roost sites following translocation has been widely reported,
although how they do it is not fully understood. Vision has been reported to be an important factor, since blinded *Myotis sodalis* showed considerably less homing ability than did
sighted ones (Barbour *et al.*, 1966), and smell also has an effect, but only close to the roost
(Davis, 1966). Homing ability, as might be expected, has been shown to be most developed
in migratory bat species (Wason, 1978) and therefore *Plecotus* species may be expected to
be relatively poor at finding their way home. In fact, few investigations appear to have been
carried out. Ryberg (1947) showed that *P. auritus* were able to find their way back to roosts
from about 60 km away – a distance in the same range as the longest natural flights of these
bats (Gaisler and Hanak, 1969). Also, two captive *P. auritus* which escaped in Aberdeen
were found to have returned to their roost 45 km away within 10 days (M.A. Anderson,
unpublished). Cockrum (1956) found that only four *C. townsendii*, out of a total of 54
released, had returned to their roost 45 km away within 2 days, and concluded that homing ability in this species was poorly developed. This appears to confirm that non-migratory
bat species are relatively inefficient at homing. Because *Plecotus* bats do not fly long distances normally, they are likely to be familiar with only limited geographic areas. Their
flight is energetically expensive compared with that of most other species (Chapter 2) and
they avoid flying across open spaces. They thus have all the hallmarks of being stationary
species which remain in a limited area and do not have well-developed homing ability,
although they are able to find their way back to roosts over distances of up to 60 km without apparent difficulty.

PARASITES

Compared with many insectivorous bats, *Plecotus* harbour relatively few ectoparasites and infestations on individuals are usually light, particularly those on adults; Stebbings (1966) reported that juveniles frequently harboured higher numbers. Low infestations of ectoparasites are probably connected with small colony size in these bats – parasites such as mites and fleas thrive in large numbers on hosts which live in close contact with each other and between which transfer is easy. Long-eared bats live in small colonies which are often divided into several groups within large roof spaces and so there is relatively little contact. They also move between main and temporary roosts (Chapter 6), thus further reducing the opportunity for parasite numbers to increase.

Ectoparasites

The commonest of these are fleas and mites. Very occasionally a nycteribiid fly is reported to occur on long-eared bats, although neither *Plecotus* species is considered to be a natural host for these (Hutson, 1984). Kristofik (1982) recorded one specimen of *Nycteribia schmidlii* on a male *P. auritus* in the Slovak Republic; he considered its presence to be 'casual' and suggested it was a stray from a member of another bat species roosting in the vicinity. Nycteribiidae (Order Diptera) are minute, wingless parasites of bats; they have long legs and have become highly specialized on their way of life.

Fleas

Fleas (Order Siphonaptera) are small, wingless insects which are laterally flattened in shape and which live parasitically on mammals and birds. The larvae are non-parasitic. Ischnopsyllidae are a family of specialist bat fleas (Figure 7.2), and several species of these have been recorded on long-eared bats. Haitlinger and Ruprecht (1992) found *Ischnopsyllus hexatinus* on *P. auritus* in Poland and this species also occurs on the same host in Britain (Stebbings, 1977). *Nycteridopsylla longiceps* occurs rarely on *P. auritus* in winter (Swift, 1991).

Mites

Mites (Class Arachnida; Order Acari) are very numerous and widespread and many are parasitic. The cephalothorax and abdomen are fused so that the body essentially consists of one piece (Figure 7.2) and most species have eight legs. The family most often found on long-eared bats are Spincturnidae, and the species *Spincturnix plecotina* has been collected from *P. auritus* in Britain (Stebbings, 1977), Poland (Haitlinger and Ruprecht, 1992) and Korea (Kim and Lee, 1990). Other species of mite recorded from *Plecotus* species include *Ornithonyssus pipistrelli*, *Neomyobia plecotia* (Swift, 1991) and *Leptotrombidium russicum* (Haitlinger and Ruprecht, 1992).

Internal Parasites

Gardner *et al.* (1987) examined blood smears of 12 British bat species, including *P. auritus* but not *P. austriacus*, for parasites. The number in *P. auritus* was low, the only organism found being *Grahamella* species. This is an intraerythrocytic bacterium found in a wide range of mammals. It is transmitted by fleas and is not considered to be harmful to the host.

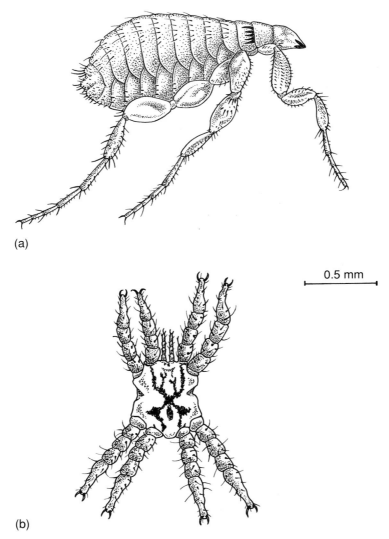

0.5 mm

(a)

(b)

FIG 7.2 *A flea of the family Ischnopsyllidae (a) and a mite (b) typical of those ectoparasitic on long-eared bats.*

PREDATION

In the tropics, specialist hawks prey exclusively on bats, but in Europe most incidences of predation on bats by birds appear to be occasional and opportunistic. However, although bats are of minor importance in the diet of the birds which catch them, this does not mean that occasional predation is trivial from the perspective of the bat, and the need to avoid predation exerts considerable influence on aspects of their behaviour.

Predation by Birds

Corvids take some bats in the USA and Africa (Rosevear, 1965) and gulls have been observed to catch one in Britain (Cleeves, 1969), but a survey of all records showed that predation on bats by these groups is negligible (Speakman, 1991a). Hawks and falcons catch very few, reflecting the diurnal activity of these birds. The few bats they do take are likely to be of species which emerge early in the evening, before twilight (e.g. serotines, *Eptesicus serotinus*). Long-eared bats, which emerge much later, are very unlikely to encounter them. However long-eared bats which fly in daylight for any reason (see below) run a much higher risk, as is shown in a report by Simms (1977). A male and a female kestrel, *Falco tinnunculus*, were observed pursuing a group of eight long-eared bats during an early evening in August and one bat was caught.

There is evidence from extensive dietary studies in Europe that bats regularly turn up in the diets of owls. Tawny (*Strix aluco*) and barn (*Tyto alba*) owls are the most important predators, and long-eared owls (*Asio otus*) also prey on them. Barn owls generally forage in open country such as over fields, but tawny owls forage predominantly in closed habitats, mainly woodland, copses and wooded gardens, and long-eared owls also prefer wooded areas, particularly coniferous and mixed woodland (Glue, 1970); the latter two species might therefore be expected to prey to a greater extent on long-eared bats, which also prefer such habitats. Glue (1970) analysed 119 pellet samples, each consisting of between 22 and 52 individual barn owl pellets. Out of a total of 31 491 prey items from these pellets, he found the remains of 11 bat skeletons, including one of *P. auritus*. In Poland, Ruprecht (1979) found that both tawny and barn owls preyed on bats and that *P. auritus* was one of the commonest bat species in the pellets of tawny owls. The tawny owl seemed to be a more specialist predator of bats than was the barn owl, although of 21 bat species which occur in Poland, remains of 20 were found in barn owl pellets; these included both *P. auritus* and *P. austriacus*. In a later study (Ruprecht, 1990), this author estimated that bat remains accounted for 0.81% of the contents of tawny and barn owl pellets in western Poland. The frequency of different bat species in the pellets reflected their relative abundance in the area, indicating that owls were not being selective. This was confirmed in another Polish study (Lesinski, 1989), which found that *P. auritus* remains occurred more frequently than did those of *P. austriacus* in barn owl pellets, reflecting the higher local abundance of *P. auritus*. Occasionally, however, individual owls do prey on bats in a highly opportunistic way. Jentzsch (1992) reported that one barn owl, which lived close to a *Myotis myotis* roost in southern Germany, appeared to have become adept at catching these bats – 9.1% of its diet consisted of *M. myotis*, which must have had a considerable adverse effect on the bats' population locally. *M. myotis* is the species most preyed upon by owls in Europe. *Plecotus* are generally less common in pellets, constituting only 0.61% of the content of pellets in some areas (Lipej and Gjerkes, 1992). Speakman (1991a), in a comprehensive review of predation by birds on bats, attempted to assess the impact this predation has on bat populations in Britain. From published records, he estimated the total population of birds which may prey on bats, the total annual food intake of these birds and the proportion of their diet which was likely to consist of bats. From these figures he estimated the total number of bats eaten in a year. This included 8783 bats eaten by barn owls, 168 850 by tawny owls and 10 205 by long-eared owls. Next, Speakman estimated the total population of bats in Britain and their overall mortality rates from published reports. From these he calculated the total number of bats which die in the country in a year. This figure was about 1.82 million, of which 201 415 were calculated to be killed by birds, indicating that avian predators accounted for around 11.1% of the total annual mortality of all bats in Britain.

The UK population of *P. austriacus*, whose roosts are few and whose range is very limited in Britain, has been estimated at around 1500 individuals (Stebbings and Griffiths, 1986) and its annual mortality rate is 0.33 (Stebbings, 1970). The total population of *P. auritus* is not known, but its population density (Boyd and Stebbings, 1989; Speakman *et al.*, 1991a) was calculated by Speakman (1991a) to be about one-tenth that of *P. pipistrellus* and its range in Britain to be about 80% of the area inhabited by pipistrelles. He therefore estimated the population to be about 8% of that of pipistrelles, which is around 4.631 million (Walsh *et al.*, 1987), or about 370 000. The annual mortality rate of *P. auritus* is 0.242 (Stebbings, 1977). From these figures, if it is assumed that birds prey equally on all bat species, avian predation accounts for about 9950 brown and 55 grey long-eared bats every year.

Speakman's (1991a) figure of 11.1% for the impact of predation by birds on bat mortality is surprisingly high, given the low incidence of bats in the diets of these birds. It is also strange that predation on bats is not reported more often, particularly that by diurnal birds such as kestrels. Speakman (1991a) estimated that 8406 bats are killed by kestrels every year, which implies that 23 are attacked every day by these birds, but kestrels chasing bats is still a rarely recorded event. The reason for this is the large population of kestrels in the UK. In order for 23 bats to be killed every day, an individual kestrel would only need to catch one once in 20 years. High owl populations in the UK probably also account for the relatively low proportion of bats in their diets. Because owl populations are nationally high, their rate of predation on bats need only be relatively low to produce a noticeable effect. It cannot therefore be argued that predation is too low in this country to produce an effect on the behaviour of bats such as *Plecotus* species, and it is highly probable that behaviour such as late emergence, selection of roosts close to woodland and the use of flyways are connected with predator avoidance.

Predation by Mammals

The most significant mammalian predator of long-eared bats in Britain and Europe is almost certainly the domestic cat, *Felis catus*. In the Netherlands, records of predation on bats by cats are almost four times more frequent than those of predation on them by owls (Bekker and Mostert, 1990), and bats which roost in houses are especially vulnerable to cat predation. Unlike birds of prey, domestic cats live in close proximity to humans and have no fear of approaching human dwellings – they are thus far more likely than owls to attack bats in the immediate vicinity of the roost. They are agile and adept at climbing and can therefore get into a position to attack bats as they emerge. They may even be able to get into some attics where long-eared bats roost and attack them there. Bruijn (1990) photographed the activities of a cat which was suspected of killing a number of bats (mainly *P. pipistrellus* and *P. auritus*) roosting in a tower. The cat was filmed entering the tower through a ventilation opening, climbing 80 steps to the loft and then attacking the roosting bats. Before its activities were curtailed by fixing a grill to the ventilation opening, it had killed at least 50 bats. Many had been regurgitated or rejected uneaten, a feature common in cat predation. Like many insectivores such as shrews and moles, bats are apparently unpalatable to cats, but this does not deter them from killing large numbers, perhaps in the hope of finding one which tastes better!

Anecdotal evidence suggests that most long-eared bat predation by cats occurs as the bats emerge in the evening. Cats climb on to window sills or roofs and capture the bats as they drop through the exit hole from the roost. Many cats become very skilled at this activity and can have a serious effect on a colony. Many of the long-eared bats brought to me as casualties have been rescued from cats, and those found are likely to form only a small proportion of those caught. Slow-flying bats such as *Plecotus* species are particularly vulnerable. Bagley and Jacobs (1985) recorded high mortality in a colony of the related species *C. townsendii virginianus* due to a domestic cat catching them on emergence. The colony's maternity roost was in a cave whose entrance was grilled, and the cat had become adept at catching bats as they flew through the grill.

Daylight Flying

Bats are almost exclusively nocturnal, but observations and reports indicate that they do occasionally fly during daylight. Because daylight flying is so unusual, naturalists tend to notice and record instances of it, and Speakman (1990) conducted a survey in which he sought as many observations as possible from all over Britain in an attempt to discover how prevalent daylight flying was and what the reasons were for its occurrence. A total of 420 records were received, about one-third of which were of flights during winter (October–March). In the remaining two-thirds, a peak of activity occurred during April; activity in both summer and winter was greatest in the middle of the day, between 1200 and 1600 hours. The number of bats involved in each sighting varied between 1 and 200, but around 90% were of single individuals. Speakman concluded from data in the survey that the main purpose of daylight flights in summer was to compensate for energy deficits caused by inadequate food intake during nocturnal foraging – if poor weather reduced bats' ability to feed, possibly for several nights, they emerged during daylight as an emergency measure. The prevalence of flights in April reflected the lower insect population at that time and the bats' subsequent need to supplement night feeding. This was supported by the finding that bats at high latitude were more likely to fly by day than were those further south, since short nights further added to their inability to meet energy demand in cold or wet conditions. In winter, daylight flying occurred because periods of arousal from hibernation (Chapter 8) did not always coincide with periods of darkness. If bats aroused during daylight and conditions were suitable for foraging, they emerged both to feed and to drink.

Of the 420 records of bats flying in daylight, 16 were of *P. auritus* and one of *P. austriacus*, although some of the 153 unidentified bats may also have been *Plecotus* species. Speakman (1990) observed that *P. auritus* thus flew in daylight very infrequently, although the number of flights made by this species (16) and the number made by *P. pipistrellus* (154) appear to be in approximately the same proportion as their populations in Britain, since the *P. auritus* population was estimated by Speakman (1991a) to be 8% of that of *P. pipistrellus*. There was therefore no evidence that long-eared bats were less inclined to fly by day than any other species, despite their normal habit of foraging late at night rather than in twilight. Overall, however, the survey showed that daylight flights were rare, and

Speakman (1990) calculated that bats of all species were about 100 times less likely to fly by day than by night.

Since peak insect availability occurs in mid to late afternoon in temperate regions (Rydell and Speakman, 1995) and since bats frequently have to resort to energy saving behaviour such as torpor and clustering during reproduction when demand is high, Speakman (1991b) next sought reasons to explain why daylight flying does not occur more frequently. Four alternative hypotheses were examined:

- Direct competition with insectivorous birds (e.g. house martins) may reduce the amount of food bats could acquire by day.
- Mobbing by birds (e.g. crows) which are neither predators nor competitors may reduce feeding efficiency.
- Overheating caused by the incidence of sunlight on bats' dark, uninsulated wings may mean they are unable to dissipate heat generated in flight (Speakman and Hays, 1992).
- Daylight flying may expose bats to an unacceptably high risk of attack by diurnal avian predators.

Speakman's (1990) survey showed that encounters between daylight flying bats and mobbing birds were rare and trivial and could not explain the infrequency of daylight flying. Interactions with avian aerial insectivores were also infrequent (they occurred in only 1.4% of records), and a separate study (Vernier, 1990) found no evidence of competition with hirundine birds. Fossil evidence also makes the competition hypothesis unlikely – by the early to mid Eocene, microchiropteran bats were already specialized for echolocation but passerine birds, including Hirundinidae, did not appear before the Oligocene (Rydell and Speakman, 1995); bats therefore had no potential competitors during the Eocene. However, the fossil history of owls dates back to the Palaeocene and that of other predatory birds such as hawks to the early Eocene (Rydell and Speakman, 1995) and thus there were potential predators of bats at the time their nocturnal habits were evolving.

In order to investigate the predation and overheating hypotheses, Speakman (1991b) conducted a further analysis on data from his daylight flying survey and also investigated flying behaviour in captive *P. pipistrellus* and *P. auritus*. Experiments were performed to establish the effect of light on the flying behaviour of the bats and whether there was any effect of radiant heat on body temperature. Individual bats of both species flew for a significantly greater percentage of time in the dark than in the light; there was no difference between the species and both avoided flying in the light. There was also no significant difference in either species between the body temperatures of bats measured at the end of flights in the dark and in the light, indicating that avoidance of light was not mediated by overheating. Overheating was thus not the proximal cue which caused the bats' avoidance of flying in the light, although it could not be ruled out as an ultimate factor influencing the reason for the avoidance of daylight flying. The survey (Speakman, 1990) also showed that bats did not particularly avoid flying on hot, sunny days, suggesting that, at least in the UK, overheating does not have a significant effect.

The most likely factor which causes bats to be nocturnal thus appears to be predation, and the results of the survey (Speakman, 1991b) support this. Of the 420 reports of daylight flights, 3.1% included observations of interactions with cats or with avian predators including kestrels, merlins (*Falco columbarius*), sparrowhawks (*Accipiter nisus*) and

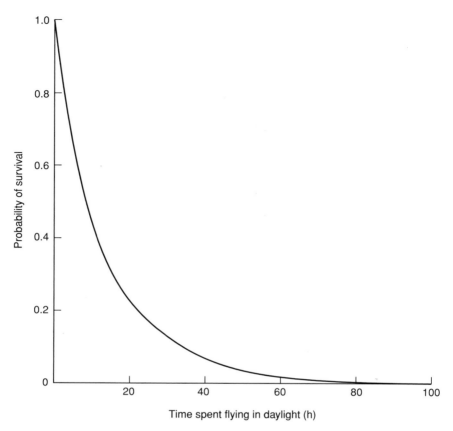

FIG 7.3   *Probability of surviving predation attempts against time spent flying in daylight for bats in the UK (reproduced with permission from Speakman, 1991b).*

black-headed gulls (*Larus ridibundus*). In at least 1.2% of the 420 reports, the bat was killed. Speakman estimated, from data in the survey, that on average a bat flying in daylight would be fatally attacked about once in every 14.3 h of flight. A bat flying in daylight for 64 h would have a 99% chance of being killed (Figure 7.3). This is about 100 times the estimated risk of death by nocturnal predation, and strongly supports the hypothesis that avoidance of diurnal predators is the reason why bats are very largely nocturnal.

CHAPTER 8

Hibernation

BATS living in temperate regions face an annual problem of food shortage, since few arthropods are available during winter. All animals which depend on seasonal food sources have the same problem and several solutions have evolved. Animals may switch food sources temporarily, e.g. the bank vole, *Clethrionomys glareolus*, may eat dead leaves in mid winter when its normal diet of seeds, fruits and leaves of woody plants is not available (Watts, 1968). However, this option is not open to bats because no appropriate alternative foods are available to them. Migration to lower latitudes is common among bird species and has also evolved among some bats. In Europe, species such as *P. pipistrellus* and *N. noctula* migrate over large distances, particularly in northern parts of their range (Strelkov, 1969). The third strategy is hibernation, an option open only to animals, such as temperate zone bats, which can become torpid. Bats sometimes use both strategies – pipistrelles and noctules, when they migrate, do so from summer to winter roosts, which are usually further south, and there they hibernate. Stationary species such as long-eared bats, whose summer and winter roosts are close to each other, rely entirely on hibernation as a strategy to survive cold winters and severely curtailed food supplies.

HETEROTHERMY, TORPOR AND HIBERNATION

Heterothermy is a specialized form of endothermy found mainly among small, temperate zone mammals. A heterothermic animal is able to vary its body temperature but, unlike ectothermic animals such as reptiles, heterotherms are able to control the fall in body temperature and also to restore high body temperature independently of ambient temperature. They do this using heat generated by mobilization of fat stored in the body.

Torpor is defined as a state in which an animal allows its body temperature to fall below its active endothermic level. The drop in temperature is controlled and, at low ambient temperature, can be maintained within narrow limits by metabolic processes. Hibernation is an extended form of torpor which may last for days or weeks and which occurs in response to a prolonged fall in ambient temperature and a reduction in food supply. It is not, however, continuous torpor which lasts all winter. Ransome (1971) proposed that it differs from short-term torpor used by bats during summer only in how often arousal occurs. In summer, a bat arouses frequently (hence the term 'Tagesschlaflethargie' (day-sleep lethargy) used by Eisentraut, 1937), while in winter arousals may occur days or weeks apart (Brack and Twente, 1985; Twente *et al.*, 1985; Thomas, 1995a).

119

Altringham (1996) listed four features of torpor in an attempt to define it in physiological terms:

- It involves a controlled reduction of body temperature, typically to within 1–2°C of ambient temperature.
- Heart rate, oxygen consumption, breathing rate and metabolic rate all fall as the body temperature drops.
- Peripheral vasoconstriction occurs and, at extremes of temperature, blood flow is restricted to a few vital organs for much of the time.
- The torpid animal is able to arouse spontaneously, independently of ambient temperature.

Timing of Hibernation

Stebbings (1970) recorded that *P. austriacus* in southern England began to hibernate earlier than *P. auritus*; whereas most *P. austriacus* from a colony were hibernating by late October or early November, *P. auritus* from the same roost were still active in early November and the whole colony was not in hibernation before the end of November. In central Europe, Hurka (1971) similarly found that *P. austriacus* began to hibernate in October. In Poland, Harmata (1973), who did not distinguish between the two species, found that *Plecotus* bats first appeared in hibernacula at the beginning of November and stayed there until mid March. Stebbings (1970) found that female *P. austriacus* began to emerge from hibernation in late March and by early April, all bats of this species were active. *P. auritus* were all active by mid April. In Europe, bats of both species ended hibernation in late March (Harmata, 1973), although Horacek (1975) found that a few *P. auritus* remained in hibernacula until early April.

Fat Accumulation Prior to Hibernation

All hibernating bats accumulate fat during late summer and autumn and this is used as an energy store for winter. The weight gain can be considerable – Ransome (1990) recorded that the fattest individuals of *Rhinolophus ferrumequinum* in his studies gained 75–80% of their lean weight during October, although weight gain, even among bats of the same species, was very variable. Hale (1980) caught a total of 12 *P. auritus* in mist nets during a study of bird migration in England and recorded the weights of these before releasing them. On 26 August, the average weight of males among netted individuals was 6.50 g ($n=3$) and that of females 7.65 g ($n=2$). On 13 October, the average weights of bats was 9.25 g ($n=2$) for males and 10.82 g ($n=5$) for females, which indicated that the average weight of bats sampled had increased by 41% over a period of 7 weeks. This gain is high compared with most bat species, in which pre-hibernal weight gain is around 25–30% (Humphrey and Kunz, 1976). In Spain, weight gain in *P. auritus* at the same time of year was found to be less; individual adult females sampled weighed an average of 9.0 g in July and 11.2 g in October, representing a gain of 25% (Benzal, 1991). The difference between the bats in the two studies was that those in Spain had a higher minimum weight than those in England. Either the true minimum weight in the Spanish bats was missed or else long-eared bats at this lower latitude never lose as much fat and so their weight never falls below about 9 g.

High pre-hibernal weight gain was also found in the plecotine species *C. townsendii*, in which fat accumulation accounted for 50% of the weight of males and 57% of that of females immediately before hibernation (Humphrey and Kunz, 1976). These authors suggested that large weight gain may have compensated for the high frequency with which the species moved hibernation sites during winter and the consequent high rate at which they used up energy.

Funakoshi and Uchida (1982) suggested that pre-hibernal weight increase in bats depends on an endogenous circannual rhythm which is independent of the timing of the reproductive cycle, since late births during a summer had no effect on pre-hibernal weight gain among vespertilionid bats in their study. They also suggested that the most likely Zeitgeber, or exogenous timing factor, was ambient temperature.

Weight Loss During Hibernation

Stebbings (1970) estimated weight loss during hibernation in southern England to be 22% in *P. auritus* and 29% in *P. austriacus*. Grey long-eared bats aroused more often during winter and changed hibernation sites more frequently, which accounted for their higher weight loss. Stebbings attributed this to unsuitable hibernating conditions for this species in Britain, which forced bats to arouse often to feed. He suggested that *P. austriacus* are confined to the extreme south of the country because this is the only part where the number of insects flying in winter is high enough to allow them to do so.

SITE SELECTION

Hibernation Sites

Plecotus species hibernate in caves, both natural ones and man-made structures such as mines, quarries and underground fortifications. They are also among the European bats most likely to be found in buildings, mainly cellars, and they may spend at least part of the winter in tree holes. In general, they choose relatively cool sites and move between hibernacula more frequently than do most European bats.

Daan and Wichers (1968) found that *Plecotus* species spent less time in winter in a system of artificial limestone caves than did any of the other eight species which used the caves. Their stay was confined to a period in the middle of winter, and it was presumed that they spent the rest of the time in cooler sites such as trees. However, in Poland long-eared bats were found to spend more time in underground sites, particularly in a system of fortifications (Bernard *et al.*, 1991). In Sweden, where there are few natural caves, *P. auritus* have been recorded hibernating in mines and limestone quarries, and 34% of the bats in one mine in the south of the country were of this species (Gerrell, 1980–81). Where the two *Plecotus* species hibernate in the same sites in central Europe, *P. austriacus* has been found to select slightly warmer microclimates (Hurka, 1971; Horacek, 1975).

When long-eared bats hibernate in buildings, cellars are the commonest sites for them, although one specimen of *P. austriacus* was found in December in a disused brick kiln in the Netherlands (Glas, 1982). In Germany, a solitary *P. austriacus* hibernated in a castle cellar near Berlin (Haensel and Nafe, 1993), where Haensel (1994) reported that *P. auritus* was the most numerous bat species hibernating in underground cellars of barns and houses. Cellars are also common sites to find *P. austriacus* in the Czech Republic (Horacek, 1975) and in Germany (Haensel, 1994). Both Gerrell (1980–81) and Rydell (1989c) reported extensive use of stone-built cellars by *P. auritus* in Sweden. These cellars, which are very common in the south of the country, are detached from houses and have a vaulted roof. They were traditionally used for storing potatoes, but nowadays are frequently empty. Gerrell (1980–81) found that *P. auritus* was the most numerous bat species in them in winter. Rydell (1989c) searched stone cellars in many rural areas in Sweden for signs of bats and found that 63% of intact cellars, but only 11% of derelict ones, contained such signs. Rydell concluded that these sites were important hibernacula for *P. auritus*. The condition of the cellar was obviously important, and thus there was a need to preserve them in good repair, although bats were not deterred by the cellars fulfilling their normal function of storing potatoes. Occupation was found to be highest in those containing many crevices, which were used as roost sites.

Changing Sites by Bats

Long-eared bats change their hibernation sites frequently during winter. Daan (1970) used automatic flash photography in a cave system in the Netherlands to monitor site-changing activity by bats. He found that *Plecotus* species made more flights inside the caves and changed hibernation sites more often than did individuals of several *Myotis* species which also hibernated there. Bezem *et al.* (1964) studied movements of *P. auritus* in a complex system of artificial limestone caves and found that, statistically, this species showed a preference for roosting in the cool outer region of the caves, up to 50 m from the entrance. However, in severely frosty weather, they migrated to the warmer inner region, more than 50 m from the outside. This indicated that long-eared bats changed sites within hibernacula in response to changes in ambient temperature. Kuipers and Daan (1970) also studied internal migration in the same cave system. Their study involved a number of species including grey and brown long-eared bats. Parts of the caves where relatively warm air could flow into the entrance area from outside were avoided by long-eared bats early in the winter; they hibernated in the deeper areas, which were cooler. As the entrance area cooled down with cold air flowing from outside, they moved into it from the inner areas. However, in one part of the system, different air flow meant that the entrance area was the coolest part all winter; in this section, long-eared bats spent all their hibernation period in the entrance area.

Temperature

All records available show that long-eared bats prefer lower ambient temperatures at which to hibernate than do most other European species. Daan and Wichers (1968) reported that the average temperature in a limestone cave close to hibernating *Plecotus* species ranged from 0–5.3°C, which was lower than that close to any of the other eight species in the same cave. Harmata (1969, 1973) measured the preferred hibernating temperatures of several European species, both under natural conditions and in the laboratory. In captivity, *P. auritus* chose to hibernate at temperatures of 1–8°C, with most individuals selecting 6°C (Harmata, 1969). Temperatures selected in the laboratory were generally slightly higher than those selected in the wild. In another study under natural conditions, long-eared bats (no distinction made between species) hibernated at temperatures of between –3 and 11°C, with most individuals choosing areas at around 7°C (Harmata, 1973). Gaisler (1970) used a natural situation to show that *Plecotus* prefer to hibernate at low temperatures. A cave in the Czech Republic was divided into two parts by a wooden wall and one section was considerably warmer than the other; a number of long-eared bats regularly hibernated in the cooler section. One autumn, the wall was broken down, allowing warm air into the cooler part of the cave, and the following winter no *Plecotus* bats hibernated there. They returned gradually after the wall was restored. Nagel and Nagel (1991) reported that *P. auritus* in Germany hibernated at a mean ambient temperature of 4°C. Harmata (1969) found that *P. auritus* remained active at temperatures as low as 1°C, which may explain why they require low temperatures for hibernation and why they may be found in summer roosts well into autumn (Chapter 6). Harmata (1969) reported that the only other European species which showed a similar preference for low hibernation temperatures was *Barbastella barbastellus*, another member of the plecotine group (see Chapter 1). Other plecotine bats (e.g. *C. townsendii*; Humphrey and Kunz, 1976) have also been found to prefer temperatures in the same range. Both long-eared bats and barbastelles are also able to tolerate lower extremes of temperature than are other species in Europe – Abelencev *et al.* (1956) reported that *P. auritus* could survive at temperatures as low as –7.5°C and *B. barbastellus* several degrees below this.

Where data are available for brown and grey long-eared bats separately, they indicate that the ranges of temperatures at which they hibernate are similar – Horacek (1975) found *P. austriacus* hibernating at 2–9°C – but that *P. austriacus* in general prefer slightly warmer hibernacula.

Humidity

Relative humidity in bat hibernacula is generally high (Altringham, 1996) and is likely to be higher in caves than in buildings. Speakman and Racey (1989) proposed that hibernating bats are more at risk from dehydration than from starvation and that the main purpose of most winter flights is to drink rather than to feed. By selecting humid hibernacula, bats are able to reduce water loss while they are torpid and so have to arouse less often. Daan and Wichers (1968) found the relative humidity of limestone caves around hibernating *Plecotus* to be 95–100%. Similar high humidity was found in caves containing hibernating long-eared bats in Russia (75–100%; Lesinski, 1986) and Poland (range 55–100%, average 84%; Bogdanowicz and Urbanczyk, 1983).

Altitude

There are a number of reports from Europe that long-eared bats use hibernacula at high altitude. In southern Germany, Nagel *et al.* (1983–4) found *P. auritus* and a few *P. austriacus* in caves at 700–800 m above sea level, while very few were found below this altitude and negligible numbers hibernated below 500 m. In summer, however, almost all bats in the area were found at lower altitudes. It was therefore apparent that long-eared bats moved into the mountains in winter, probably because temperatures in caves there were lower. A cave at 800 m above sea level in the area was found to be 2–3°C cooler than one at 300 m above sea level. Nagel and Nagel (1991) similarly found that *P. auritus* in Germany preferred cooler sites at high altitude in which to hibernate.

Sites Chosen within Hibernacula

Bezem *et al.* (1964) described three possible positions for bats within hibernacula:

- they may hang freely from a horizontal surface such as a ceiling
- they may hang in contact with a wall
- they may be in crevices, either deep ones such as bore holes in quarries or shallow ones such as indentations in rock.

The nine species hibernating in a large system of artificial caves in the Netherlands were ranked by these authors in order of their inclination to hibernate in crevices, from *Rhinolophus hipposideros*, which was always found hanging freely from the roof, to *P. pipistrellus*, which invariably hibernated deep in crevices: *R. hipposideros*, *Myotis emarginatus*, *M. myotis*, *M. dasycneme*, *M. nattereri*, *M. mystacinus* and *P. auritus*, *M. daubentonii*, *P. pipistrellus*. *P. auritus* was thus in the middle of the range and was usually found either in contact with a wall or in crevices. They used both shallow and deeper fissures. In the same caves, however, Daan and Wichers (1968) always found long-eared bats (no distinction was made between the two species) in crevices – they were never on walls.

Horacek (1975) found differences in the hibernation sites used by *P. auritus* and *P. austriacus* in the Czech Republic. Within a limestone quarry, *P. auritus* were usually found in larger galleries, and individuals hibernated in crevices or bore holes, mostly at depth (Figure 8.1). They appeared to prefer sites where ambient temperature fluctuated little (hence their preference for deeper crevices) and where the range was 2–7°C. *P. austriacus* hibernated in warmer parts of the quarry (2–9°C), often in smaller galleries and in sites subjected to considerable temperature changes. They were never found deep in crevices, but preferred to be on walls or at the entrances to crevices (Figure 8.2). Horacek (1975) also frequently found *P. austriacus* in cellars during winter, and concluded that they were more likely than *P. auritus* to hibernate in synanthropic sites.

In general, both species of long-eared bats hibernate singly or in very small groups of two or three individuals (Harmata, 1973). When they are in such small groups, individual bats do not form direct body contact with each other, and huddles or clusters have not been reported. *Plecotus* bats are, occasionally, found in larger groups with other species which have similar thermal preferences (Bogdanowicz, 1983), but they do not form large clusters.

AROUSAL

Arousal is the process by which bats actively emerge from a state of torpor. They may become active in response to disturbance in the hibernaculum, but arousal also occurs routinely under natural conditions. The process involves the use of brown adipose tissue, which is found in the neck and scapular region in temperature zone bats. Observations of long-eared bats active in winter under natural conditions (e.g. Daan, 1970) suggest they

FIG 8.1　*Hibernation sites commonly occupied by* P. auritus.

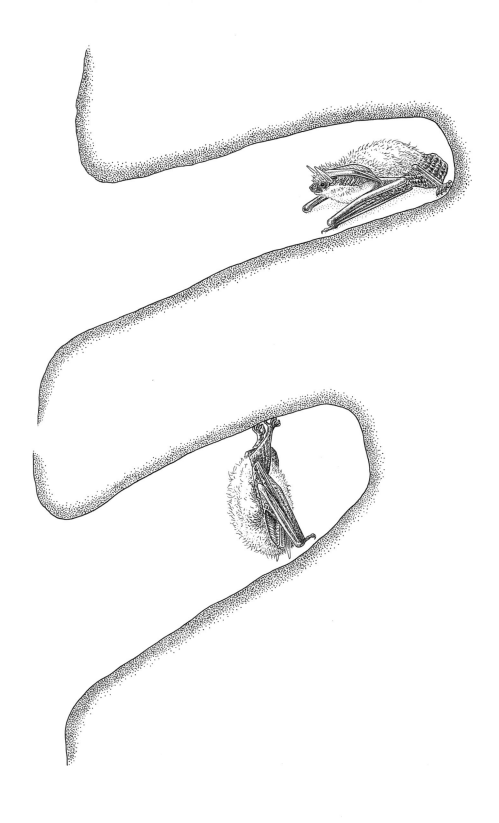

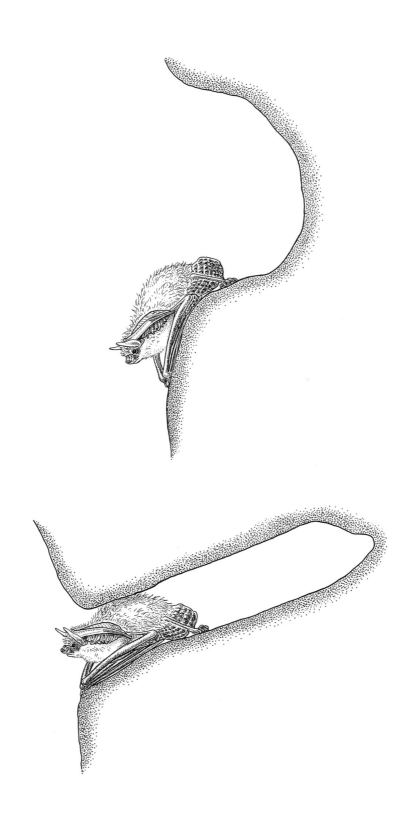

arouse relatively frequently compared with most other species. Daan (1973) found that among bats of three species of *Myotis*, arousal occurred on average every 20 days during mid winter. In October and in early spring activity was clearly nocturnal but during the middle of winter bats aroused at any time of day, and daylight flights occurred. This pattern was consistent with arousal being controlled by a free-running endogenous rhythm. In autumn and spring, with shorter periods of torpor, the rhythm was entrained to arousals at dusk. A similar situation was found to exist in the American species *Myotis lucifugus* by Thomas (1995a), using radio telemetry in order to avoid disturbing bats and so causing non-natural arousals. Bats aroused every 15–20 days at random times – there was no tendency to become active at dusk. Thomas considered that the frequency of arousal was most probably governed by water loss in bats and their consequent need to become active in order to drink.

Frequency of arousal in *P. auritus*, and the factors governing it, have been studied under semi-natural conditions (Hays *et al.*, 1992) and are discussed below.

WINTER ACTIVITY

Bats which arouse from torpor may then leave the hibernaculum and fly actively. Stebbings (1966, 1970) reported intermittent activity among both *P. auritus* and *P. austriacus* throughout winter, including one flight at midday on a January day when the air temperature was below 0°C and snow was lying. Avery (1985) investigated winter activity in *P. pipistrellus* in southern England and found that bats emerged during all winter months, that activity levels were higher on warm, calm nights and that level of activity was correlated with daytime temperature and not with the temperature the night before.

The primary function of winter flights is not clear. Feeding may take place during them (Ransome, 1968; Avery, 1985) and both Avery (1985) and Brigham (1987) suggested that the need to feed was the most important stimulus. However, Speakman and Racey (1989) concluded, from a study on captive *P. pipistrellus*, that hibernating bats would die of dehydration before they starved and that winter flights were initiated by the need to drink. They suggested that bats which fed during winter flights did so in order to cover the energetic cost of the flight, but that this was not their main purpose. Because in a natural situation bats almost always eat and drink during flights, it is difficult to separate the two activities. In an attempt to clarify the situation in *P. auritus*, Hays *et al.* (1992) investigated the daily food and water consumption and the individual probability of emergence in a captive colony. The bats were kept in a free-flight enclosure in which they were exposed to natural photoperiod and environmental temperature and where they had unlimited access to drinking water but only periodic access to food. They hibernated in a small wooden box inside the enclosure. Activity was monitored by two Doppler radar units interfaced to a microcomputer. During the experiment, which took place between January and March, bats were subjected to 11 days with access to water only, then 14 days with access to food and water, 11 days with water only and finally 15 days with food and water. The bats were weighed at the beginning and end of each period, but otherwise were completely undisturbed. Physical conditions in the roost box were within the range found in natural hibernacula – the mean

FIG 8.2 *Hibernation sites commonly occupied by* P. austriacus.

relative humidity was 82% and the temperature was 3.4–12.4°C. The results of the study showed that the probability that bats would emerge increased when there was food available and when it was warmer. Food consumption was significantly and positively correlated with the mean temperature at night in the flight enclosure; bats were more active and ate and drank more on warmer nights. When food was not available, bats emerged on 14 out of 22 nights and when food was available, they emerged on 28 out of 29 nights. Emergence thus occurred frequently even when food was not available, suggesting that in this species winter flights may be almost a daily occurrence except in very cold weather. The authors proposed that, in *P. auritus*, winter flights may not be initiated by the onset of either dehydration or starvation. Rather, at typical winter temperatures, bats may fly whenever possible, almost daily, in order to ensure that neither water nor food reserves approach critical levels. Prolonged bouts of torpor (more than a few days) only occur if ambient temperature drops to less than about 4°C.

Hays *et al.*'s (1992) study also showed that winter activity in *P. auritus* was strictly nocturnal. The time of initial activity was strongly correlated with the time of sunset (Figure 8.3), with first emergence occurring a mean interval of 64.4 min after sunset. It therefore appears that, in this species, frequent and regular activity in winter prevents the endogenous rhythm controlling arousal from becoming free-running and maintains entrainment to the light–dark cycle. Daylight flying does occasionally occur (Speakman, 1990), but probably only in response to extended cold spells and subsequent long periods of torpor.

The reason why *P. auritus* flies more frequently in winter than many other species may be connected with its habit of gleaning much of its food (Chapter 3). While most bat species will only be able to feed on nights when the air temperature is above the threshold for insect flight (which varies for different species but is in the range of 5–10°C; Taylor, 1963; Rydell, 1989a), long-eared bats are able to glean insects crawling on vegetation at lower temperatures. Their foraging method also allows them to feed on diapausing insects

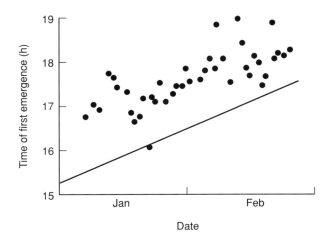

FIG 8.3   *The time of first emergence of* P. auritus *hibernating in semi-natural conditions, plotted against date during January and February. The line represents the time of sunset at 57 °N (reproduced with permission from Hays* et al., *1992).*

(Roer, 1969). There is thus more accessible food available to long-eared bats than to non-gleaning species, even on colder nights. However, they are more active on warmer nights, and during mild spells in winter they spend less time in torpor and feed for longer (Hays *et al.*, 1992). They also drink more on nights when food is available, suggesting that most of the water drunk is to balance the water loss incurred as a result of staying active and feeding.

EFFECTS OF DISTURBANCE ON HIBERNATING BATS

Disturbance inside hibernacula has long been considered a cause of the decline of bat populations. Besides deliberate destruction of colonies, inadvertent disturbance by tourists and speleologists and by conservationists and biologists monitoring population is thought to have had a detrimental effect. Disturbance causes unnatural arousal in hibernating bats, which then use up energy resources and may in consequence run out of energy and die before the end of winter. Large-scale handling and ringing of hibernating bats was identified as having a major adverse effect on bat numbers (Punt, 1970), and Gaisler *et al.* (1981) demonstrated that population reductions in some cave-dwelling species were a direct consequence of their own research activities. Stebbings (1966, 1969) noted that handling and weighing a long-eared bat caused it to lose 0.18 g per day, which he estimated to be 3–4 times the normal daily weight loss of a torpid bat. Therefore a bat handled six times during a winter could lose 3–4 weeks' worth of hibernation time due to loss of fat and this could make the difference between surviving and not doing so. Krzanowski (1961) reported similar weight losses due to handling in cave-dwelling bats in Poland.

As a result of findings such as these, guidelines were drawn up recommending that visits to hibernacula should be restricted to 2–3 per winter and bats should not be handled, photographed using flash or exposed to bright torchlight, excessive noise or smoking (Hutson and Mickleburgh, 1988). However, the relative effects of different stimuli were unknown, so in a series of laboratory experiments on captive bats, Speakman *et al.* (1991b) assessed the frequency and magnitude of arousals provoked by various tactile and non-tactile stimuli. Bats of six species including *P. auritus* were kept in a cool flight room where food and water were constantly available. Individuals were weighed and then placed in a respiratory chamber at a temperature of 1–5°C through which cool air flowed; they were then left undisturbed until they had become torpid. After this, energy expenditure was calculated from oxygen consumption. Inside the chamber, bats were subjected to non-tactile stimuli which included torchlight, photographic flash, sound, human speech and bursts of warm air for 7–10 min. Tactile stimulus was provided by handling the bat in the chamber through a rubber glove fitted to the roof. A positive response was defined as a significant increase in energy expenditure above the pre-stimulation torpid rate, and response was monitored until the bat returned to torpor. The susceptibility of bats to all five non-tactile stimuli was low. *P. auritus* responded to only two of them – one individual to photographic flash and another to warm air. In both cases, the degree of disturbance was low and the time before the bat again became torpid was short. However, tactile stimulus elicited a response in every case and the frequency of response was significantly higher than that for non-tactile stimuli. The energy expenditure per response was also significantly higher (Figure 8.4); the authors calculated that the average extra energy expended by brown long-eared bats during a response to a non-tactile stimulus was 8 J, but that expended in response to a

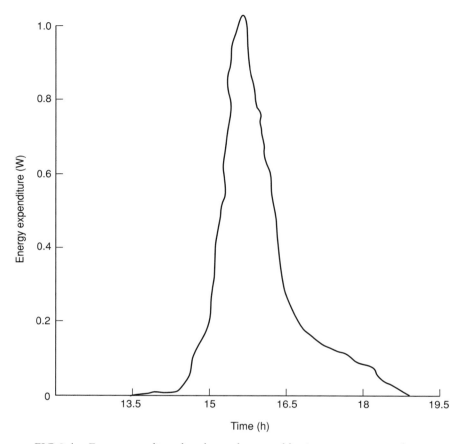

FIG 8.4 *Energy expenditure by a brown long-eared bat in response to a tactile stimulus administered during a period of torpidity in a respiratory chamber. The base line represents the energy expenditure in torpor before stimulation (reproduced with permission from Speakman* et al., *1991b).*

tactile one was 3578 J, or almost 450 times higher. While a non-tactile stimulus would cause a negligible decrease in the maximum possible duration of hibernation, a tactile one could result in hibernation time being shortened by up to 6–7 days. Heavy individuals used up more energy in these responses than did lighter ones, and the level of response was also higher at warmer ambient temperature – disturbances at 10°C had the greatest effect.

Thomas (1995b) investigated disturbance in a wild population of about 1300 *M. lucifugus* hibernating in a cave and his findings in this species conflicted with those of Speakman *et al.* (1991b) with respect to non-tactile stimuli. Infra-red motion detector data loggers set up in the cave recorded that visits by workers resulted in a dramatic increase in flight activity, beginning 30 min after the visit, peaking 1–1.75 h later and remaining significantly higher than normal for up to 8.5 h. Thomas attributed this activity to a 'knock on' effect; a few bats which had been active at the time of the visit following natural arousals became active and they flew in the cave, causing others to arouse. The difference in response between these bats and *P. auritus* may be due to their different hibernation behaviour – while *M. lucifugus* huddle in large clusters, *P. auritus* are solitary and therefore less susceptible to mass disturbance. Bats are also less susceptible to disturbance immediately after they re-enter torpor following arousal (Thomas, 1995b). Since long-eared bats arouse frequently, it is possible that they are always in this less susceptible state (termed the refractory period) when they are torpid. Finally, it has been suggested (Coles *et al.*, 1989; see Chapter 2) that long-eared bats fold their ears when torpid in order to reduce their sensitivity to aural stimuli and prevent frequent unnecessary arousals. The response to tactile stimuli is far more acute and has evolved as a form of predator-avoiding behaviour.

CHAPTER 9

Long-Eared Bats and Humans

THE preceding chapters have shown that long-eared bats are among the European species most closely associated with humans and that their behaviour, ecology and survival are strongly influenced by the activities of people. Interaction with humans has both beneficial and detrimental effects on these bats – while habitat destruction, urbanization and the large-scale use of chemicals on crops and roof timbers are undoubtedly bad influences, we have for many years provided long-eared bats with shelter, warmth, hibernacula and foraging areas. There is an argument that *P. austriacus* might not have become a European species at all had it not been provided with warm lofts in which to roost, cellars in which to hibernate and gardens and orchards in which to forage.

The last 20 years have seen a significant increase in interest in bats both by conservationists and by the general public. Bats now have legal protection in most European countries and there is increasing awareness of the dangers they face and the need to prevent further population declines. Of all mammals, they have had one of the worst public images over the years, but with the advent of bat groups and their drive to educate the public about the realities, as opposed to the superstition, of bats, this is at last beginning to improve.

POSITIVE HUMAN INFLUENCES

The main benefits long-eared bats have obtained from humans are those of shelter, warmth and suitable places to hibernate. *P. austriacus* is almost always found in house or church lofts in summer, while *P. auritus* seems to depend more and more on similar roost sites, particularly at high latitude. Mining and quarrying operations have led to the existence of underground hibernation sites in areas where no natural caves exist, and this has allowed long-eared bats to colonize such areas. Cellars are also important hibernation sites. Gardens and orchards provide foraging sites, particularly for grey long-eared bats; because *Plecotus* species always forage close to roosts, the provision of these sites has allowed them to roost in places which would otherwise have been unsuitable. Deciduous and mixed woodland, which was often planted round large country houses in the eighteenth and nineteenth centuries, has had the same effect, with particular benefit to *P. auritus*.

THREATS TO BATS

Habitat Destruction

Loss of deciduous woodland arguably presents the most serious threat to long-eared bats. Large-scale arable farming has led to the removal of many wooded areas. The associated loss of hedges has also removed essential flyways along which long-eared bats move between foraging sites, thus making many sites inaccessible. The move towards intensive grazing of livestock has had the same effect. Heavily fertilized and grazed fields produce little diversity of insects and no tree cover and are thus unsuitable foraging sites. Destruction of woodland and of flyways has removed protection from predators as well as access to insect food and has made large areas of land into 'no-go' areas for bats. Coniferous plantations, particularly large ones, are less favourable foraging sites than deciduous or mixed woodland. When long-eared bats do forage there, they have been found to use the edges and to avoid the interior (Entwistle *et al.*, 1996); most of a large, densely planted forest will thus not be used.

Another threat connected with modern agriculture is barbed wire. *P. auritus* has been found among several bat species which face a very real danger of becoming impaled during foraging, and newly-flying juveniles are most at risk (Hinkel and Rackow, 1994). Barbed wire is generally dangerous to wildlife and these authors suggested that caring farmers might consider replacing it with other wire. Accidents to young bats also occur with cacti and other thorny plants, but no practical solution to this hazard could be suggested.

Roost Destruction

Long-eared bats require large old houses in rural areas in which to roost (Chapter 6), and these are declining in number. Although some other house-dwelling species such as pipistrelles have adapted to use modern suburban housing estates, these are not a suitable alternative for *Plecotus* species. *P. austriacus* is better adapted to live in towns than is *P. auritus* because it can forage in gardens and parks, but it still requires old houses with large gardens, which are in short supply in the inner parts of cities. Also, modern policies on domestic hygiene do not, in general, include the concept of humans sharing their houses with other species (except those kept as pets), and thus many house owners insist that bat colonies are removed or excluded. Deliberate destruction or persecution of colonies is also a serious problem, although legal protection and public education has reduced this threat to some extent.

Poisoning

Crop spraying and treatment of roof timbers against wood-boring insects expose bats to the dangers of chemical poisoning. Extensive spraying of crops, particularly with organochlorines, leads to a build-up of residues in insects, which are then eaten by the bats. Long-eared bats, because they roost in direct contact with timbers in attics, are also highly vulnerable to poisoning by the chemicals used in timber treatment; this is discussed below.

Disturbance

As discussed in Chapter 8, long-eared bats are vulnerable to disturbance in hibernacula and also to deliberate destruction while they are hibernating. Summer colonies are more tolerant of disturbance in the roost than are many European species, but excessive upheaval can cause them to abandon roosts. There is also evidence that excessive capture, handling and ringing during study by scientists may be detrimental.

BATS AND THE LAW

In Britain, bats of all species have full legal protection under the Wildlife and Countryside Act 1981. Under this act, it is illegal for anyone not in possession of an appropriate licence intentionally to kill, injure or handle a bat of any species, to possess or offer for sale a bat, whether alive or dead (unless it was obtained legally) or to disturb a roosting bat. All procedures such as ringing, radio telemetry, photography inside roosts and handling bats inside or outside roosts for scientific purposes require special research licences (issued by Scottish Natural Heritage, English Nature or the Countryside Council for Wales, depending on the country where the work is to be carried out), and visits to houses which involve entering roosts require the possession of a Roost Visitor's licence. All work concerned with visits to hibernacula also requires to be licensed. The only bats which may be handled without a licence are those in the living space (not the attic) of a dwelling house; these may be removed gently and placed outside. The law also allows sick or injured bats to be tended or to be moved in order to obtain help for them.

Roosts, as well as bats, are fully protected under the act. It is an offence to damage, destroy or obstruct access to any place which bats use for shelter or protection, whether bats are actually present or not, except if that place is the living space of a house. Before any such action is taken, the appropriate statutory nature conservation body must be consulted and allowed time in which to advise. All procedures such as timber treatment, re-roofing, rewiring or plumbing in attics where bats roost (even if there are no bats in residence at the time) require prior consultation and advice from Scottish Natural Heritage, English Nature or the Countryside Council for Wales. The above is a general guide only and further details may be obtained from Sections 9–11, 16–27 and 69 of the Wildlife and Countryside Act 1981. Most other European countries have laws which provide similar protection for bats.

The Wildlife and Countryside Act has been criticized because it affords equal protection to all bat species and may be considered unnecessary for the most abundant bats such as pipistrelles. The reasons for the blanket protection are the alarming decline in numbers which has taken place in recent years among all species including pipistrelles (Stebbings, 1988) and the difficulty in distinguishing between species. The latter point is illustrated very well by long-eared bats – *P. austriacus* is one of Britain's rarest bats, while *P. auritus* is probably our second commonest species and in less urgent need of protection. However, if both were not protected, then anybody prosecuted for harming a grey long-eared bat could claim that they thought it was brown! If experts have difficulty telling the two apart, it is unreasonable to expect members of the general public to be able to do so. Extra protection may be given to rarer species by the creation of SSSIs (Sites of Special Scientific Interest) at their roosts or hibernacula (Mitchell-Jones *et al.*, 1993). The guidelines for the selection of sites to be given SSSI status (published in 1989 by the Nature Conservancy Council) specify that all traditional breeding roosts of *P. austriacus* be included, and certain mixed assemblages of different species are also protected in this way.

PUBLIC RELATIONS

Bat workers have long contended that Dracula has a lot to answer for. The myth of bats flying around castles late at night and turning into blood-sucking vampires has, over many years, had a very strong grip on the collective public imagination. Because bats are difficult to study, nocturnal and slightly mysterious, superstitions that they suck blood and get caught in human hair have persisted and it is an uphill task persuading people that they are, in reality, likeable animals which do very little harm to anybody and are wonderful examples of evolutionary diversity. If Beatrix Potter had written about a bat, it might all have been different!

The formation of local bat groups has been a major asset in improving bats' public image. There are now groups of bat enthusiasts in most areas of Britain and they are able to give talks to school groups and others about bats, their biology and habits. The more people understand these animals, the less they fear them. Bat group members are also able to visit householders who have become unwilling hosts to colonies of bats and to give them advice and information. With help and support of this kind, many roost owners come not only to tolerate their bats, but also to like and protect them.

Because long-eared bats live in apices of roofs, they are easily visible to roost owners and are thus among the species most often reported to bat groups. The most frequently given reasons for householders wishing to exclude bats from their homes are smell, accumulation of droppings and urine, noise, fear of damage to property and fear of health hazards. Because long-eared colonies are mostly small (fewer than 30 bats), noise and smell are not so much of a problem as they are with species which live in much larger colonies. They are, in any case, relatively quiet bats and it is rare to hear them from outside the roost. Accumulation of droppings is also a less serious problem than in many other species because of their small colonies, although over many years they can build up under the ridge where the bats roost. Where they are a problem, bat groups have eased the situation by removing droppings from attics (they make excellent garden compost) and then placing a row of sheets of newspaper under the ridge to collect any more. On subsequent 'clean-up' visits, the newspapers can be removed and replaced. In *Plecotus* roosts, another problem is caused by the bats' habit of flying inside the roost. This results in scattered droppings and sticky patches of urine round the attic, often on owners' possessions which have been stored there. The only answer to this seems to be to cover stored items with dust sheets which can be taken outside, shaken and replaced periodically.

When householders are afraid of bats damaging the structure of their house, roost visitors are able to reassure them that no bats chew woodwork or build nests, as do rodents, and there is no danger of electric wiring being damaged. The main danger to humans, as well as to bats, is that a bat may fall into an uncovered water tank and drown. Since this could present an obvious health hazard to humans, householders are strongly advised to cover water tanks in attics where bats roost. Long-eared bats are in particular danger from drowning in attic tanks because they fly inside roosts, and juveniles making their first practice flights are especially vulnerable. There is also a danger from basins and buckets placed in attics to catch rainwater from roof leaks. In order to prevent unnecessary deaths and to avoid having smelly dead bats in the attic, it is advisable to cover such containers with fine mesh to prevent bats from falling in.

Bats in the tropics are carriers of the fungal disease histoplasmosis and of viral rabies. Histoplasmosis is not a problem in Europe, but in recent years a rabies-like virus has been identified and occurs very rarely in several bat species in Europe. In June 1996, a Daubenton's bat, *Myotis daubentonii*, found in a distressed state in a south coast port in England, was discovered to be infected with the same virus (European Bat Lyssavirus type 2). The bat had probably arrived from mainland Europe on a ship and there was no evidence that this was other than a rare, isolated incident in Britain; over 2000 freshly dead bats have been tested for rabies infection during the last 10 years and all have been negative. The incidence of bat rabies in Europe is extremely low, and there have been no cases of the virus being passed from bats to other mammals. The risk from bats is therefore minimal, but because of the seriousness of the disease members of the public are currently advised not to handle bats which are obviously distressed or in unusual places such as lying on the ground. Instead, they should contact the relevant statutory nature conservation body or their local bat group to deal with the situation.

EFFECTS OF RESEARCH ON BATS

It is a source of concern among bat research workers that their activities in the field and the techniques they use may adversely affect bat populations or cause colonies to abandon roosts. Unless dead bodies are found, data are difficult to collect because bats are small, mobile and may disappear leaving no evidence of their fate.

Disturbance in Summer Roosts

Excessive disturbance inside roosts may cause colonies to leave, but in general long-eared bats are less susceptible than many other species. Because of the nature of their roosts, they are more likely to move into less accessible roof compartments following disturbance than to abandon the roost altogether. When abandonment does occur, it is usually temporary and, since long-eared bats frequently move to cool alternative roosts in summer (Entwistle, 1994), it is, in any case, often difficult to attribute such desertion to disturbance.

Disturbance in Hibernacula

This has been discussed in Chapter 8. The consensus of opinion appears to be that touching hibernating *Plecotus* bats should be avoided as much as possible. Non-tactile stimuli cause far less disturbance, but in general studies on hibernating bats should only be carried out for very good reasons.

Transmitters

The effects of attaching radio transmitters to small species such as long-eared bats have also been discussed (Chapter 4). Provided the weight of the transmitter does not exceed a maximum of 10% of the weight of the bat, adverse effects are not apparent on adults. Workers in Europe have avoided tagging juveniles or pregnant females in order to minimize the stress caused, and transmitters have deliberately been attached to larger individuals.

Ring Damage

During early banding studies (e.g. Herreid *et al.*, 1960), rings applied to bats were found to cause injuries, but design has improved over the years and large-scale damage to bones or wing membranes is now less common. Barclay and Bell (1988) stress that rings should be applied loosely enough to slide freely along the forearm but not so loosely that they could slide over the wrist or elbow. In a long-term study of *P. auritus* in Scotland (Entwistle *et al.*, 1994), 526 bats were ringed over 13 years. Significant ring damage was not reported among bats which were recaptured, although occasional injuries were found. The study used rings marketed by the Mammal Society; these have been found to cause minimal injury. Perez-Barberia (1991) reported that 8.2% of adult *P. austriacus* recaptured after ringing showed signs of forearm or patagium damage. Damage among this species was higher than in others in the area of Spain where the study was carried out, and the degree depended on the quality of rings used. Most ringing injuries are caused by bats chewing at rings, and *P. austriacus* are relatively aggressive bats (Stebbings, 1970) which may therefore have a higher tendency to chew rings than have other species. More data are needed, but it appears that caution should meanwhile be exercised if grey long-eared bats have to be banded.

The DLW Technique

This method of investigating energy expenditure (Chapter 5) involves taking blood samples from and injecting bats peritoneally with water containing labelled isotopes of oxygen and hydrogen. Among some small mammals, use of the technique has been associated with reduced survival rates linked to suborbital bleeding (Frase *et al.*, 1990). Speakman and Racey (1987) used it to investigate energy budgets in *P. auritus* and the bats used were also ringed as part of a longer term population study. Entwistle *et al.* (1994) compared the estimated survival rate of recaptured bats which had been subjected to DLW treatment with that of ones which had not in order to investigate the long-term effects of the technique. Recapture rates of bats caught more than 6 months after initial ringing suggested that the treatment had no significant effect on long-term survival, other than the initial effects of capture, handling and ringing.

REMEDIAL TIMBER TREATMENT

Vulnerability of Bats

Around the time that the Wildlife and Countryside Act 1981 came into effect, a number of cases of bats dying in attics following remedial treatment of roof timbers against insect or fungal infestations were attributed to poisoning by the chemicals used (Jeffries, 1972) and such poisoning was considered by conservationists to be a major cause of declines in bat numbers (Stebbings and Griffiths, 1986). Voûte (1980–81) reported high mortality in a colony of *Myotis dasycneme* following treatment, in their absence, of their roost with a mixture of lindane, PCP and DDT, and numerous other records from around Europe also pointed to the susceptibility of bats to these chemicals.

Bats are more vulnerable to remedial timber treatment in houses than are other mammals for a number of reasons. They roost in direct contact with roof timbers and spend most of their time there – in summer, long-eared bats spend at least 18 h inside the roost every day. They are small and therefore their faces are close to the roof beams during roosting and they breathe air from a narrow boundary layer which, due to imperfect mixing, contains a higher concentration of any pesticide vapour than does air further from the wood (Mitchell-Jones *et al.*, 1989). Bats also groom themselves thoroughly every day, and during this activity they lick their fur and flight membranes and may ingest any pesticide which has rubbed off onto them. The possession of wing membranes gives bats a high surface area/volume ratio and thus makes them very vulnerable to picking up large amounts of chemical. Natural oils in their fur and from facial glands may further compound the problem by dissolving lipid-soluble pesticides. Bats also undergo considerable weight changes due to mobilization of fat, for example during hibernation or in the period following weaning in juveniles. At such times organochlorines in the body fat become more concentrated in remaining lipids, including those in the brain. Deaths of bats due to elevated levels of organochlorines in the brain have been reported following migration, and also in British species at the end of hibernation (Jeffries, 1972).

Although not as common as the pipistrelle in Britain, *P. auritus* is the species most frequently encountered by surveyors in roof spaces (Mitchell-Jones *et al.*, 1989), probably because long-eared bats enter roof voids while pipistrelles tend to roost under eaves or in similar crevices. Long-eared bats choose to roost in the parts of attics most likely to be sprayed during treatment, and are therefore probably the species most at risk from chemicals. It is significant that, in Britain, more reported instances of dead bats being found following timber treatment have involved long-eared bats than any other species in recent years (Mitchell-Jones *et al.*, 1989). Roer (1987) similarly recorded that both *P. auritus* and *P. austriacus* have suffered high mortality from the use of organochlorines in Germany.

Chemicals Used

Surface spraying against infestations of the furniture beetle, *Anobium punctatum* (woodworm), is by far the most frequently used form of remedial treatment, accounting for about 90% of all treatments carried out in Britain. Most chemicals used are therefore insecticides, and they are usually applied in hydrocarbon solvents or, for recently introduced chemicals, in water-based emulsions. Until the late 1980s, treatment was almost always with organochlorine chemicals. Dieldrin was withdrawn by voluntary agreement in 1984, but lindane (gamma HCH or BHC) continued to be used despite its known high toxicity to mammals. In infestations where the death watch beetle, *Xestobium rufovillosum*, is involved, higher concentrations of insecticide and the application of pastes or pressure injection are frequently considered necessary because of the more serious structural damage this beetle can do.

Pyrethroids, which are artificial forms of the naturally occurring insecticide pyrethrum (a plant extract), were developed at the Rothampstead Institute and became commercially available during the 1980s. They are now widely used, despite initial reservations in the industry that they might be more expensive and less durable than lindane. Studies (Baker and Berry, 1980; Berry, 1983) have shown them to be as effective as lindane and probably even longer lasting because they suffer less from volatile loss. The two commercially available forms, permethrin and cypermethrin, can be used effectively in roof spaces at concentrations which make the cost of spraying an attic with them very similar to that of spraying it with lindane.

When infestations such as dry rot are present, fungicide sprays are used. In the past, 'dual purpose' sprays were often applied in the hope of preventing fungi from appearing, but these were not effective, since surface spraying is of little use in remedial treatment of fungal deterioration and provides little protection against future infestations (Mitchell-Jones *et al.*, 1989). For many years the fungicide used for almost all treatments was pentachlorophenol (PCP), but concern about its effect on human health has now reduced its use to a few serious cases, and it is usually applied as a paste. Other fungicides used include tributyltin oxide (TBTO), Borester-7 and metal soaps such as zinc naphthanate, zinc octoate and copper naphthanate.

Toxicity to Bats

Although lindane was suspected, from evidence in the field in several European countries, to be highly toxic to bats, and although it was formerly used to kill bats deliberately to rid houses of them (Taylor, 1987), commercial companies which manufactured and applied the chemical were able to claim that evidence of its harmfulness was anecdotal and did not exclude other possibilities, such as that affected bats had ingested lethal substances while feeding. In order to establish the dangerous nature of timber treatment chemicals to bats, laboratory experiments under controlled conditions were undertaken (Racey and Swift, 1986). The experiments involved pipistrelles (*P. pipistrellus*), but there has never been any evidence that they are any more or less susceptible to organochlorine poisoning than other species, and it is generally accepted that all European bats, including both long-eared species, are equally vulnerable. In the experiments, groups of pipistrelles were kept in plywood-lined cages which had been treated with various chemicals in accordance with their manufacturers' instructions. In all cases where the cages had been treated with either lindane or PCP or a mixture of the two, all the bats died within a few days. TBTO was found to cause higher mortality than occurred in untreated control cages, but the increase was not statistically significant. Lindane and PCP were fatal to bats even in a cage which had been treated 14 months previously, indicating little reduction in toxicity with time. When bats were prevented by an inner cage made of nylon netting from roosting in direct physical contact with treated wood, they still died, indicating that breathing vapour from the chemicals was also fatal. Bats in cages treated with permethrin, cypermethrin, deltamethrin, copper naphthanate, Borester-7 or zinc octoate survived as well as did those in untreated control cages, indicating that these chemicals had low toxicity to bats. Boyd *et al.* (1988) confirmed and extended Racey and Swift's (1986) findings with respect to lindane. Their experiments involved keeping groups of pipistrelles in large outdoor enclosures; each contained five pine roosting boxes, four of which had been treated with lindane. Initially, the boxes were treated at a lower concentration than is used commercially in order to investigate sublethal effects, but in a later experiment they were treated at a level similar to that used in roof spaces. The bats displayed no preference for roosting in the untreated box and results showed that, at the higher concentration level, five out of seven bats died. Carcase analysis showed that all, including the two which survived, contained very high levels of lindane. The levels in the survivors were as high as the levels in those which died, but the survivors were significantly heavier and so may have been more resistant to the toxic effects.

The above experiments showed clearly that both lindane and PCP are lethal to bats. Lindane is picked up very easily from treated surfaces, and a whole body level of about 30 ppm caused death in pipistrelles (Boyd *et al.*, 1988). In a number of fatal incidents involving wild bats where lindane was implicated, the levels were found to be at least as high as this and the contorted positions of the dead bats confirmed that lindane poisoning had occurred. As a result of the experiments and of this sort of evidence in the wild, the use of lindane in attics where bats roost is now illegal under the Wildlife and Countryside Act 1981. All commercially available preparations containing lindane must contain a warning that they are dangerous to bats and must not be used in roosts. All major manufacturers now produce suitable treatments based on permethrin or cypermethrin, which are safe for use in roosts. Spraying must be carried out when bats are not present. When fungicides are needed, zinc or copper naphthanate, Borester-7, zinc octoate and acypetacs-zinc can legally be used in roosts provided bats are not present at the time, but TBTO should be avoided. PCP is now rarely used for spraying and its use in pastes is confined to a few exceptional cases.

STREET LAMPS AND URBANIZATION

Because many insects are positively phototactic, street lamps, which are a common feature in villages and small towns as well as in cities, are likely to affect the distribution of flying insects at night. Some bat species are able to exploit the situation by feeding on moths and other insects round the lights, but others appear to avoid them.

Types of Lamp

The commonest types of street lamp in Europe are mercury vapour lights, which give out a blue-white light and emit a considerable fraction of their energy in the ultraviolet part of the spectrum; low-pressure sodium lamps, which give out a monochromatic orange light; and high-pressure sodium lamps, which give out bright orange light but, because they contain mercury vapour as well as sodium, also emit some ultraviolet light. Mercury vapour lamps were found to attract five times more insects in Sweden (Rydell, 1992) and eight times more insects in southern England (Blake *et al.*, 1994) than did either sodium type. High-pressure sodium lamps attracted significantly more insects than did low-pressure ones in the same study (Rydell, 1992).

Attractiveness to Bats

Two surveys involving travelling by car along lit and unlit stretches of road and using sight and ultrasonic bat detectors to monitor bat numbers (Rydell, 1992; Blake *et al.*, 1994; Rydell and Racey, 1995) showed that bat density was significantly higher along stretches of road with streetlamps than along unlit stretches and that the highest bat activity occurred around mercury vapour lamps. Along roads lit by mercury vapour lamps in Britain and in Sweden, densities as high as 5 bats km^{-1} were recorded (Rydell and Racey, 1995).

Not all bat species exploit street lights. While individuals of fast-flying species known to use long-range calls and to feed in open situations (e.g. *Nyctalus, Eptesicus, Vespertilio* and *Pipistrellus* species) were found to forage round street lamps (Rydell, 1992), others, particularly *Myotis* species and *P. auritus*, appeared to avoid them and were only detected in unlit areas (Figure 9.1). Other bats which do not appear to exploit streetlamps for

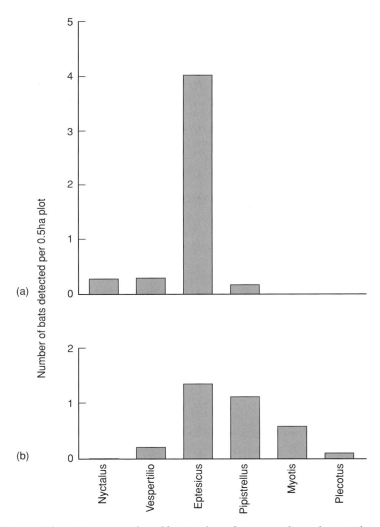

FIG 9.1   *The minimum number of foraging bats of six genera detected per 0.5 ha plot in southern Sweden (a) in villages with street lamps (n = 8 plots) and (b) in other habitats away from street lamps (n = 35 plots). Each plot was searched visually and using an ultrasonic bat detector. Long-eared bats (Plecotus) were detected only in areas away from lights (reproduced with permission from Rydell, 1992).*

feeding include *Rhinolophus* species (Jones *et al.*, 1995). These bats all fly relatively slowly and manoeuvrably and use either very long, high-frequency, narrow-band calls or broad-band echolocation pulses with fast repetition rate; both types of call are suitable for foraging in cluttered situations (Baagøe, 1987). It is thus possible that *P. auritus* does not forage round street lamps either because its method of foraging is unsuitable for catching insects flying fast in open situations or because it avoids the light in order to reduce exposure to predators.

Bauerova (1982) observed *P. austriacus* foraging round street lamps in the Czech Republic. Although large numbers of small moths swarmed round a light, the bat ignored them and, on eight occasions, pursued and caught large moths in fast flight. Grey long-eared bats thus appear to differ from brown ones in this aspect of behaviour; they do exploit streetlamps and use the opportunity provided to pursue large moths in free flight. Avoiding flying in the light does not seem to be important to this species. Another observation from Europe confuses the issue further; Barataud (1990) studied a mixed colony of *P. auritus* and *P. austriacus* and during this study he analysed perch remains from under a willow tree situated directly beneath a street lamp. Over 60% of the remains were from larvae and adults of moth species whose larvae feed on willow leaves, and it thus appeared that at least one *Plecotus* bat exploited insects in this tree. The author did not state which species used the perch – if it was *P. auritus*, then the presence of the streetlight does not seem to have deterred it from feeding there, mainly by gleaning. If the bat was an individual of *P. austriacus*, then it must have gleaned far more than this species is reported to do, in order to have caught the larvae. It is possible that *P. auritus* are not deterred by light and that they do glean around street lamps on occasions when the opportunity arises. If this is the case, then their normal avoidance of street lamps is due to their inability to exploit a situation in which moths are flying fast and in the open, rather than to a need to avoid predation. Further research is needed.

Implications for Long-eared Bats

The limited evidence so far available indicates that *P. austriacus* is able to exploit street lamps for foraging but that *P. auritus*, in general, is not. Illuminated roads will probably continue to be available in the future, unlike many other bat habitats which are becoming fewer, and this will benefit *P. austriacus*. There has, however, been a tendency in recent years in Europe to replace mercury vapour lights with sodium ones, which use less energy and which do not require the processing or handling of poisonous mercury (Rydell and Racey, 1995), and sodium lamps have been shown to attract far fewer insects. They are thus of less benefit to grey long-eared bats than are mercury vapour ones.

The effect of street lamps on *P. auritus* is uncertain. Rydell and Racey (1995) suggested that some species may avoid crossing lit areas and may thus be prevented by street lamps from reaching important foraging areas. This has not been shown to be the case for *P. auritus*; Howard (1995) found that individuals commuting from a roost to foraging areas were not deterred by a powerful halogen light shining across their normal flyway. However, it is possible that a street lamp may attract moths to it from a considerable surrounding area. Dark parts of this area will thus contain few moths and so foraging there may become unprofitable.

Urbanization

P. austriacus thrives in villages and small towns where there are houses in which to roost and close-by gardens, orchards and parks in which to forage. It also appears to be well adapted to living in city suburbs in some regions – Gaisler and Bauerova (1985–6) found four nursery colonies in built-up areas in the city of Brno and frequently netted individuals in the suburbs. Because it does not depend on woodland but prefers to forage in places such as gardens and parks, it may be found in most urban situations except inner cities.

P. auritus, on the other hand, depends on woodland and rarely occurs in urban situations. Gaisler and Bauerova (1985–6) found these bats only occasionally around Brno and only on the extreme outer limits of the city. Entwistle *et al.* (1997) found no roosts within the city of Aberdeen, and Hanak (1969) and Gaisler (1979) similarly found no roosts within cities. *P. auritus* thrives in rural areas and in small villages. Increasing urbanization in many countries thus presents a major threat to the species and has been suggested as a reason for population declines in recent years (Speakman *et al.*, 1991a).

BAT BOXES

Artificial roosts in the form of boxes similar to bird nesting boxes are used by bats in some areas and schemes involving their use can be successful in establishing bat populations, particularly in areas where few other roost sites exist. Early designs of bat box are similar to bird boxes except that entry is through a slit at the bottom instead of a round hole and the inside of the box is grooved to allow bats to cling to it (Figure 9.2). Boxes are made of untreated wood and hung on trees or buildings. Their orientation does not seem to be important, and in most schemes boxes are placed in groups, with individuals facing in several directions so that bats have a choice. Boxes have a removable lid to allow inspection. Their height does not seem to be critical with regard to whether or not bats use them, but in general they are placed as high as possible in trees to reduce the dangers of predation or vandalism. Apart from the original wooden boxes, several different designs are currently in use, including one made of a mixture of concrete and sawdust (Figure 9.3), which appears to be successful in attracting bats.

Bat box schemes have been found to be most successful, in terms of bats using them, when they are established in areas containing few buildings which could be used as roosts and no tree holes or other natural roosts. Large coniferous plantations are often in isolated areas and tree holes are rare in conifers; it is therefore not surprising that the most successful schemes are in coniferous forests (e.g. Altringham and Bullock, 1988; Boyd and Stebbings, 1989; Benzal, 1991). Schemes in upland areas have been reported to attract more bats than do those at lower altitude (Luger, 1977; Benzal, 1991), and this has been attributed to fewer alternative roosts being available at higher altitude.

Apart from their conservation purpose of providing roosts and attracting bats to new areas, bat boxes are popular with both the public and bat groups – they are a practical method of helping in bat conservation and, when they do attract bats, they can clearly be seen to be having a positive effect. They can also provide valuable information on bat populations. Long-term assessments of survival, sex ratios and population dynamics (Boyd and Stebbings, 1989; Benzal, 1991) have been made using bat box schemes.

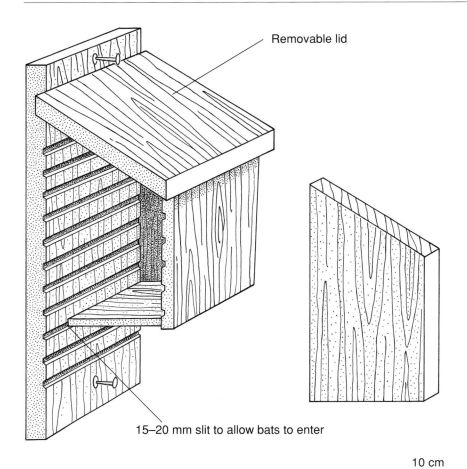

Removable lid

15–20 mm slit to allow bats to enter

10 cm

FIG 9.2 *A wooden bat box with one side removed, showing the grooved interior, removable lid and entry slit. The box is made of rough, untreated wood and is nailed to a tree or building.*

Use by Long-eared Bats

P. auritus is one of the European species which most frequently uses bat boxes and one of the few which forms nursery colonies in them. Because this species occupies tree holes, bat boxes resemble their natural roosts. They also make extensive use of woodland, where most bat box schemes are situated. Altringham and Bullock (1988) set up a scheme in a coniferous forest in south-east Scotland, in an area where there were very few alternative roost sites. Within 3 years, 60% of the boxes had been used. While *P. pipistrellus*, the most numerous species in the boxes, used them only for mating, the two other species found, *P. auritus* and *Myotis nattereri*, both formed nursery colonies. Stebbings and Walsh (1985) found that *P. auritus* was the commonest species using boxes in a scheme in northern England, while

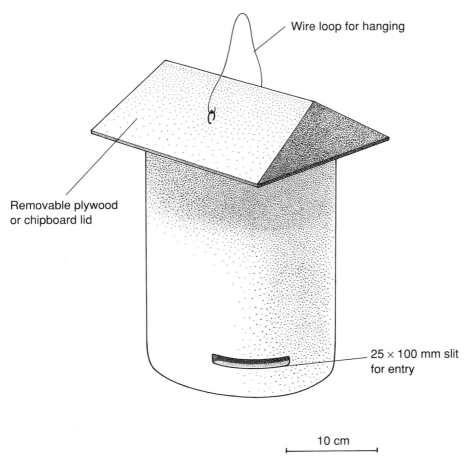

Wire loop for hanging

Removable plywood
or chipboard lid

25 × 100 mm slit
for entry

10 cm

FIG 9.3 *A concrete–sawdust bat box, consisting of a hollow cylinder with walls approximately 4 cm thick. There is a slit at the bottom for entry and the roof is removable to allow inspection. The box is hung from a tree branch by a wire loop.*

Bamford (1985) reported that this species was found in bird nest boxes in a larch (*Larix leptolepis*) plantation in Wales. Schwenke (1988) estimated that the installation of bat boxes to a density of 0.11 ha^{-1} and the increase in bird boxes to 0.66 ha^{-1} in a forest in Germany increased the bat population from 279 to 462 over a period of 5 years. In another part of Germany, Nagel and Nagel (1988) found that the installation of bat boxes in a forest area dramatically increased the population of bats, especially of *P. auritus*. Once attracted to the area by these boxes, bats also roosted in bird boxes which had previously been present but had not been occupied by bats.

Both Schwenke (1988) and Taake and Hildenhagen (1989) reported that *P. auritus* roosted preferentially in concrete–sawdust boxes rather than in wooden ones. Taake and Hildenhagen (1989) suggested this may have been because concrete–sawdust boxes have better insulation; they heat up more slowly than wooden ones when exposed to the sun and remain warm for longer, thus undergoing less fluctuation in temperature.

P. austriacus rarely uses bat boxes. As a strictly house-dwelling species which always seeks warm attics and which is not known to use tree holes, it appears to avoid boxes, and schemes in forest areas have had no success in attracting it. The only report of grey long-eared bats being found in boxes is from Poland (Kowalski and Lesinski, 1994), where more than half the 21 species known to occur were found in boxes, at least occasionally. *P. austriacus* used them rarely, and were only ever found in boxes attached to buildings. Thus, although boxes in forests appear to be of no use for conservation of this species, boxes on buildings may be of benefit in places where suitable house roosts are in short supply.

Practical Conservation Measures

As knowledge of the biology, ecology and behaviour of long-eared bats accumulates, it is becoming easier to identify the most important aspects of their conservation and to direct projects towards their specific needs. While recent legislation has concentrated on summer roosts, it is now becoming obvious that foraging habitats and hibernacula are also in need of protection.

Foraging Areas

Deciduous woodland should be protected, particularly areas close to *P. auritus* roosts. Where woodland is being destroyed on a large scale, it is sometimes possible to preserve parts of it, and even a fair-sized copse round a house can be sufficient to support a colony. Hedges, treelines and other features which may be used as flyways should also be preserved, since the absence of such features can make patches of woodland inaccessible. Small-scale projects to plant and protect joining strips of woodland between patches of forest and between roosts and foraging areas are currently being carried out in many areas and are beneficial to long-eared bats.

Where coniferous woodland dominates, the quality can be improved by dividing dense blocks of trees up by clearings and rides. Such practices will increase the edge habitat available and so benefit long-eared bats. Bat box schemes also make coniferous plantations more accessible by providing roost sites. If possible, the quality of coniferous woodland should be improved by the planting of some deciduous trees; even a line round the edge is of benefit. The planting of mixed or of deciduous woodlands in preference to purely coniferous ones should be encouraged wherever possible.

Tree Holes

Hollow trees and old, deciduous trees with hollow branches should be preserved wherever possible as potential roost sites. Such sites are typically used only as cool, temporary roosts (Entwistle, 1994) and so may be unoccupied most of the time; this does not make them any less important to the bats. Fuhrmann and Godmann (1991) investigated different types of cavity in deciduous trees and found that slow-flying species such as *P. auritus* and *Myotis bechsteinii* use low cavities, such as are found in old coppiced woods. Old trees and stumps are therefore important to long-eared bats and should be protected. When hollow trees have to be felled, they should always be carefully checked first for roosting bats – many unnecessary deaths occur during felling operations.

Roosts

Long-eared bats show a high degree of fidelity to nursery roosts. They have been shown to be selective in picking houses in which to roost (Entwistle *et al.*, 1997) and suitable houses may not be as plentiful as has been assumed until recently. Eviction of a colony could therefore have serious consequences and it is important for conservationists to make every effort to persuade roost owners to be tolerant of their bats. Advice and support are needed, and practical assistance such as with removing droppings from attics can make the difference between bats being allowed to stay and being excluded. Because of long-eared bats' vulnerability to timber treatment chemicals, vigilance is necessary in roosts to ensure that treatment is carried out with appropriate chemicals and in the absence of bats. Prosecution after bats are killed may prevent further incidents but does not help the dead bats. The energy and diligence of bat group members is invaluable in monitoring roosts and the health of the bats in them.

Old farm buildings, like tree holes, are important as temporary roosts. They should be preserved wherever possible and checked carefully for signs of roosting bats before being demolished or renovated.

Hibernacula

Besides protecting caves and mines, which is a conservation measure needed for most hibernating bats, help can also be provided for long-eared bats by building artificial hibernacula. Several projects in Germany have recently shown the benefits of such structures. Albers (1993, 1994) recorded that a conservation group, in cooperation with the German armed forces, renovated several old military bunkers and disused cellars and a derelict water pumping station. *P. auritus* was the species which made most use of the buildings, and bats moved in during the first winter after restoration was completed. Use was made by the bats of the crevices incorporated into the ceilings and walls. A similar project near Cologne (Buchen, 1992) involved the construction of an artificial gallery to replace some of the mines and quarries in the area which have been filled in or blocked up. Two years after construction, five species, including *P. auritus*, were found to hibernate in the gallery.

Other conservation projects on hibernacula have included surveys to amass information on the use of various structures. Rydell's (1989c) survey of storage cellars in Sweden emphasized their importance to *P. auritus* (Chapter 8) and Haensel (1994) reported that seven bat species hibernated in cellars round Brandenburg in Germany. His survey concentrated on collecting information which could be used to restore cellars in such a way as to make them suitable as bat hibernacula.

Bat conservation has made great strides during the last 10 years. Appreciation of the problem of declining numbers of individuals and the need to find and implement conservation measures have become firmly established and the public are beginning to see them as a group in need of protection and not as a pest. Considerable advances are also being made in our understanding of the ecological requirements of bats, and long-eared bats, as species which live in close proximity to humans, are among those whose needs are beginning to be understood. They are also very attractive animals which greatly help the conservationists' attempts to persuade the public to become more 'bat friendly'. There is, however, no room for complacency – these bats, their roosts and their habitats are still very much in need of active conservation. Because the general public interprets kindness to animals as meaning kindness to nice animals, it is essential to portray long-eared bats as nice animals. It is the responsibility of us all to protect and conserve our wildlife and to ensure a secure future for these beautiful and fascinating bats.

APPENDIX 1

Scientific and Common Names of Bat Species

Antrozous pallidus	pallid bat
Barbastella barbastellus	barbastelle
Cardioderma cor	African false vampire bat
Cloeotus percivali	short-eared trident bat
Corynorhinus mexicanus	Mexican big-eared bat
Corynorhinus rafinesquii	Rafinesque's, or eastern, big-eared bat
Corynorhinus townsendii ingens	Ozark big-eared bat
Corynorhinus townsendii townsendii	Townsend's, or western, big-eared bat
Corynorhinus townsendii virginianus	Virginia big-eared bat
Eptesicus fuscus	big brown bat
Eptesicus nilssonii	northern bat
Eptesicus serotinus	serotine
Euderma maculatum	spotted bat
Idionycteris phyllotus	Allen's big-eared bat
Lasiurus cinereus	hoary bat
Lasiurus cinereus semotus	Hawaiian hoary bat
Lavia frons	yellow-winged bat
Miniopterus schreibersii	long-fingered bat
Myotis bechsteinii	Bechstein's bat
Myotis blythii	lesser mouse-eared bat
Myotis dasycneme	pond bat
Myotis daubentonii	Daubenton's bat
Myotis emarginatus	notch-eared bat
Myotis evotis	long-eared *Myotis*
Myotis lucifugus	little brown bat
Myotis myotis	greater mouse-eared bat
Myotis mystacinus	whiskered bat
Myotis nattereri	Natterer's bat
Myotis septentrionalis	northern long-eared bat
Myotis sodalis	social bat
Nyctalus noctula	noctule
Otomops spp.	big-eared free-tailed bats

Pipistrellus pipistrellus	pipistrelle
Plecotus auritus	brown long-eared bat
Plecotus austriacus	grey long-eared bat
Plecotus taivanus	Taiwan long-eared bat
Plecotus teneriffae	Tenerife long-eared bat
Rhinolophus ferrumequinum	greater horseshoe bat
Rhinolophus hipposideros	lesser horseshoe bat
Tadarida brasiliensis	Mexican free-tailed bat
Vespertilio murinus	particoloured bat

APPENDIX 2

Care of Stranded or Injured Bats

STRANDED BATS

OCCASIONALLY, bats enter houses or other buildings and become trapped. After flying around inside for some time, they become exhausted and may later be found and rescued. Their immediate need is to be given food and water, after which most recover rapidly and can be released. Water is best offered on a very fine paintbrush. Initially, this can be brushed against the bat's lips, after which the bat will usually lap from the brush. In summer, enough insects to revive a bat can usually be caught with a butterfly net. Small flies, caddis flies or moths are all accepted by long-eared bats and are relatively easy to collect; they are best offered mashed up and held in a blunt pair of tweezers. When no insects are available, mashed mealworms (see below) can be given instead. At first, food may have to be pushed gently into the bat's mouth, but as it recovers it will snap at it avidly. Hungry, dehydrated bats are always torpid when found, but as they are fed they can be felt to warm up. Once warm and fully active, they should be released as soon as possible. If the whereabouts of the roost is known, the bat can be placed in it. If not, it should be released around dusk outside the building where it was found. Provided it is warm and active, it will fly from an outstretched hand of its own accord. It should not be thrown into the air because if it is not fully warmed up it may fall to the ground and be injured or even accidentally stood on.

INJURIES

Bats with serious injuries or infections require attention from a veterinary surgeon. Relatively few vets have much experience in dealing with bats, but there are some who specialize in treating this group. Local RSPCA officers, the Bat Conservation Trust (see below) or local veterinary surgeries can advise on how to obtain expert treatment.

Wing injuries are the commonest cause of disablement in bats. Those with broken finger bones usually recover and the bones sometimes heal on their own, usually through the formation of callouses round the break. In such cases, the bat will be able to fly again, but many bats with wing bone fractures do not regain the ability to fly. Broken humeri or forearms are far more serious. These can sometimes be pinned in larger species, but in bats as small as *Plecotus* pinning is rarely successful. In any case, infection is always a serious risk, and for many bats with these injuries, amputation of the wing is the only possible treatment. Many workers feel that humane destruction is a kinder alternative for the bat.

151

KEEPING BATS IN CAPTIVITY

The law allows sick or injured bats to be kept in captivity if they do not have a realistic chance of surviving in the wild, but it should be stressed that they should only be kept captive if there really is no alternative. Those who undertake the care should be aware that bats live long lives and that the commitment could be for a number of years. Many bat groups have among their members an expert carer who can advise on keeping bats and who may be prepared to take on the care of new cases. Captive bats in bat groups fulfil a useful publicity function – they can be taken to lectures and demonstrations to enable members of the public to see and handle live bats.

Cages made of wood or metal lined with wood are suitable for housing long-eared bats. The wood must be untreated and rough enough to allow bats to grip. Mesh on the top or front must be fine enough to prevent them from escaping and there should be a dark compartment for sleeping. Paper towels on the cage floor make cleaning easy. Bats which are capable of flight remain much healthier if they have daily access to a large room or enclosure where they can fly freely and safely. Water must be freely available, and is best provided in a shallow dish or a small bird feeder attached to the side of the cage. Where possible, bats should be fed on freshly caught insects such as moths or flies. This is not always practicable and such food can be supplemented with or replaced by mealworms (*Tenebrio* spp.), available from pet shops or by mail order. These should, however, be supplemented with vitamins, since they lack some nutrients found in wild insects. Vitamin supplements such as 'Vitament' may be sprinkled onto food or, in soluble form, added to drinking water. An adult *P. auritus* will require about 25–30 mealworms or 2.5–3.0 g of insects per day, although most carers feed to appetite, particularly if the bat is able to fly daily – those which cannot fly can become obese if overfed.

REARING BABY BATS

Rearing abandoned or orphaned infants is time-consuming, difficult and frequently unsuccessful – again, bat groups may be able to provide contact with experts in this field. A milk substitute has to be administered until the infant is about 4 weeks old, and this is best given through a pipette or on a very fine paintbrush. The most successful foods are reported to be diluted cow's milk (1 : 1 milk : water) or a bitch-milk substitute such as 'Lactol'. Baby bats have to be fed at least every 2–3 h throughout the day and after feeding the baby should be washed very gently with cotton buds dipped in water to simulate the grooming action of its mother. Infants should be kept at a constant temperature of about 30°C. Weaning is also a difficult process, since many captive juveniles seem very reluctant to start eating mealworms or insects – much time and patience is needed. It is generally considered that bats reared in captivity should not be released; bats have complex social behaviour, much of which is learned from conspecifics, and hand-reared infants do not acquire this learning and are unlikely to survive in the wild.

APPENDIX 3

Useful Contact Addresses in the UK

The Bat Conservation Trust (BCT)   15 Cloisters House, 8 Battersea Park Road, London SW8 4BG. Telephone 0171 627 2629. Fax 0171 627 2628. BCT is involved in education, advice and promotion of conservation of bats in Britain. It acts as a coordination centre for bat groups and is also actively involved in research concerned with bat conservation.

Local Bat Groups   There are around 90 of these, covering most areas in the country. The names and addresses of contact persons for individual groups can be obtained from BCT.

The Mammal Society   15 Cloisters Business Centre, 8 Battersea Park Road, London SW8 4BG. Telephone 0171 498 4358. Fax 0171 498 4459. This society promotes the study of mammals, including bats, by amateur naturalists and professional scientists. It designs and supplies bat rings and also produces a number of publications relevant to the study of bats.

Scottish Natural Heritage (SNH)   12 Hope Terrace, Edinburgh EH9 2AS. Telephone 0131 554 9797.

English Nature   Northminster House, Peterborough PE1 1UA. Telephone 01733 340345.

Countryside Council for Wales (CCW)   Plas Penrhos, Ffordd Penrhos, Bangor, Gwynedd LL57 2LQ. Telephone 01248 370444.

These three statutory nature conservation organizations are responsible for advising Government on nature conservation in the UK. They give advice on bat problems under the Wildlife and Countryside Act 1981, enforce protection for all bats under this law and also administer the licensing system.

World Wide Fund for Nature (WWF)   Panda House, Weyside Park, Godalming, Surrey GU7 1XR. Telephone 01483 426444.

Fauna & Flora International (FFI)   Great Eastern House, Tenison Road, Cambridge CB1 2DT. Telephone 01223 571000.

Vincent Wildlife Trust (VWT)   10 Lovat Lane, London EC3R 8DT. Telephone 0171 283 2089.

The above three voluntary organizations all include promotion of bat conservation in their work.

Royal Society for the Prevention of Cruelty to Animals (RSPCA) Causeway, Horsham, Sussex RH12 1HG. Telephone 01403 264181.

Scottish Society for the Prevention of Cruelty to Animals (SSPCA) 19 Melville Street, Edinburgh EH3 7PL. Telephone 0131 225 6418.

References

Abelencev, V., Pidoplicko, I.G. and Popov, B.M. (1956). Fauna Ukrainy 1. Ssavei. Insectivora, Chiroptera. AN. USSR *Inst. Zool:* 229–446.

Achyra, L. and Fenton, M.B. (1992). Echolocation behaviour of vespertilionid bats (*Lasiurus cinereus* and *Lasiurus borealis*) attacking airborne targets including arctiid moths. *Can. J. Zool.,* 70: 1292–1298.

Adam, M.D., Lacki, M.J. and Barnes, T.G. (1994). Foraging areas and habitat use of the Virginia big-eared bat in Kentucky. *J. Wildlife Management,* 58(3): 462–469.

Aellen, V. (1971). Le chauvre-souris *Plecotus austriacus* (Fischer) en Suisse. *Congr. Suisse Speleol. Neuchatel,* 1970, Act.4: 167–172.

Aellen, V. (1983–4). Migrations de chauves-souris en Suisse. Note complémentaire. *Myotis,* 21–22: 185–189.

Agee, H.R. (1967). Response of the acoustic cell of the bollworm and tobacco budworm to ultrasound. *J. Economic Entomol.,* 60: 366–369.

Agee, H.R. (1969). Response of flying bollworm moths and other tympanate moths to pulsed ultrasound. *Ann. Entomol. Soc. America,* 62: 801–807.

Ahlén, I. (1981). *Identification of Scandinavian bats by their sounds.* Report No.6, Dept. Wildlife Ecol. Swedish Univ. Agric. Sci.

Ahlén, I. and Gerell, R. (1989). Distribution and status of bats in Sweden. In: *European Bat Research 1987* (Hanak, V., Horacek, I. and Gaisler, J., eds). Charles University Press, Prague: 319–325.

Albers, S. (1993) Bau von Fledermauswinterquarterieren durch die Bundeswehr in Munster (Landkreis Soltau Fallingbostel). *Nyctalus, Berlin,* 4: 462–464.

Albers, S. (1994). Bau von funf Fledermaus-Winterquartieren in Raum Bispingen, Landkreis Soltau-Fallingbostel (nordostliches Niedersachsensen). *Nyctalus, Berlin,* 5: 191–195.

Aldridge, H.D.J.N. (1987). Turning flight of bats. *J. Exp. Biol.,* 128: 419–425.

Aldridge, H.D.J.N. and Brigham, R.M. (1988). Load carrying and manoeuverability in an insectivorous bat: a test of the 5% 'rule' of radio-telemetry. *J. Mamm.,* 69: 378.

Altringham, J.D. (1996). *Bats. Biology and Behaviour.* Oxford University Press, Oxford.

Altringham, J. and Bullock, D. (1988). Bat boxing in Fife. *Batchat (NCC),* 11: 4–7.

Anderka, F.W. and Angehrn, P. (1992). Transmitter attachment methods. In: *Wildlife Telemetry. Remote Monitoring and Tracking of Animals* (Priede, I.G. and Swift, S.M., eds). Ellis Horwood, Chichester: 135–146.

Anderson, M.E. and Racey, P.A. (1991). Feeding behaviour of captive brown long-eared bats, *Plecotus auritus. Anim. Behav.,* 42: 489–493.

Anderson, M.E. and Racey, P.A. (1993). Discrimination between fluttering and non-fluttering moths by brown long-eared bats, *Plecotus auritus. Anim. Behav.,* 46: 1151–1155.

Anthony, E.L.P. (1987). The role of the anterior pituitary and the hypothalamus in controlling reproductive cycles in bats. In: *Recent Advances in the Study of Bats* (Fenton, M.B., Racey, P.A. and Rayner, J.M.V., eds). Cambridge University Press, Cambridge: 421–439.

Arlettaz, R. (1996a). Feeding behaviour and foraging strategy of free-living mouse-eared bats, *Myotis myotis* and *Myotis blythii*. *Anim. Behav.*, **51**: 1–11.

Arlettaz, R. (1996b). Foraging behaviour of the gleaning bat *Myotis nattereri* (Chiroptera, Vespertilionidae) in the Swiss Alps. *Mammalia*, **60**(2): 181–186.

Arlettaz, R. and Perrin, N. (1995). The trophic niches of sympatric sibling *Myotis myotis* and *M. blythii*: do mouse-eared bats select prey? In: *Ecology, Evolution and Behaviour of Bats* (Racey, P.A. and Swift, S.M., eds). *Symp. Zool. Soc. London*, **67**: 361–376.

Arnold, H.R. (1993). *Atlas of Mammals in Britain*. Inst. Terr. Ecol., London: 64–67.

Aschoff, J. (1966). Circadian activity pattern with two peaks. *Ecology*, **47**(4): 657–662.

Audet, D. (1990). Foraging behaviour and habitat use by a gleaning bat, *Myotis myotis* (Chiroptera, Vespertilionidae). *J. Mamm.*, **71**(3): 420–427.

Avery, M.I. (1985). Winter activity of pipistrelle bats. *J. Anim. Ecol.*, **54**: 721–738.

Azzaroli-Puccetti, M.L. and Zava, B. (1988). New data on the Chiroptera of the Cape Verde Islands (North Atlantic). *Mus. Reg. di Scienze Nat. Boll. (Torino)*, **6**(2): 603–616.

Baagøe, H.J. (1980–81). Danish bats, status and protection. *Myotis*, **18–19**: 16–17.

Baagøe, H.J. (1987). The Scandinavian bat fauna: adaptive wing morphology and free flight in the field. In: *Recent Advances in the Study of Bats* (Fenton, M.B., Racey, P.A. and Rayner, J.M.V., eds). Cambridge University Press, Cambridge: 57–74.

Bagley, F. and Jacobs, J. (1985). Census technique for endangered big-eared bats proving successful. *Endangered Species Techn. Bull.*, **10**(3): 5–7.

Baker, J.M. and Berry, R.W. (1980). Synthetic pyrethroid insecticides as replacements for chlorinated hydrocarbons for the control of wood-boring insects. *Holz als Roh- und Werkstoff*, **38**: 121–127.

Baker, R.J. (1970). Karyotypic trends in bats. In: *Biology of Bats*, Vol. 1 (Wimsatt, W.A., ed.). Academic Press, New York: 65–96.

Bamford, R. (1985). Nestboxes in forestry plantations. *Quart. J. Forestry*, **79**(3): 153–158.

Barataud, M. (1990). Eléments sur le comportement alimentaire des Oreillards brun et gris, *Plecotus auritus* (Linnaeus, 1758) et *Plecotus austriacus* (Fischer, 1829). *Le Rhinolophe*, 7: 3–10.

Barbour, R.W. and Davis, W.H. (1969). *Bats of America*. University Press, Kentucky, Lexington.

Barbour, R.W., Davis, W.H. and Hassell, M.D. (1966). The need of vision in homing by *Myotis sodalis*. *J. Mamm.*, **47**(2): 356–357.

Barclay, R.M.R. (1991). Population structure of temperate zone insectivorous bats in relation to foraging behaviour and energy demand. *J. Anim. Ecol.*, **60**: 165–178.

Barclay, R.M.R. (1995). Does energy or calcium availability constrain reproduction in bats? In: *Ecology, Evolution and Behaviour of Bats* (Racey, P.A. and Swift, S.M., eds). *Symp. Zool. Soc. London*, **67**: 245–258.

Barclay, R.M.R. and Bell, G.P. (1988). Marking and observational techniques. In: *Ecological and Behavioural Methods for the Study of Bats* (Kunz, T.H., ed.). Smithsonian Institute Press, Washington: 59–76.

Barrett-Hamilton, G.E.H. (1907). Description of two new species of *Plecotus*. *Ann. & Mag. Nat. Hist.*, **20**: 520–521.

Barrett-Hamilton, G.E.H. (1910). *A History of British Mammals*. 1. Bats. Gurney & Jackson, London.

Bauer, K. (1960). Die Saugetiere des Neusiedlersee-Gebietes (Osterreich). *Bonn. Zool. Beitr.*, **11**: 141–344.

Bauerova, Z. (1982). Contribution to the trophic ecology of the grey long-eared bat, *Plecotus austriacus. Fol. Zool.*, **31**(2): 113–122.

Bauerova, Z. and Zima, J. (1988). Seasonal changes in visits to a cave by bats. *Fol. Zool.*, **37**(2): 97–111.

Beck, A. (1995). Faecal analysis of European bat species. *Myotis*, **32–33**: 109–119.

Bekker, J.P. and Mostert, K. (1990). Predation on bats in the Netherlands: facts and assumptions. Abstract, 5th European Bat Res. Symp. Nyborg, Denmark.

Bell, T. (1874). *A History of British Quadrupeds*. Van Voorst, London.

Benzal, J. (1991). Population dynamics of the brown long-eared bat (*Plecotus auritus*) occupying bird boxes in a pine forest plantation in central Spain. *Neth. J. Zool.*, **41**(4): 241–249.

Bernard, R., Glazaczow, A. and Samolag, J. (1991). The overwintering bat colony in Strzaliny (northwestern Poland). *Acta. Zool. Cracoviensa*, **34**(2): 453–461.

Berry, R.W. (1983). Recent developments in the remedial treatment of wood-boring insect infestations. *Biodetermination*, **5**: 154–165.

Bertrand, A. (1992). Donnees preliminaires sur les chauves-souris de la haute chain pyrenéenne (Pyrenées argiégeoises). *Mammalia*, **56**(2): 290–292.

Best, T.L., Carey, S.D., Caesar, K.G. and Henry, T.H. (1992). Distribution of bats (Mammalia: Chiroptera) in coastal plain caves of southern Alabama. *Nat. Spel. Soc. Bull.*, **54**(2): 61–65.

Bezem, J.J., Sluiter, J.W. and van Heerdt, P.F. (1964). Some characteristics of the hibernating locations of various species of bats in South Limburg. 1. *Proc. Koninkl. Akademie van Wetenschappen Amsterdam* C, **67**(5): 325–350.

Billington, G. (1993). *BAT groups*, No.7. Bat Conservation Trust, London.

Bingley, W. (1809). *Memoirs of British Quadrupeds*. Darton & Harvey, London.

Blake, D., Hutson, A.M., Racey, P.A., Rydell, J. and Speakman, J.R. (1994). Use of lamplit roads by foraging bats in southern England. *J. Zool. London*, **234**: 453–462.

Bogdanowicz, W. (1983). Community structure and interspecific interactions in bats hibernating in Poland. *Acta. Theriol.*, **28**: 357–370.

Bogdanowicz, W. and Owen, R.D. (1996). Landmark-based size and shape analysis in systematics of the plecotine bats. In: *Advances in Morphometrics* (Marcus, L.F. *et al.*, eds). Plenum Press, New York.

Bogdanowicz, W. and Urbanczyk, Z. (1983). Some ecological aspects of bats hibernating in city of Poznum. *Acta. Theriol.*, **28**: 371–385.

Booth, C. and Booth, J. (1994). *The Mammals of Orkney*. Kirkwall.

Borg, J., Fiore, M., Violani, C. and Zava, B. (1990). Observations on the Chiropterofauna of Gozo, Maltese Islands. *Mus. Reg. Sci. Nat. Boll. (Torino)*, **8**(2): 501–516.

Boyd, I.L., Myhill, D.G. and Mitchell-Jones, A.J. (1988). Uptake of Gamma-HCH by pipistrelle bats and its effect on survival. *Env. Pollution*, **51**: 95–111.

Boyd, I.L. and Stebbings, R.E. (1989). Population changes of brown long-eared bats (*Plecotus auritus*) in bat boxes in Thetford Forest. *J. Appl. Ecol.*, **26**: 101–112.

Boye, P., Pott-Dorfer, B., Dorfer, K. and Demetropoulous, A. (1990). New records of bats (Chiroptera) from Cyprus and notes on their biology. *Myotis*, **28**: 93–100.

Brack, V. and Twente, J.W. (1985). The duration of the period of hibernation of three species of vespertilionid bats. 1. Field studies. *Can. J. Zool.*, **63**: 2952–2954.

Bradbury, J.W. (1977a). Lek mating behaviour in the hammer-headed bat. *Z. Tierpsychol.*, **45**: 225–255.

Bradbury, J.W. (1977b). Social organization and communication. In: *Biology of Bats*, Volume 3 (Wimsatt, W.A., ed.). Academic Press, New York: 1–72.

Brigham, R.M. (1987). The significance of winter activity by the big brown bat (*Eptesicus fuscus*): the influence of energy reserves. *Can. J. Zool.*, **65**: 1240–1242.

Brosset, A. (1966). *La Biologie des Chiroptères*. Masson, Paris: 240.

Brown, J., Flinders, I. and Richardson, P.W. (1983). The use of church porches by bats. *J. Zool. London*, **200**: 292–295.

Brown, L.N. and Brown, C.K. (1993). First record of the eastern big-eared bat (*Plecotus rafinesquii*) in southern Florida. *Florida Scientist*, **56**(1): 63–64.

Brown, P. (1976). Vocal communication in the pallid bat, *Antrozous pallidus*. *Z. Tierpsychol.*, **41**: 34–54.

Brown, P.E. and Grinnell, A.D. (1980). Echolocation ontogeny in bats. In: *Animal Sonar Systems* (Busnel, R.G. and Fish, J.F., eds). Plenum Press, New York: 355–377.

Bruijn, Z. (1990). Domestic cat *Felis catus* as a predator of bats. *Lutra*, **33**(1): 30–34.

Buchen, C. (1992). Bau eines kunstlichen Stollens als Fledermaus-Winterquartier. *Nyctalus, Berlin*, **4**: 269–273.

Buchler, E.R. (1976). A chemiluminescent tag for tracking bats and other small nocturnal animals. *J. Mamm.*, **57**: 173–176.

Bullock, D.J., Combes, B.A., Eales, L.A. and Pritchard, J.S. (1987). Analysis of the timing and pattern of emergence of the pipistrelle bat (*Pipistrellus pipistrellus*). *J. Zool. London*, **211**: 267–274.

Castor, C., Dettmer, K. and Juptner, S. (1993). Von Tagesmenu zum Gestamptfrabspectrum des Grauen Langohrs (*Plecotus austriacus*) – 2 Jahre Freilandarbeit furden Fledermausschutz. *Nyctalus, Berlin*, **4**: 495–538.

Catto, C. (1994). *Bat Detector Manual*. Bat Conservation Trust, London.

Catto, C.M.C., Racey, P.A. and Stephenson, P.J. (1995). Activity patterns of the serotine bat (*Eptesicus serotinus*) at a roost in southern England. *J. Zool. London*, **235**: 635–644.

Clark, B.S., Leslie, D.M. and Carter, T.S. (1993). Foraging activity of adult female Ozark big-eared bats (*Plecotus townsendii ingens*) in summer. *J. Mamm.*, **74**(2): 422–427.

Cleeves, T.R. (1969). Herring gull catching and eating bat. *British Birds*, **62**: 333.

Cockrum, E.L. (1956). Homing, movements and longevity of bats. *J. Mamm.*, **37**(1): 48–57.

Coles, R.B., Guppy, A., Anderson, M.E. and Schlegel, P. (1989). Frequency sensitivity and directional hearing in the gleaning bat *Plecotus auritus* (Linnaeus 1758). *J. Comp. Physiol. A*, **165**: 269–280.

Corbet, G.B. (1964). The grey long-eared bat *Plecotus austriacus* in England and the Channel Islands. *Proc. Zool. Soc. London*, **143**(3): 511–515.

Corbet, G.B. (1970). Vagrant bats in Shetland and the North Sea. *J. Zool. London*, **161**: 281–282.

Corbet, G.B. (1971). Provisional distribution maps of British mammals. *Mamm. Rev.*, **1**: 95–142.

Corbet, G.B. and Hill, F.E. (1991). *A World List of Mammalian Species*, 3rd edn. British Museum (Natural History), London.

Cormack, R.M. (1964). Estimates of survival from the sighting of marked animals. *Biometrika*, **51**: 429–434.

Cranbrook, Earl of (1963a). Folding of the ears of a long-eared bat (*Plecotus auritus*). *Suffolk Nat. Trans.*, **11**(5): 386–387.

Cranbrook, Earl of (1963b). Notes on the feeding habits of the long-eared bat. *Suffolk Nat. Trans.*, **11**(2): 1–3.

Crucitti, P. (1989). Distribution, diversity and abundance of cave bats in Latium (central Italy). In: *European Bat Research 1987* (Hanak, V., Horacek, I. and Gaisler, J., eds). Charles University Press, Prague.

Daan, S. (1970). Photographic recording of natural activity in hibernating bats. *Bijd. Dierk.*, **40**: 13–16.

Daan, S. (1973). Activity during natural hibernation in three species of vespertilionid bats. *Neth. J. Zool.*, **23**: 1–71.

Daan, S. (1980). Long term changes in bat populations in the Netherlands: a summary. *Lutra*, **22**: 95–106.

Daan, S. and Wichers, H.J. (1968). Habitat selection of bats hibernating in a limestone cave. *Sonderdruck aus Z. f. Saugetierkunde Bd.*, **33**(5): 262–287.

Dapson, R.W., Studier, E.H., Buckingham, M.J. and Studier, A.L. (1977). Histochemistry of odiferous secretions from the integumentary glands in three species of bats. *J. Mamm.*, **58**: 531–535.

Davis, R. (1966). Homing performance and homing ability in bats. *Ecol. Monographs*, **36**(3): 202–237.

Davis, R.B., Herreid, C.F. and Short, H.L. (1962). Mexican free-tailed bats in Texas. *Ecol. Monographs*, **32**: 311–346.

De Blase, A.F. (1980). The bats of Iran: systematics, distribution, ecology. *Fieldiana Zool.* N.S. **4**: 1–424.

De Coursey, G. and de Coursey, P.J. (1964). Adaptive aspects of activity rhythms in bats. *Biol. Bull.*, **126**: 14–27.

De Fanis, E. and Jones, G. (1995a). Post-natal growth, mother–infant interactions and development of vocalizations in the vespertilionid bat *Plecotus auritus*. *J. Zool. London*, **235**: 85–97.

De Fanis, E. and Jones, G. (1995b). The role of odour in the discrimination of conspecifics by pipistrelle bats. *Anim. Behav.*, **49**: 835–839.

De Paz, O. (1984). On the distribution of genus *Plecotus* (Chiroptera: Vespertilionidae) in the Iberian Peninsula and Balearic Isles. *Mammalia*, **48**: 585–591.

Dulic, B. (1980). Morphological characteristics and distribution of *Plecotus auritus* and *Plecotus austriacus* in some regions of Yugoslavia. *Proc. 5th Int. Bat Res. Conference*: 151–161.

Dunning, D.C. and Roeder, K.D. (1965). Moth sounds and the insect-catching behaviour of bats. *Science, New York*, **147**: 173–174.

Eisentraut, M. (1936). Beitrag zur Mechanik des Fledermausfluges. *Z. wiss. Zool.*, **148**: 159–188.

Eisentraut, M. (1937). Die Wirkung neidriger Temperaturen auf die Embryonentwichlung bei Fledermausen. *Biol. Zbl.*, **57**: 59–74.

Eisentraut, M. (1950). Die Ernahung der Fledermause. *Zool. Jb.*, **79**: 115–177.

Ekman, M. and de Jong, J. (1996). Local patterns of distribution and resource utilization of four bat species (*Myotis brandti, Eptesicus nilssoni, Plecotus auritus* and *Pipistrellus pipistrellus*) in patchy and continuous environments. *J. Zool. London*, **238**: 571–580.

Ellis, S.E. (1993). Tabanidae as dietary items of Rafinesque's big-eared bat: implications for its foraging behaviour. *Entomol. News*, **104**(3): 118–122.

Entwistle, A.C. (1994). Roost ecology of the brown long-eared bat (*Plecotus auritus*) in northeast Scotland. Unpublished PhD thesis, University of Aberdeen, UK.

Entwistle, A.C., Racey, P.A. and Speakman, J.R. (1996). Habitat exploitation by a gleaning bat, *Plecotus auritus*. *Phil. Trans. R. Soc. Lond.* B, **351**: 921–931.

Entwistle, A.C., Racey, P.A. and Speakman, J.R. (1997). Roost selection by the brown long-eared bat (*Plecotus auritus*). *J. Appl. Ecol.*, **34**: 399–408.

Entwistle, A.C., Racey, P.A. and Speakman, J.R. (in press). The reproductive cycle and determination of sexual maturity in male brown long-eared bats, *Plecotus auritus. J. Zool. London.*

Entwistle, A.C., Speakman, J.R. and Racey, P.A. (1994). Effect of using the doubly labelled water technique on long-term recapture in the brown long-eared bat (*Plecotus auritus*). *Can. J. Zool.*, **72**: 783–785.

Erkert, H.G. (1982). Ecological aspects of bat activity rhythms. In: *Ecology of Bats* (Kunz, T.H., ed). Plenum Press, New York: 201–242.

Erkert, H.G. and Kracht, S. (1978). Evidence for ecological adaptation of circadian systems. *Oecologia (Berl.)*, **32**: 71–78.

Farney, J. and Fleharty, E.D. (1969). Aspect ratio, loading, wing span and membrane areas of bats. *J. Mamm.*, **50**(2): 362–367.

Faure, P.A., Fullard, J.H. and Dawson, J.W. (1993). The gleaning attacks of the northern long-eared bat, *Myotis septentrionalis*, are relatively inaudible to moths. *J. Exp. Biol.*, **178**: 173–189.

Fedyk, A. and Fedyk, S. (1970). Karyotypes of some species of vespertilionid bats from Poland. *Acta Theriol.*, **15**: 295–305.

Fedyk, S. and Ruprecht, A.L. (1983). Chromosomes of some species of vespertilionid bats. 2. Evolutionary relationships of plecotine bats. *Acta Theriol.*, **28**(10): 171–182.

Fenton, M.B. (1995). Constraint and flexibility – bats as predators, bats as prey. In: *Ecology, Evolution and Behaviour of Bats* (Racey, P.A. and Swift, S.M., eds). *Symp. Zool. Soc. London*, **67**: 277–289.

Fenton, M.B. and Bell, G.P. (1981). Recognition of species of insectivorous bats by their echolocation calls. *J. Mamm.*, **62**: 233–243.

Fenton, M.B. and Fullard, J.H. (1979). The influence of moth hearing on bat echolocation strategies. *J. Comp. Physiol.* A, **132**: 77–86.

Fenton, M.B. and Fullard, J.H. (1981). Moth hearing and the feeding strategies of bats. *Am. Scientist*, **69**(3): 266–275.

Findley, J.S. (1993). *Bats: A Community Perspective.* Cambridge University Press, Cambridge.

Fluckiger, P.F. and Beck, A. (1995). Observations on the habitat use for hunting by *Plecotus austriacus* (Fischer, 1829). *Myotis*, **32–33**: 121–122.

Forrest, T.G., Read, M.P., Farris, H.E. and Hoy, R.R. (1997). A tympanal hearing organ in scarab beetles. *J. Exp. Biol.*, **200**: 601–606.

Frase, B.A., Pizzuto, T.M. and Getz, L.L. (1990). Survivorship of bled voles measured by recapture. *J. Mamm.*, **71**: 104–105.

Freeman, P.W. (1981). Correspondence of food habits and morphology in insectivorous bats. *J. Mamm.*, **62**(1): 166–170.

Frost, D.R. and Timm, R.M. (1992). Phylogeny of plecotine bats (Chiroptera: Vespertilionidae): summary of the evidence and proposal of a logistically consistent taxonomy. *Am. Mus. Navitates*, **3034**: 1–16.

Fuhrmann, M. and Godmann, O. (1991). Naturliche quartiere de waldflederemause schutzen! Konsequenzen aus einer Baumhohlenuntersuchung in Rheingau. *AFZ–Allgemeine–Forst Zeitschrift*, **49**(19): 982–983.

Fuhrmann, M. and Seitz, A. (1992). Nocturnal activity of the brown long-eared bat (*Plecotus auritus* L.1758): data from radiotracking in the Lenneburg forest near Mainz (Germany). In: *Wildlife Telemetry. Remote Monitoring and Tracking of Animals* (Priede, I.G. and Swift, S.M., eds). Ellis Horwood, Chichester: 538–548.

Fullard, J.H. (1987). Sensory ecology and neuroethology of moths and bats: interactions in a global perspective. In: *Recent Advances in the Study of Bats* (Fenton, M.B., Racey, P.A. and Rayner, J.M.V., eds). Cambridge University Press, Cambridge: 244–272.

Fullard, J.H. (1992). The neuroethology of sound production in tiger moths (Lepidoptera, Arctiidae). 1. Rhythmicity and central control. *J. Comp. Physiol.* A, **170**: 575–588.

Fullard, J.H. and Yack, J.E. (1993). The evolutionary biology of insect hearing. *Tree*, **8**(7): 248–252.

Funakoshi, K. and Uchida, T.A. (1982). Annual cycles of body weight in the Namie's frosted bat *Vespertilio superans superans. J. Zool. London*, **196**: 417–430.

Gaisler, J. (1966). A tentative ecological classification of colonies of the European bats. *Lynx, Praha*, **6**: 35–39.

Gaisler, J. (1970). Remarks on the thermopreferendum of palearctic bats in their natural habitats. *Proc. 2nd Int. Bat Res. Conf*: 33–35.

Gaisler, J. (1979). Ecology of bats. In: *Ecology of Small Mammals* (Stoddart, D.M., ed.). Chapman & Hall, London: 281–342.

Gaisler, J. (1983–4). Bats of northern Algeria and their winter activity. *Myotis*, **21–22**: 89–95.

Gaisler, J. and Bauerova, Z. (1985–6). The life of bats in a city. *Myotis*, **23–24**: 211–215.

Gaisler, J., Chytil, J. and Vlasin, M. (1990). The bats of south Moravian lowlands (Czechoslovakia) over thirty years. *Prirodovedne Prace Ustavu Ceskoslovenske Academie ved V Brne*, **24**(9): 1–50.

Gaisler, J. and Hanak, V. (1964). Netopyr dlouhouchy *Plecotus austriacus*, Fischer 1829 v Bulharsku. *Zool. Listy*, **1**: 31–38.

Gaisler, J. and Hanak, V. (1969). Summary of the results of bat banding in Czechoslovakia, 1948–1967. *Lynx*, **10**: 25–34.

Gaisler, J., Hanak, V. and Horacek, I. (1980–81). Remarks on the current status of bat populations in Czechoslovakia. *Myotis*, **18–19**: 68–75.

Gaisler, J., Zukal, J., Nesvadbova, J., Chytil, J. and Obuch, J. (1996). Species diversity and relative abundance of small mammals (Insectivora, Chiroptera, Rodentia) in the Palava biosphere reserve of UNESCO. *Acta Soc. Zool. Bohem.*, **60**: 13–23.

Gardner, R.A., Molyneux, D.H. and Stebbings, R.E. (1987). Studies on the prevalence of haematozoa of British bats. *Mamm. Rev.*, **17**(2/3): 75–80.

Gerell, R. (1980–81). Bat conservation in Sweden. *Myotis*, **18–19**: 11–15.

Gerell, R. and Lundberg, K. (1985). Social organization in the bat *Pipistrellus pipistrellus. Behav. Ecol. Sociobiol.*, **16**: 177–184.

Glas, G.H. (1982). Records of hibernating barbastelle and grey long-eared bats in the Netherlands outside the southern Limburg cave area. *Lutra*, **25**: 15–16.

Glue, D.E. (1970). Avian predator pellet analysis and the mammalogist. *Mamm. Rev.*, **1**: 53–62.

Gould, E. (1955). The feeding efficiency of insectivorous bats. *J. Mamm.*, **36**: 399–406.

Gould, E. (1971). Studies of maternal–infant communication and development of vocalization in the bats *Myotis* and *Eptesicus. Communications Behav. Biol.*, **5**: 263–313.

Greenaway, F. and Hutson, A.M. (1990). *A Field Guide to British Bats*. Bruce Coleman, Uxbridge, UK.

Griffin, D.R. (1958). *Listening in the Dark*. Yale University Press, New Haven, CT.

Gustafson, A.W. and Damassa, D.A. (1987). Binding of sex steroids to plasma proteins: relation to androgen resistance and asynchronous reproductive patterns in hibernating bats. In: *Recent Advances in the Study of Bats* (Fenton, M.B., Racey, P.A. and Rayner, J.M.V., eds). Cambridge University Press, Cambridge: 442–458.

Haensel, J. (1994). Zum Fledermaus-Winterbestand zahlreicher in der Stadt Baruth vorhandener, teils verfallsgefahrdeter Erdkeller – Vorabeit fur ein Schutzprogramm. *Nyctalus, Berlin*, **5**(3/4): 249–273.

Haensel, J. and Nafe, M. (1993). Flavismus bei einem Braunen Langohr (*Plecotus auritus*) erhebliche Farbaufhellung bei einem Grauen Langohr (*Plecotus austriacus*). *Nyctalus, Berlin*, **4**: 465–468.

Haeussler, U. and Braun, M. (1991). Collection of indigenous bats (Mammalia: Chiroptera) of the Staatliches Museum fur Naturkinde Karlsruhe; Part 2: *Plecotus. Carolinea*, **49**: 101–114.

Haitlinger, R. and Ruprecht, L. (1992). Parasitic arthropods (Siphonaptera, Diptera, Acari) of bats from the western part of the Biatowieza forest. *Nyctalus, Berlin*, **4**(3): 315–319.

Hale, J. (1980). Weight variation in long-eared bats. *J. Brit. Mus.*, **1980**: 296–297.

Hall, E.R. (1981). *The Mammals of North America*, 2nd edn. Wiley, New York.

Hanak, V. (1962). Graues Mausohr (*Plecotus austriacus*) – neues Mitglied der Fledermausfauna der Tschechoslowakei. *Cas. nar Mus.*, **131**: 87–96.

Hanak, V. (1966). Ergebnisse der Fledermausberingung in der Sowjet union. *Myotis*, **4**: 12–18.

Hanak, V. (1969). Okologische Bemerkungen zur Verbreitung der Langohnen (Gattung *Plecotus* Geoffroy, 1818) in der Tschechoslowakei. *Lynx*, N.S. **10**: 35–39.

Handley, C.O. (1959). A revision of American bats of the genera *Euderma* and *Plecotus. Proc. US Nat. Mus.*, **110**: 95–246.

Harmata, W. (1969). The thermopreferendum of some species of bats (Chiroptera). *Acta Theriol.*, **14**(5): 49–62.

Harmata, W. (1973). The thermopreferendum of some species of bats (Chiroptera) in natural conditions. *Zeszyty Naukowe Uniwersytetu Jagiellonskiego*, **19**: 127–141.

Harmata, W. (1987). Results of bat-banding in Poland in the years 1954–1974. *Myotis*, **25**: 113–116.

Haskell, P.T. and Belton, P. (1956). Electrical responses of certain lepidopterous tympanal organs. *Nature, London*, **177**: 139–140.

Hays, G.C., Speakman, J.R. and Webb, P.I. (1992). Why do brown long-eared bats (*Plecotus auritus*) fly in winter? *Physiol. Zool.*, **65**(3): 554–567.

Hayward, A.F. and Teagle, W.G. (1961). Some observations on the medial lobules of the ears of the long-eared bat *Plecotus auritus* (Linnaeus). *Proc. Zool. Soc. London*, **137**: 469–473.

Heerdt, P.F. and Sluiter, J.W. (1958). Longevity in bats. *Natuurhistorische Maandblad*, **38**: 47.

Heerdt, P.F. and Sluiter, J.W. (1961). New data on longevity in bats. *Natuurhistorische Maandblad*, **3–4**: 36.

Heise, G. and Schmidt, A. (1988). Contribution to the social organization and ecology of the brown long-eared bat (*Plecotus auritus*). *Nyctalus, Berlin*, **2**: 445–465.

Helversen, O. and Weid, R. (1990). The distribution of some bat species in Greece. *Bonn. Zool. Beitr.*, **41**(1): 9–22.

Herreid, C.F. (1964). Bat longevity and metabolic rate. *Exp. Geront.*, **1**: 1–9.

Herreid, C.F., Davis, R.B. and Short, H.L. (1960). Injuries due to bat banding. *J. Mamm.*, **41**: 398–400.

Hill, J.E. and Smith, J.D. (1984). *Bats. A Natural History*. British Museum (Natural History), London.

Hinkel, A. and Rackow, W. (1994). Unfalle von Fledermausen auf Kletten, Kakteen oder Stacheldracht. *Nyctalus, Berlin*, **5**: 3–10.

Horacek, I. (1975). Notes on the ecology of bats of the genus *Plecotus* Geoffroy, 1818 (Mammalia: Chiroptera). *Vestnik Ceskoslovenske Spolecnosti Zool.*, **34**: 195–210.

Howard, R.W. (1995). *Auritus. A Natural Hsitory of the Brown Long-Eared Bat*. William Sessions, York, UK.

Hughes, P.M. and Rayner, J.M.V. (1991). Addition of artificial loads to long-eared bats *Plecotus auritus*: handicapping flight performance. *J. Exp. Biol.*, **161**: 285–298.

Hughes, P.M., Speakman, J.R., Jones, G. and Racey, P.A. (1989). Suckling behaviour in the pipistrelle bat (*Pipistrellus pipistrellus*). *J. Zool. London*, **219**: 665–670.

Humphrey, S.R. and Kunz, T.H. (1976). Ecology of a Pleistocene relict, the western big-eared bat (*Plecotus townsendii*), in the southern great plains. *J. Mamm.*, **57**(3): 470–494.

Hurka, L. (1971). Zur Verbreitung und Okologie der Fledermause der Gattung *Plecotus* in Westbohmen. *Fol. Mus. Rerum Nat. Bohemiae Occidentalis*, **1**: 1–24.

Husar, S. (1976). Behavioural character displacement: evidence of food partitioning in insectivorous bats. *J. Mamm.*, **57**(2): 331–338.

Hutson, A.M. (1984). Keds, flat-flies and bat flies, Diptera, Hippoboscidae and Nycteribiidae. *Handbook of Identification British Insects*, Vol. 10; Part 7. Royal Entomological Society, London: 1–40.

Hutson, A.M. (1991). Grey long-eared bat at Brighton. *Bat News No.23*. Bat Conservation Trust, London.

Hutson, A.M. (1996). Recent reports and news. *Bat News (BCT)*, **41**: 6.

Hutson, A.M. and Mickleburgh, S. (1988). *Bats Underground: A Conservation Code*. Fauna and Flora Preservation Society, London.

Ibanez, C. and Fernandez, R. (1986). Systematic status of the long-eared bat *Plecotus teneriffae* Barrett-Hamilton 1907 (Chiroptera; Vespertilionidae). *Saugetierkunde Mitt.*, **32**: 143–149.

Jeffries, D.J. (1972). Organochlorine insecticide residues in British bats and their significance. *J. Zool. London*, **166**: 245–263.

Jenni, L. (1978). L'activité ornothologique au col de Bretolet en 1977. *Nos Oiseaux*, **34**: 245–256.

Jenni, L. (1981). L'activité ornothologique au col de Bretolet en 1980. *Nos Oiseaux*, **36**: 109–112.

Jentzsch, M. (1992). Fledermause als Eulenbeute im Sudharz und Helme–Unstrut–Gebiet. *Nyctalus*, **4**: 428–431.

Jenyns, L. (1829). The distinctive characters of two British species of *Plecotus*, supposed to have been confounded under the name of the long-eared bat. *Trans. Linn. Soc. London*, **16**(1833): 53–60.

Jeuniaux, C. (1961). Chitinase, an addition to the list of hydrolases in the digestive tract of vertebrates. *Nature, London*, **192**: 135–136.

Johnson, C.G. (1950). A suction trap for small airborne insects which automatically segregates the catch into successive hourly samples. *Ann. Appl. Biol.*, **37**: 80–91.

Johnson, C.G. and Taylor, L.R. (1955). The development of large suction traps for airborne insects. *Ann. Appl. Biol.*, **43**(1): 51–62.

Jones, C. and Suttkus, R.D. (1975). Notes on the natural history of *Plecotus rafinesquii*. *Occas. Pap. Mus. Zool. La. State Univ.*, **47**: 1–14.

Jones, G. (1990). Prey selection by the greater horseshoe bat (*Rhinolophus ferrumequinum*): optimal foraging by echolocation? *J. Anim. Ecol.*, **59**: 587–602.

Jones, G. (1994). Scaling of wingbeat and echolocation pulse emission rates in bats: why are aerial insectivorous bats so small? *Functional Ecol.*, **8**: 450–457.

Jones, G., Duvergé, P.L. and Ransome, R.D. (1995). Conservation biology of an endangered species: field studies of greater horseshoe bats. In: *Ecology, Evolution and Behaviour of Bats* (Racey, P.A. and Swift, S.M., eds). *Symp. Zool. Soc. London*, **67**: 309–324.

Jones, G. and Rydell, J. (1994). Foraging strategy and predation risk as factors influencing emergence time in echolocating bats. *Phil. Trans R. Soc. Lond. B*, **346**: 445–455.

Jooris, R. (1980). Additional data on the distribution of *Plecotus austriacus* (Fischer 1829) in the low lying districts of Belgium with a critical assessment of biometrical data of the two *Plecotus* species. *Lutra*, **23**: 3–11.

Kihlstrom, J.E. (1972). Period of gestation and body weight in some placental mammals. *Comp. Biochem. Physiol.*, **43A**: 673–679.

Kim, M.H. and Lee, H.P. (1990). Studies on Spincturnicidae (Acari: Mesostigmata) parasitic on bats in Korea. *Korean Archaeology*, **6**(1): 139–148.

Kleiman, D.G. (1969). Maternal care, growth rate and development in the noctule (*Nyctalus noctula*), pipistrelle (*Pipistrellus pipistrellus*) and serotine (*Eptesicus serotinus*) bats. *J. Zool. London*, **157**: 187–211.

Kolb, A. (1950). Beitrage sur Biologie einheimischer Fledermause. *Zool. Jb. Abt. Syst. Okol. Georgr. Tiere*, **78**: 547.

Koopman, K.F. and Jones, J.K. (1970). Classification of bats. In: *About Bats: a Chiropteran Symposium* (Slaughter, B.H. and Walton, D.W., eds). Southern Methodist University Press, Dallas, Texas: 22–28.

Kovtun, M.F. and Zhukova, N.F. (1994). Feeding and digestion intensity in chiropterans of different trophic groups. *Fol. Zool.*, **43**(4): 377–386.

Kowalski, M. and Lesinski, G. (1994). Bats occupying nest boxes for birds and bats in Poland. *Nyctalus, Berlin*, **5**(1): 19–26.

Krauss, A. (1978). Materials on foodstuff of long-eared bat (*Plecotus auritus* L). *Zool. Abh. Staalisches Mus. Tierkunde in Dresden*, **34**: 325–337.

Kristofik, J. (1982). Reports of flies of the family Nycteribiidae (Diptera) in the territory of Slovakia. *Biologia (Bratislava)*, **37**: 191–197.

Krystufek, B. (1980). Some notes on long-eared bats (Gen. *Plecotus* Geoffroy, 1818, Chiroptera, Mammalia) in Slovenia. *Biosistematika*, **6**(1): 113–115.

Krzanowski, A. (1961). Weight dynamics of bats wintering in the cave at Pulawy (Poland). *Acta Theriol.*, **4**: 249–264.

Kuipers, B. and Daan, S. (1970). 'Internal migration' of hibernating bats: response to seasonal variation in cave microclimate. *Bijd. Dierkunde*, **40**(1): 51–55.

Kunz, T.H. (1973). Population studies of the cave bat (*Myotis velifer*): reproduction, growth and development. *Occ. Pap. Mus. Nat. Hist. Kansas*, **15**: 1–43.

Kunz, T.H. (1974). Feeding ecology of a temperate insectivorous bat (*Myotis velifer*). *Ecology*, **55**(4): 693–711.

Kunz, T.H. (1987). Post-natal growth and energetics of suckling bats. In: *Recent Advances in the Study of Bats* (Fenton, M.B., Racey, P.A. and Rayner, J.M.V., eds). Cambridge University Press, Cambridge: 396–420.

Kunz, T.H. and Stern. A.A. (1995). Maternal investment and post-natal growth in bats. In: *Ecology, Evolution and Behaviour of Bats* (Racey, P.A. and Swift, S.M., eds). *Symp. Zool. Soc. Lond.*, **67**: 123–138.

Kunz, T.H. and Whitaker, J.O. (1983). An evaluation of fecal analysis for determining food habits of insectivorous bats. *Can. J. Zool.*, **61**: 1317–1321.

Kurta, A. and Kunz, T.H. (1987). Size of bats at birth and maternal investment during pregnancy. *Symp. Zool. Soc. Lond.*, **57**: 79–106.

Kurta, A., Kunz, T.H. and Nagy, K.A. (1990). Energetics and water flux of free-living big brown bats (*Eptesicus fuscus*) during pregnancy and lactation. *J. Mamm.*, **71**(1): 59–65.

Kuzyakin, A.P. (1944). Ordo Chiroptera. In: *Mammals of USSR* (Bobrinski, N.A., ed.). Moscow.

Lacki, M.J., Adam, M.D. and Shoemaker, L.A. (1993). Characteristics of feeding roosts of Virginia big-eared bats in Daniel Boone National Forest. *J. Wildlife Mgmt*, **57**(3): 539–543.

Lanza, B. (1959). Chiroptera. In: *Fauna d'Italia*, 4. *Mammalia* (*Generalità, Insectivora and Chiroptera*) (Toschi, A. and Lanza, B., eds), Ediziona Calderini, Bologna.

Largen, M.J., Kock, D. and Yalden, D.W. (1974). Catalogue of the mammals of Ethiopia. 1. Chiroptera. *Monitore Zoologico Italiano, Supp.*, 5: 221–298.

Lehmann, J., Jenni, L. and Maumary, L. (1992). A new longevity record for the long-eared bat (*Plecotus auritus*, Chiroptera). *Mammalia*, 56(2): 316–318.

Leonard, M.L. and Fenton, M.B. (1983). Habitat use by spotted bats (*Euderma maculatum*) (Chiroptera: Vespertilionidae): roosting and foraging behaviour. *Can. J. Zool.*, 61: 1487–1491.

Lesinski, G. (1986). Ecology of bats hibernating underground in central Poland. *Acta Theriol.*, 31: 507–521.

Lesinski, G. (1989). Bats (Chiroptera) in the food of the barn owl (*Tyto alba*) (Scop.) on the Wielen upland (Poland). *Przeglad. Zool.*, 33(1): 129–136.

Lipej, L. and Gjerkes, M. (1992). Bats in the diet of owls in NW Istra. *Myotis*, 30: 133–138.

Luger, F. (1977). Untersuchungen zur Verbreitung und Lebensweise von Fledermausen in nistkasen im Geisenfelder Forst, Oberbayern. *Anzeiger fur Schadlingskunde Pflanzenschutz*, 50(12): 183–188.

Lundberg, K. and Gerell, R. (1986). Territorial advertisement and male attraction in the bat *Pipistrellus pipistrellus*. *Ethology*, 71: 115–124.

Madkour, G. (1989). Urogenitalia of Microchiroptera from Egypt. *Zool. Anzeiger*, 222(5–6): 337–352.

Maier, C. (1992). Activity patterns of pipistrelle bats (*Pipistrellus pipistrellus*) in Oxfordshire. *J. Zool. London*, 228: 69–80.

Matsumura, S. (1979). Mother–infant communication in a horseshoe bat *Rhinolophus ferrumequinum nippon*): development of vocalization. *J. Mamm.*, 60(1): 76–84.

McAney, C., Shiel, C., Sullivan, C. and Fairley, J. (1991). The analysis of bat droppings. *Occ. Pub. Mamm. Soc. London*, 14.

McLean, J.A. and Speakman, J.R. (1996). Suckling behaviour in the brown long-eared bat (*Plecotus auritus*). *J. Zool. London*, 239: 411–416.

McNab, B.K. (1971). The structure of tropical bat faunas. *Ecology*, 52(2): 352–358.

Meade, L. (1992). New distributional records for selected species of Kentucky mammals. *Trans. Kentucky Acad. Sci.*, 53(3–4): 127–132.

Menu, H. (1983). Contribution à la méthodologie de détermination des *Plecotus auritus* (Linné, 1758) et *Plecotus austriacus* (Fischer, 1829). *Mammalia*, 47(4): 588–591.

Millais, J.G. (1904). *The Mammals of Great Britain and Ireland*. Longmans, London.

Miller, L.A. (1970). Structure of the green lacewing tympanal organ (*Chrysopa carnea*, Neuroptera). *J. Morphology*, 131: 359–382.

Miller, L.A. (1971). Physiological responses of green lacewings (*Chrysopa*, Neuroptera) to ultrasound. *J. Insect Physiol.*, 17: 491–506.

Miller, L.A. (1975). The behaviour of flying green lacewings, *Chrysopa carnea*, in the presence of ultrasound. *J. Insect Physiol.*, 21: 205–219.

Mitchell-Jones, A.J. (1990). The distribution of bats in Britain 1982–87 as revealed by enquiries. *Mamm. Rev.*, 20(4): 145–157.

Mitchell-Jones, A.J., Cooke, A.S., Boyd, I.L. and Stebbings, R.E. (1989). Bats and remedial timber treatment chemicals – a review. *Mamm. Rev.*, 19(3): 93–110.

Mitchell-Jones, A.J., Hutson, A.M. and Racey, P.A. (1993). The growth and development of bat conservation in Britain. *Mamm. Rev.*, 23(3/4): 139–148.

Moffat, C.B. (1939). The mammals of Ireland. *Proc. R. Irish Acad.*, 44B: 61–128.

Morgan, P. (1989). The brown long-eared bat (*Plecotus auritus*); Mammals of Brecknock. *Breconshire Nat.*, **49**: 15–16.

Moss, C.F. (1988). Ontogeny of vocal signals in the big brown bat, *Eptesicus fuscus*. In: *Animal Sonar. Processes and Performance* (Nachtigall, P.E. and Moore, P.W.B., eds). Plenum Press, New York: 115–120.

Myers, P. (1978). Sexual dimorphism in size of vespertilionid bats. *Amer. Nat.*, **112**: 701–711.

Nagel, A., Frank, H. and Weigold, H. (1983–4). Distribution of hibernating bats in Wuerttemberg (south Germany). *Myotis*, **21–22**: 116–121.

Nagel, A. and Nagel, R. (1988). Einsatz von Fledermauskasten zur ansiedlung von Fledermausen: ein vergleich von 2 verschiedenen gebieten Baden-Wurttembergs. *Myotis*, **26**: 129–144.

Nagel, A. and Nagel, R. (1991). How do bats choose optimal temperatures for hibernation? *Comp. Biochem. Physiol.* A, **99**(3): 323–326.

Norberg, U.M. (1970a). Hovering flight of *Plecotus auritus* Linnaeus. *Bijd. tot de Dierkunde*, **40**(1): 62–66.

Norberg, U.M. (1970b). Functional osteology and myology of the wing of *Plecotus auritus* Linnaeus (Chiroptera). *Ark. Zool.*, **22**(12): 483–543.

Norberg, U.M. (1976a). Aerodynamics, kinematics and energetics of horizontal flapping flight in the long-eared bat *Plecotus auritus*. *J. Exp. Biol.*, **65**: 179–212.

Norberg, U.M. (1976b). Aerodynamics of hovering flight in the long-eared bat *Plecotus auritus*. *J. Exp. Biol.*, **65**: 459–470.

Norberg, U.M. and Rayner, J.M.V. (1987). Ecological morphology and flight in bats (Mammalia: Chiroptera): wing adaptations, flight performance, foraging strategy and echolocation. *Phil. Trans. R. Soc. Lond.* B, **316**: 335–427.

Nowak, R.M. (1991). *Walker's Mammals of the World*, 5th edn. John Hopkins University Press, Baltimore.

Obrist, M.K., Fenton, M.B., Eger, J.L. and Schlegel, P.A. (1993). What ears do for bats: a comparative study of pinna sound pressure transformation in Chiroptera. *J. Exp. Biol.*, **180**: 119–152.

O'Gorman, F. and Fairley, J.S. (1965). A colony of *Plecotus auritus* from Co. Kilkenny. *Proc. Zool. Soc. London*, **145**: 154–155.

O'Sullivan, P. (1994). Bats in Ireland. *Irish Nat. J.* (*Special Zool. Suppl.*).

Palmeirim, J.M. (1990). Bats of Portugal: zoogeography and systematics. *Univ. Kansas Mus. Nat. Hist. Misc. Pub.*, No. 82: 1–53.

Park, K.J., Masters, E. and Altringham, J.D. (in press). Social structure of three sympatric species of vespertilionid bats. *J. Zool. London*.

Pearson, O.P., Koford, M.R. and Pearson, A.K. (1952). Reproduction in the lump-nosed bat (*Corynorhinus rafinesquei*) in California. *J. Mamm.*, **33**: 273–320.

Pennycuick, C.J. (1975). Mechanics of flight. In: *Avian Biology*, Vol. 5 (Farner, D.S., King, J.R. and Parkes, K.C., eds). Academic Press, London: 1–73.

Perez-Barberia, F.J. (1991). Evaluation of damages produced by ringing in *Plecotus austriacus* Fischer, 1829 (Chiroptera, Vespertilionidae). *Misc. Zool.* (*Barcelona*), **15**: 209–213.

Piechoki, R. (1966). Uber die Nachweise der Langohr-Fledermause *Plecotus auritus* L. und *Plecotus austriacus* Fischer im mitteldeutschen Raum. *Hercynia*, **3**: 407–415.

Pollack, G.S. (1994). Synaptic inputs to the omega neuron of the cricket *Teleogryllus oceanicus*: differences in EPSP waveforms evoked by low and high sound frequencies. *J. Comp. Physiol.* A, **174**: 83–89.

Poulton, E.B. (1929). British insectivorous bats and their prey. *Proc. Zool. Soc. London*, **19**: 277–302.

Priede, I.G. (1992). Wildlife telemetry: an introduction. In: *Wildlife Telemetry. Remote Monitoring and Tracking of Animals* (Priede, I.G. and Swift, S.M., eds). Ellis Horwood, Chichester: 3–25.

Punt, A. (1970). Round table discussion on bat conservation. *Proc. 2nd Int. Bat Res. Conf*: 3–4.

Qumsiyeh, M.B., Disi, A.M. and Amr, Z.S. (1992). Systematics and distribution of the bats (Mammalia: Chiroptera) of Jordan. *Dirasat Series B. Pure & Appl. Sci.*, **19**(2): 101–118.

Racey, P.A. (1969). Diagnosis of pregnancy and experimental extension of gestation in the pipistrelle bat, *Pipistrellus pipistrellus*. *J. Reprod. Fert.*, **19**: 465–474.

Racey, P.A. (1972). Viability of bat spermatozoa after prolonged storage in the epididymis. *J. Reprod. Fert.*, **28**: 309–311.

Racey, P.A. (1973). Environmental factors affecting the length of gestation in heterothermic bats. *J. Reprod. Fert. Suppl.*, **19**: 175–189.

Racey, P.A. (1974a). The reproductive cycle in male noctule bats, *Nyctalus noctula*. *J. Reprod. Fert.*, **41**: 169–182.

Racey, P.A. (1974b). Ageing and assessment of reproductive status of pipistrelle bats, *Pipistrellus pipistrellus*. *J. Zool. London*, **173**: 264–271.

Racey, P.A. (1975). The prolonged survival of spermatozoa in bats. In: *The Biology of the Male Gamete* (Duckett, J.G. and Racey, P.A., eds). *Suppl. No. 1, Biol. J. Linn. Soc.*, **7**: 385–416.

Racey, P.A. (1976). Induction of ovulation in the pipistrelle bat, *Pipistrellus pipistrellus*. *J. Reprod. Fert.*, **46**: 481–483.

Racey, P.A. (1978). The effect of photoperiod on the initiation of spermatogenesis in pipistrelle bats, *Pipistrellus pipistrellus*. *Proc. 4th Int. Bat Res. Conf.* (Olembo, R.J., Castelino, J.B. and Mutere, F.A., eds). Kenya Nat. Acad. for the Advancement of Arts and Science, Nairobi.

Racey, P.A. (1982). Ecology of reproduction. In: *Ecology of Bats* (Kunz, T.H., ed). Plenum Press, New York: 57–97.

Racey, P.A. (1991). Noctule. In: *The Handbook of British Mammals*, 3rd edn (Corbet, G.B. and Harris, S., eds). Blackwell, Oxford: 117–121.

Racey, P.A. and Speakman, J.R. (1987). The energy costs of pregnancy and lactation in heterothermic bats. In: *Reproductive Energetics in Mammals* (Loudon, A.S.I. and Racey, P.A., eds). *Symp. Zool. Soc. London*, **57**: 107–125.

Racey, P.A. and Swift, S.M. (1981). Variations in gestation length in a colony of pipistrelle bats (*Pipistrellus pipistrellus*) from year to year. *J. Reprod. Fert.*, **61**: 123–129.

Racey, P.A. and Swift, S.M. (1985). Feeding ecology of *Pipistrellus pipistrellus* (Chiroptera: Vespertilionidae) during pregnancy and lactation. 1. Foraging behaviour. *J. Anim. Ecol.*, **54**: 205–215.

Racey, P.A. and Swift, S.M. (1986). The residual effects of remedial timber treatments on bats. *Biol. Cons.*, **35**: 205–214.

Rakhmatulina, I.K. (1972). The breeding, growth and development of pipistrelles in Azerbaidzhan. *Soviet J. Ecol.*, **2**: 131–136.

Ransome, R.D. (1968). The distribution of the greater horseshoe bat, *Rhinolophus ferrumequinum*, during hibernation, in relation to environmental factors. *J. Zool. London*, **154**: 77–112.

Ransome, R.D. (1971). The effect of ambient temperature on the arousal frequency of the hibernating greater horseshoe bat, *Rhinolophus ferrumequinum*, in relation to site selection and the hibernation state. *J. Zool. London*, **164**: 353–371.

Ransome, R.D. (1990). *The Natural History of Hibernating Bats*. Christopher Helm, London.

Rayner, J.M.V. (1987). The mechanics of flapping flight in bats. In: *Recent Advances in the Study of Bats* (Fenton, M.B., Racey, P.A. and Rayner, J.M.V., eds). Cambridge University Press, Cambridge: 23–42.

Rayner, J.M.V. and Aldridge, J.N. (1985). Three-dimensional reconstruction of animal flight paths and the turning flight of microchiropteran bats. *J. Exp. Biol.*, **118**: 247–265.

Revin-Yu, V. and Boeskorov, G.G. (1989). On finding hibernation places of vespertilionid bats (Mammalia, Chiroptera) in Yakutia (USSR). *Zool. Zhurnal*, **68**(3): 150–151.

Robinson, M.F. (1990). Prey selection by the brown long-eared bat (*Plecotus auritus*). *Myotis*, **28**: 5–18.

Roeder, K.D. (1962). The behaviour of free-flying moths in the presence of artificial ultrasonic pulses. *Anim. Behav.*, **10**: 300–304.

Roeder, K.D. (1967). *Nerve Cells and Insect Behaviour*, revised edn. Harvard University Press, Cambridge, MA.

Roeder, K.D. and Treat, A.E. (1957). Ultrasonic reception by the tympanic organ of noctuid moths. *J. Exp. Zool.*, **134**: 127–158.

Roeder, K.D. and Treat, A.E. (1969). The acoustic detection of moths by bats. *Proc. 11th Int. Ent. Congress, Vienna.*

Roer, H. (1969). Zur Ernahrungsbiologie von *Plecotus auritus* (L) (Mammalia, Chiroptera). *Bonn. Zool. Beitr.*, **4**: 378–383.

Roer, H. (1973). Uber die Ursachen hoher Jugendmortalitat beim Mausohr, *Myotis myotis* (Chiroptera, Mammalia). *Bonn. Zool. Beitr.*, **24**: 332–341.

Roer, H. (1987). Erste erfahrungen mit einem permethrin-haltigen holzschutzmittel in einer wochenstube des mausohrs (*Myotis myotis*). *Myotis*, **25**: 105–111.

Rosevear, D.R. (1965). *The Bats of West Africa*. British Museum Natural History, London.

Ross, A. (1961). Notes on food habits of bats. *J. Mamm.*, **42**(1): 66–71.

Ross, A. (1967). Ecological aspects of the food habits of insectivorous bats. *Proc. West. Found. Vert. Zool.*, **1**(4): 205–263.

Roverud, R.C. (1987). The processing of echolocation sound elements in bats: a behavioural approach. In: *Recent Advances in the Study of Bats* (Fenton, M.B., Racey, P.A. and Rayner, J.M.V., eds). Cambridge University Press, Cambridge.

Ruprecht, A.L. (1971). Distribution of *Myotis myotis* (Borkhausen, 1797) and representatives of the genus *Plecotus* Geoffroy, 1818 in Poland. *Acta Theriol.*, **16**(7): 95–104.

Ruprecht, A.L. (1979). Bats (Chiroptera) as constitutents of the food of barn owls *Tyto alba* in Poland. *Ibis*, **121**: 489–494.

Ruprecht, A.L. (1983). Criteria for species identification in the genus *Plecotus* (Geoffroy (Chiroptera, Vespertilionidae). *Zool. J. (Moscow)*, **62**(8): 1252–1257 (In Russian, English summary).

Ruprecht, A.L. (1990). Bats (Chiroptera) in the food of owls in the Nadnotecka forest. *Przeglad Zool.*, **34**(2–3): 349–358.

Ryberg, O. (1947). *Studies on Bats and Bat Parasites*. Bokforlaget Svensk Natur, Stockholm.

Rydell, J. (1989a). Feeding activity of the northern bat *Eptesicus nilssoni* during pregnancy and lactation. *Oecologia*, **80**: 562–565.

Rydell, J. (1989b). Food habits of northern (*Eptesicus nilssoni*) and brown long-eared (*Plecotus auritus*) bats in Sweden. *Holarctic Ecol.*, **12**: 16–20.

Rydell, J. (1989c). Cellars as hibernation sites for bats. *Fauna och Flora (Stockholm)*, **84**(2): 43–53.

Rydell, J. (1992). Exploitation of insects around street lamps by bats in Sweden. *Functional Ecol.*, **6**: 744–750.

Rydell, J. (1993). Variation in foraging activity of an aerial insectivorous bat during reproduction. *J. Mamm.*, **74**(2): 503–509.

Rydell, J., Entwistle, A. and Racey, P.A. (1996). Timing of foraging flights of three species of bats in relation to insect activity and predation risk. *Oikos*, **76**: 243–252.

Rydell, J. and Racey, P.A. (1995). Street lamps and the feeding ecology of insectivorous bats. In: *Ecology, Evolution and Behaviour of Bats* (Racey, P.A. and Swift, S.M., eds). *Symp. Zool. Soc. London*, **67**: 291–307.

Rydell, J., Skals, N., Surlykke, A. and Svensson, M. (1997). Hearing and bat defence in geometrid winter moths. *Proc. R. Soc. Lond.* B, **264**: 83–88.

Rydell, J. and Speakman, J.R. (1995). Evolution of nocturnality in bats: potential competitors and predators during their early history. *Biol. J. Linn. Soc.*, **54**: 183–191.

Sales, G. and Pye, D. (1974). *Ultrasonic Communication by Animals*. Chapman & Hall, London: 71–97.

Schaffler, M. (1993). Beobachtung eines Jungentransports beim Braunen Langohr (*Plecotus auritus*). *Nyctalus*, 4(5): 490–491.

Schober, W. and Grimmberger, E. (1989). *A Guide to the Bats of Britain and Europe*. Hamlyn, London.

Schwenke, W. (1988). Versuche zur forderung von Waldfledermausen mittels vogel- und fledermaus-Kunsthohlen 1982–1987 in Geisenfelder Forst. *Myotis*, **26**: 145–152.

Sese, C. and Ruiz-Bustos, A. (1992). New small mammal faunas from the Pleistocene of the north of the province of Madrid (Spain). *Bol. Real Soc. Esp. Hist. Nat. Seccion Geol.*, **87**(1–4): 115–139.

Shiel, C.B., McAney, C.M. and Fairley, J.S. (1991). Analysis of the diet of Natterer's bat *Myotis nattereri* and the common long-eared bat *Plecotus auritus* in the west of Ireland. *J. Zool. London*, **223**: 299–305.

Simmons, J.A. and O'Farrell, M.J. (1977). Echolocation in the long-eared bat *Plecotus phyllotis*. *J. Comp. Physiol.*, **122**: 201–214.

Simms, C. (1977). Kestrels hunting long-eared bats. *British Birds*, **70**: 499–500.

Sluiter, J.W. and van Heerdt, P.F. (1966). Seasonal habits of the noctule bat (*Nyctalus noctula*). *Extraits des Arch. Néerlandaises de Zool.*, **16**(4): 423–439.

Southwood, T.R.E. (1966). *Ecological Methods, with Particular Reference to the Study of Insect Populations*. Methuen, London: 192–193.

Spallanzani, L. (1784). *Dissertations Relative to the Natural History of Animals and Vegetables, Translated from the Italian etc.* 8vo, London, 2 vols.

Spangler, H.G. (1988). Hearing in tiger beetles (Cicindelidae). *Physiol. Ent.*, **13**: 447–452.

Speakman, J.R. (1988). Position of the pinnae and thermoregulatory status in brown long-eared bats (*Plecotus auritus*). *J. Therm. Biol.*, **13**(1): 25–29.

Speakman, J.R. (1990). The function of daylight flying in British bats. *J. Zool. London*, **220**: 101–113.

Speakman, J.R. (1991a). The impact of predation by birds on bat populations in the British Isles. *Mamm. Rev.*, **21**(3): 123–142.

Speakman, J.R. (1991b). Why do insectivorous bats in Britain not fly in daylight more frequently? *Functional Ecol.*, **5**: 518–524.

Speakman, J.R. (1993). The evolution of echolocation for predation. *Symp. Zool. Soc. London*, **65**: 39–63.

Speakman, J.R., Bullock, D.J., Eales, L.A. and Racey, P.A. (1992). A problem defining temporal pattern in animal behaviour: clustering in the emergence behaviour of bats from maternity roosts. *Anim. Behav.*, **43**: 491–500.

Speakman, J.R. and Hays, G.C. (1992). Albedo and transmittance of short-wave radiation for bat wings. *J. Therm Biol.*, **17**(6): 317–321.

Speakman, J.R. and Racey, P.A. (1986). The influence of body condition on sexual development of male brown long-eared bats (*Plecotus auritus*) in the wild. *J. Zool. London*, **210**: 515–525.

Speakman, J.R. and Racey, P.A. (1987). The energetics of pregnancy and lactation in the brown long-eared bat, *Plecotus auritus*. In: *Recent Advances in the Study of Bats* (Fenton, M.B., Racey, P.A. and Rayner, J.M.V., eds). Cambridge University Press, Cambridge: 367–393.

Speakman, J.R. and Racey, P.A. (1988a). The doubly-labelled water technique for measurement of energy expenditure in free-living animals. *Sci. Prog. Oxford*, 72: 227–237.

Speakman, J.R. and Racey, P.A. (1988b). Validation of the doubly-labelled water technique in small insectivorous bats by comparison with indirect calorimetry. *Physiol. Zool.*, 61(6): 514–526.

Speakman, J.R. and Racey, P.A. (1989). Hibernal ecology of the pipistrelle bat: energy expenditure, water requirements and mass loss, implications for survival and the function of winter emergence flights. *J. Anim. Ecol.*, 58: 797–813.

Speakman, J.R. and Racey, P.A. (1991). No cost of echolocation for bats in flight. *Nature, London*, 350 (6317): 421–423.

Speakman, J.R., Racey, P.A., Catto, C.M.C., Webb, P.I., Swift, S.M. and Burnett, A.M. (1991a). Minimum summer populations and densities of bats in NE Scotland, near the northern borders of their distributions. *J. Zool. London*, 225: 327–345.

Speakman, J.R., Webb, P.I. and Racey, P.A. (1991b). Effects of disturbance on the energy expenditure of hibernating bats. *J. Appl. Ecol.*, 28: 1087–1104.

Spitzenberger, F. (1993). Angaben zu sommerverbreitung, bestandgrossen und siedlungsdichten einiger gebaudebewohnender fledermausarten karntens. *Myotis*, 31: 69–109.

Stebbings, R.E. (1966). A population study of bats of the genus *Plecotus*. *J. Zool. London*, 150: 53–75.

Stebbings, R.E. (1967). Identification and distribution of bats of the genus *Plecotus* in England. *J. Zool. London*, 153: 291–310.

Stebbings, R.E. (1968). Bechstein's bat (*Myotis bechsteini*) in Dorset 1965–67. *J. Zool. London*, 155: 228–231.

Stebbings, R.E. (1969). Observer influence on bat behaviour. *Lynx*, 10: 93–100.

Stebbings, R.E. (1970). A comparative study of *Plecotus auritus* and *Plecotus austriacus* (Chiroptera, Vespertilionidae) inhabiting one roost. *Bijdragen tot de Dierkunde*, 40(1): 91–94.

Stebbings, R.E. (1977). Genus *Plecotus*. Long-eared bats. In: *The Handbook of British Mammals*, 2nd edn (Corbet, G.B. and Southern, H.N., eds). Blackwell, London: 120–128.

Stebbings, R.E. (1986). *Which Bat Is It?* Mammal Society, London.

Stebbings, R.E. (1988). *Conservation of European Bats*. Christopher Helm, London.

Stebbings, R.E. (1991). Genus Barbastella. In: *The Handbook of British Mammals*, 3rd edn (Corbet, G.B. and Harris, S., eds). Blackwell, Oxford: 128–130.

Stebbings, R.E. and Griffiths, F. (1986). *Distribution and Status of Bats in Europe*. ITE/NERC, Huntingdon.

Stebbings, R.E. and Walsh, S.T. (1985). *Bat Boxes*. Fauna and Flora Preservation Society, London.

Steiner, H.M. and Gaisler, J. (1994). On a collection of bats (Chiroptera) from NE Turkey and N Iran. *Acta Sci. Nat. Brno*, 28(1): 1–37.

Strelkov, P.P. (1962). The peculiarities of reproduction in bats (Vespertilionidae) near the northern border of their distribution. *Int. Symp. Methods of Mammal Investigations, Brno 1960*: 306–311.

Strelkov, P.P. (1969). Migratory and stationary bats (Chiroptera) of the European part of the Soviet Union. *Acta Zool. Cracoviensa*, 14: 393–439.

Strelkov, P.P. (1989). New data on the structure of the baculum in Palearctic bats. 1. The genera *Myotis*, *Plecotus* and *Barbastella*. In: *European Bat Research 1987* (Hanak, V., Horacek, I. and Gaisler, J., eds). Charles University Press, Prague: 87–94.

Studier, E.H., Lysengen, V.L. and O'Farrell, M.J. (1973). Biology of *Myotis thysanodes* and *M. lucifugus* (Chiroptera, Vespertilionidae) – 2. Bioenergetics of pregnancy and lactation. *Comp. Biochem. Physiol.*, **44A**: 467–471.

Stutz, H-P.B. (1989). Altitude distribution of nursing colonies of selected Swiss bat species (Mammalia, Chiroptera). *Rev. Suisse Zool.*, **96**(3): 651–662.

Swift, S.M. (1980). Activity patterns of pipistrelle bats (*Pipistrellus pipistrellus*) in north-east Scotland. *J. Zool. London*, **190**: 285–295.

Swift, S.M. (1981). Foraging, colonial and maternal behaviour of bats in north-east Scotland. Unpublished PhD thesis, University of Aberdeen, UK.

Swift, S.M. (1991). Genus *Plecotus* (long-eared bats). In: *The Handbook of British Mammals*, 3rd edn (Corbet, G.B. and Harris, S., eds). Blackwell, Oxford: 130–138.

Swift, S.M. (1997). Roosting and foraging behaviour of Natterer's bats (*Myotis nattereri* Kuhl, 1818) close to the northern border of their distribution. *J. Zool. London*, **242**: 375–384.

Swift, S.M. and Racey, P.A. (1983). Resource partitioning in two species of vespertilionid bats (Chiroptera) occupying the same roost. *J. Zool. London*, **200**: 249–259.

Taake, K-H. (1985). Einige verhaltensokologische Aspekte der Rauber-Beute-Beziehungen europaischer Fledermause (Chiroptera). *Z. Saugetierkunde*, **50**: 202–208.

Taake, K-H. (1992). Resource utilization strategies of vespertilionid bats hunting over water in forests. *Myotis*, **30**: 7–74.

Taake, K-H. and Hildenhagen, U. (1989). Nine years inspections of different artificial roosts for forest-dwelling bats in northern Westfalia: some results. In: *European Bat Research 1987* (Hanak, V., Horacek, I. and Gaisler, J., eds). Charles University Press, Prague: 487–493.

Taylor, J.K. (1987). *Pesticide Usage, Great Britain*. Preliminary Report 53, Ministry of Agricultural Fisheries and Food, London.

Taylor, L.R. (1963). Analysis of the effect of temperature on insects in flight. *J. Anim. Ecol.*, **32**: 99–117.

Thomas, D.W. (1995a). The physiological ecology of hibernation in vespertilionid bats. In: *Ecology, Evolution and Behaviour of Bats* (Racey, P.A. and Swift, S.M., eds). *Symp. Zool. Soc. London*, **67**: 233–244.

Thomas, D.W. (1995b). Hibernating bats are sensitive to nontactile human disturbance. *J. Mamm.*, **76**(3): 940–946.

Thompson, M.J.A. (1982). A common long-eared bat *Plecotus auritus*: moth predator–prey relationship. *Naturalist*, **107**: 87–97.

Topal, G. (1958). Morphological studies on the os penis of bats in the Carpathian Basin. *Ann. Hist.-Nat. Mus. Hung.*, **50**: 331–342.

Trune, D.R. and Slobodchikoff, C.N. (1978). Position of immatures in pallid bat clusters: a case of reciprocal altruism? *J. Mamm.*, **59**(1): 193–195.

Tumlison, R. and Douglas, M.E. (1992). Parsimony analysis and the phylogeny of the plecotine bats (Chiroptera: Vespertilionidae). *J. Mamm.*, **73**(2): 276–285.

Tuttle, M.D. and Stevenson, D. (1982). Growth and survival of bats. In: *Ecology of Bats* (Kunz, T.H., ed.). Plenum Press, New York: 105–150.

Twente, J.W., Twente, J. and Brack, V. (1985). The duration of the period of hibernation in three species of vespertilionid bats. 2. Laboratory studies. *Can. J. Zool.*, **63**: 2955–2961.

Vaughan, T.A. (1976). Nocturnal behaviour of the African false vampire bat (*Cardioderma cor*). *J. Mamm.*, **57**: 227–248.

Vernier, E. (1987). *Manuale practico dei chirotteri italiani*. Unione Spel. Pordenonese – C.A.I. e Assessorato all'Ecologia, Provincia di Pordenone.

Vernier, M. (1990). Ecological observations on the evening flight of *Pipistrellus kuhlii* in the town of Padova, Italy. In: *Bat Research 1987* (Hanak, V., Horacek, I. and Gaisler, J., eds). Charles University Press, Prague: 537–541.

Voûte, A.M. (1980–81). The conflict between bats and wood preservatives. *Myotis*, **18–19**: 41–44.

Voûte, A.M., Sluiter, J.W. and Grimm, M.P. (1974). The influence of the natural light–dark cycle on the activity rhythm of pond bats (*Myotis dasycneme* Boie, 1825) during summer. *Oecologia (Berl.)*, **17**: 221–243.

Walhovd, H. and Hoegh-Guildberg, O. (1984). On the feeding habits of common long-eared bat, *Plecotus auritus*. *Flora og Fauna*, **90**: 115–118.

Walsh, S.T., Stebbings, R.E. and Thompson, M.J.A. (1987). Distribution and abundance of the pipistrelle bat *Pipistrellus pipistrellus*. *VWT report, 1987*. The Vincent Wildlife Trust, London: 43–46.

Wardhaugh, A.A. (1992). Bats and their roosts in Cleveland and north east Yorkshire. *Naturalist*, **117**: 99–108.

Wason, A. (1978). Observations on homing ability of some insectivorous bats. *Z. Saugetierkunde*, **43**: 305–306.

Waters, D.A. and Jones, G. (1994). Wingbeat-generated ultrasound in noctuid moths increases the discharge rate of the bat-detecting A1 cell. *Proc. R. Soc. Lond.* B, **258**: 41–46.

Watts, C.H.S. (1968). The foods eaten by wood mice (*Apodemus sylvaticus*) and bank voles (*Clethrionomys glareolus*) in Wytham Woods, Berkshire. *J. Anim. Ecol.*, **37**: 25–41.

Webb, P.I. (1995). The comparative ecophysiology of water balance in microchiropteran bats. In: *Ecology, Evolution and Behaviour of Bats* (Racey, P.A. and Swift, S.M., eds). *Symp. Zool. Soc. London*, **67**: 203–218.

Webb, P.I., Speakman, J.R. and Racey, P.A. (1993). Defaecation, apparent absorption efficiency and the importance of water obtained in the food for water balance in captive brown long-eared (*Plecotus auritus*) and Daubenton's (*Myotis daubentoni*) bats. *J. Zool. London*, **230**: 619–628.

Webb, P.I., Speakman, J.R. and Racey, P.A. (1994). Post-prandial urine loss and its relation to ecology in brown long-eared (*Plecotus auritus*) and Daubenton's (*Myotis daubentoni*) bats (Chiroptera: Vespertilionidae). *J. Zool. London*, **233**: 165–173.

Webb, P.I., Speakman, J.R. and Racey, P.A. (1995). Evaporative water loss in two sympatric species of vespertilionid bat, *Plecotus auritus* and *Myotis daubentoni*: relation to foraging mode and implications for roost site selection. *J. Zool. London*, **235**: 269–278.

Weidinger, K. (1994). Bat communities of three small pseudokarstic caves in eastern Bohemia (Czech Republic). *Fol. Zool.*, **43**(4): 455–464.

Werner, T.K. (1981). Responses of nonflying moths to ultrasound: the threat of gleaning bats. *Can. J. Zool.*, **59**: 525–529.

Whitaker, J.O. and Black, H.L. (1976). Food habits of cave bats from Zambia, Africa. *J. Mamm.*, **57**: 199–204.

Whitaker, J.O., Shalmon, B. and Kunz, T.H. (1994). Food and feeding habits of insectivorous bats from Israel. *Z. Saugetierkunde*, **59**: 74–81.

White, F.B. (1877). Untitled communication. *Nature, London*, **15**: 293.

Wickler, W. and Uhrig, D. (1969). Verhalten and okologische Nische de Gelbflugelfledermaus, *Lavia frons*. *Z. Tierpsychol.*, **26**: 726–736.

Wijngaarden, A. van (1962). De grijze Grootoorvleermuis, *Plecotus austriacus* (Fischer), in Nederland gevonden. *Lutra*, **4**: 20–21.

Wilde, C.J., Kerr, M.A., Knight, C.H. and Racey, P.A. (1995). Lactation in vespertilionid bats. In: *Ecology, Evolution and Behaviour of Bats* (Racey, P.A. and Swift, S.M., eds). *Symp. Zool. Soc. London,* **67**: 139–149.

Wilkinson, G.S. (1995). Information transfer in bats. In: *Ecology, Evolution and Behaviour of Bats* (Racey, P.A. and Swift, S.M., eds). *Symp. Zool. Soc. London,* **67**: 345–360.

Yager, D.D. and Hoy, R.R. (1986). The cyclopean ear: a new sense for the praying mantis. *Science,* **231**: 727–729.

Yoshiyuki, M. (1991). A new species of *Plecotus* (Chiroptera, Vespertilionidae) from Taiwan. *Bull. Science Mus. Series A* (*Zoology*), **17**(4): 189–195.

Zeng, C. and Wang, S. (1989). On the bat fauna and bat conservation in China. In: *European Bat Research 1987* (Hanak, V., Horacek, I. and Gaisler, J., eds). Charles University Press, Prague.

Zima, J. and Horacek, I. (1985). Synopsis of karyotypes of vespertilionid bats (Mammalia: Chiroptera). *Acta Univ. Carolinae Biologica 1981*: 311–329.

Index

Page numbers in *italics* refer to illustrations.